BENEFICIAL INSECTS

Nature's alternatives to chemical insecticides:
animal predation, parasitism, disease organisms

BENEFICIAL INSECTS

BY LESTER A. SWAN

HARPER & ROW, PUBLISHERS   New York • Evanston • London

FOR CRAIG AND WADE, AND NILES TOO

FIRST EDITION

LIBRARY OF CONGRESS CATALOG CARD NUMBER: 64-12705

God has lent us the earth for our life. It is a great entail. It belongs as much to those who are to come after us; and we have no right, in anything we do or neglect, to involve them in unnecessary penalties, or deprive them of benefits which it was in our power to bequeath.

—JOHN RUSKIN

CONTENTS

D. A. Chant, Chairman and Professor
Department of Biological Control
University of California, Riverside, California

FOREWORD

The chemical method of controlling insect pests has been severely criticized of late. This is partly because of genuine drawbacks to the use of pesticides: the hazards of misuse to man and animals, the development of resistance in insects, resurgence, residues, and so on. It is also partly because of largely unfounded but nonetheless real hysteria over their immediate toxicity and the possibility that prolonged sublethal doses may produce cancer in human beings or in other ways be harmful to life. In all the smoke and fire of controversy one inescapable fact is too often overlooked: pesticides are not good strategic weapons to use against insect enemies because their effects are not lasting. Pesticides are merely temporary palliatives, not permanent solutions, to the problem of protecting our forests and crops from insect pests. For this reason, even if pesticides were free from other drawbacks, we would still be poorly advised to rely on them exclusively.

Scientists who are convinced of the disadvantages of pesticide use have realized the need to supplement the chemical method with alternatives. Chief among these is biological control. The general public has also become aware of biological control as a result of the storm of criticism of pesticides in all media of communication. For the scientist, information on biological control is continually being presented in the technical and research papers published in scientific journals. These are not generally available to the public, and even if they were, most nonscientists would lack the background and training to understand them fully. There is a need, then, for an accurate and comprehensive popular text on biological control methods for the lay reader with an interest in the subject. This need is particularly acute just now because of the present focus of interest on biological control. In response to this need, Mr. Swan has provided a text that will supply the general reader with all the information required to understand biological control and to appreciate both its present role in pest control and its great future potential.

It is, besides, a fascinating account of the lives and behavior of insects that live at the expense of others and to our benefit, as well as of the phenomena of parasitism and predation in general. It contains much to interest the naturalist that is not related directly to the economic implications of these phenomena.

To keep his book to a reasonable size, Mr. Swan has followed normal practice in confining his treatment of biological control to the use of parasites, predators, and diseases against insect pests. Biological control thus defined, is not the only alternative to the use of pesticides. Other methods have been tried successfully and still others will undoubtedly be developed in the future. The day will come when scientists will have the information and the ability to blend all methods into control practices that will be the very best for specific times and conditions. That day will be with us all the sooner thanks to public awareness and understanding of biological control, for it is from the public that the research scientist gains his support. This book will help to provide just such an understanding; it needs no further justification.

INTRODUCTION

The effects of DDT and the newer insecticides on man and other animals have been the subject of bitter controversy for fifteen years or more. One of the first to suggest that the use of DDT might be involved with certain unfortunate trends in public health was Dr. Morton Biskind, a toxicologist. Many articles and scientific papers, and a few books, have been written on the effect of pesticides on birds and mammals, and several groups have objected to mass spraying—especially aerial applications—of pesticides. When extensive wildlife losses were evident after spraying or dusting large areas, strong protests came from sportsmen's organizations, the National Audubon Society, and various other conservation groups. But the greatest impact by far has come, and in a very short time, from a single book. I refer, of course, to Rachel Carson's *Silent Spring*, which drew the attention of so many (including President Kennedy) that these protests could no longer be dismissed. The net result so far has been the report, *Use of Pesticides*, by the President's Science Advisory Committee, and a hearing before a subcommittee of the Senate, chaired by Senator Hubert Humphrey of Minnesota.

The planning and preparation of this book have taken six years; its appearance at this time is coincidental. It does not presume to be a "follow-up" of Miss Carson's work; that, as one editor has suggested, would be "a terrific assignment." It does, however, suggest a positive approach to some of the problems Miss Carson brought to the public's attention. The object is to show how a natural check on destructive insect populations is provided by the insects themselves and by organisms causing insect diseases. These in turn can be used for biological control —that is, without the use of conventional insecticides. The beneficial insects treated here as examples are arranged according to the broad groupings of orders and families; this seemed to be the best way of glimpsing the whole spectrum of beneficial insects. It is hoped that the reader may catch something of the wonder and fascination of these creatures. The material is based on the scientific literature and other sources in this field. Though scientific names of the insects are used, the book is intended for the lay reader, and the treatment is nontechnical. Some readers may wish to look first at the brief explanation of how insects and their close relatives are classified in Appendix A.

Few students of biological control would say that such control is the solution to all our problems with insects; nevertheless, a leader in this field has asserted that "with sufficient knowledge, all pests can be controlled biologically." There seems to be general agreement that more research on biological control is needed. As Senator Gruening pointed out in the pesticide hearings, "Research is essential and very desirable. We need more of it. But then the question is, what becomes of the results of the research?" Much of the knowledge already gained through research in biological control is not used.

We need again the kind of effort that was exerted some years back by the USDA and cooperating state agencies on biological control of the gypsy moth, the European corn borer, the oriental fruit moth, and the Japanese beetle. This kind of effort is being made today in Canada to protect the forests, and in California to protect citrus and other crops. Some predators, parasites, and disease organisms can be used effectively as "biological insecticides"—where introduced insects or organisms control pest populations for a season or until harvest but do not become a permanent part of the new environment and therefore must be recolonized at intervals. Very few of these agents are available to growers, partly for lack of cheap methods of production but mostly for lack of demand. Cheap methods of production have been worked out in some notable instances and could undoubtedly be worked out for others. Biological control can be integrated with chemical control, thereby reducing the quantity of chemicals required; poisonous residues on the plants are thus reduced and more beneficial insects survive. We find notable examples of this in the apple-growing area of Annapolis Valley, Nova Scotia, and in California. Other programs of this kind could be worked out in other areas and for various crops.

We need more people trained in the field of biological control to work with farmers and orchardists, and to determine when control measures are necessary and what kind should be used. The present haphazard application of pesticides—often for "insurance" rather than any real need—is wasteful, hazardous, and unscientific. These poisons are peddled like any other commodity—by high pressure salesmen—to individuals and community representatives, many of whom are not well enough informed to know when the material should be applied. The "do-it-yourself" doctors are not the only ones guilty of excesses. One professional conservationist was prompted to remark of the commercial sprayers, "If I were to comment on their practices, it would be libelous. They're out to promote business, instead of insuring the public welfare. These people often spray too often and too much, and use sprays that are too poisonous."

A witness at the 1963 pesticide hearings, Dr. Mitchell R. Zavon, commented that "the spray gun is now used more than the hoe" (by the householder) and that "rare is the housewife who does not have a can of 'bug-killer' handy for stalking flies, ants, clothes moths, or any other insect that moves across the threshold." This is taught in the biology textbooks at an early age—or was in our community until a few years ago. A volume called *Modern Biology*, for the secondary school level, contains a chapter on the control of insect pests that reads in places like a promotional piece for the insecticide industry. Commenting on the effectiveness of DDT against household pests and the convenience of aerosol bombs, the authors recommend that all windows and doors of the house be closed every few weeks and each room sprayed by opening up the valve on the bomb for thirty seconds. The mist, they explain, will settle to the floor and "kill all hidden pests." While this magic is taking place, a family outing for an hour or two is suggested. The student is assured that "DDT is not poisonous to man" and that "no precautions are necessary." Senator Abraham Ribicoff—who originally presided at the pesticide hearings—has suggested that promotional materials encourage the use of insecticides in the home when there is really no need for them, and that a "return to the old fashioned fly swatter might not be a bad idea . . ." The production of insecticide aerosols increased steadily during the last decade, from 22.6 million units in 1951 to 94.2 million units in 1962.

The statistics on pesticide sales and use in this country provide some food for thought, however gratifying they may be to the manufacturers and their stockholders. Sales of synthetic organic pesticidal chemicals by primary producers amounted to $346,-441,000 in 1962 compared to $302,955,000 in 1961, an increase of 14.4 per cent; and the latter figure was an increase of 15.7 per cent over the previous year. Judging by the trend since 1957 an increase of 10 to 12 per cent was anticipated for 1963. The value of exports of all kinds of pesticides in 1962 was $130,720,000—up 22 per cent over the previous year. That in 1962 production was slightly less than in the previous year for some major pesticides— among them DDT—indicates the growing importance of proprietary chemicals produced by single firms and marketed under a baffling profusion of trade names. The estimated volume of pesticide usage in the United States in 1962 was 820 million pounds, valued at $300 million. In 1960 almost 52 million acres ·were treated by aerial application. In acreages treated with chemicals in 1958—for control of insects, plant diseases, and weeds—the corn belt (Ohio, Indiana, Illinois, Iowa, and Missouri) led all other regions with 21.6 million acres, followed closely by the northern plains states (North Dakota, South Dakota, Nebraska, and Kansas), and the southern plains states (Oklahoma and Texas).

With a business of these proportions and the idea of insect "eradication" so firmly planted in both individual and official minds, any attempt at reform is bound to meet resistance. Decisions to blanket vast areas, including densely populated urban ones, are usually made by state pest control bodies on the basis of trappings. In 1962, after 208 Japanese beetles had been collected in 725 traps in one township of Berrien County, in western Michigan, it was decided to spread 30,000 pounds of 10 per cent granular dieldrin on 1,357 acres; after 2,253 beetles had been caught in 1,573 traps in Monroe county and 523 beetles in 1,117 traps in Lenawee County, in southeastern Michigan—where they were said to be spilling over from Ohio—it was decided to apply 1,600,000 pounds of the same material over 80,000 acres using converted B-25 bombers. This application—agricultural officials referred to it as a "chemical blanket"—covered an area 15 miles long and 7 miles wide. It was made late in the season on an emergency basis, at a cost of $336,400 shared equally by the state and federal departments of agriculture. The same area had been treated similarly in 1959 and 1960 with aldrin, which is supposedly effective for four or five years. Even if there were no other objections this would not seem to be good economics. One of the most effective biological control agents—an organism causing the "milky disease" of Japanese beetles—has been available commercially (under license from the USDA) as a spore dust since 1944; it was applied extensively under USDA auspices, and with great success, from 1939 to 1948. Initially this treatment would be more expensive than the use of chemicals; but the spores carrying the bacteria that cause the disease persist in the soil for a long time and might well be less expensive in the long run even at present-day costs. Increased production of the material would no doubt reduce costs and bring about improvement in production methods, reducing costs still further. In the East, repeated sprayings are made for gypsy moth "eradication." Another biological control agent—also a bacterium, *Bacillus thuringiensis*—is effective against this pest, but there seems to be no more official enthusiasm for it than for the "milky disease" organisms.

In its report, *Use of Pesticides,* the President's Science Advisory Committee concludes that "biological methods of insect control have received relatively little attention in the United States by comparison with the great emphasis on chemical control." It injects a note of skepticism, however, with the statement that "success has not been frequent," and with its reference to such weaknesses as that "parasites and predators . . . kill some but not all" host insects, and that "the host may become resistant." Insect "eradication" has become a fetish; there is talk about the "eradication" of the fire ant, the Japanese beetle, or the gypsy moth as though these insects might be wiped out completely—which of course they never are even with chemicals. Biological control (whether with predators, parasites, or disease organisms), as the phrase itself implies, is not based on the "eradication" concept; some hosts must survive to maintain the beneficial insects, and in the case of disease organisms, hosts are needed to spread the contagion. If a sufficient number of pests are destroyed to make the crop profitable, the control may be considered successful; and it may also be more lasting than "eradication."

As far as resistance is concerned, only one major pest, the larch sawfly, has so far developed resistance to a biological control agent (a parasite), and this may quite possibly be overcome by releasing selected strains of the parasite. It might be possible to push biological control to the point where resistance became a problem, but so far there hasn't been much pushing. Many of the most important insect pests do now have resistance to chlorinated hydrocarbon and phosphate insecticides. The biological control techniques that seem most to have impressed the President's Science Advisory Committee are "prevention of reproduction" (the release of sterile males) and "the use of attractants" (chiefly sex lures); these are stressed also by USDA scientists. This attitude of skepticism, which seems to be shared by the Secretary of Agriculture, prompted Senator Ribicoff, during the pesticide hearings, to ask Secretary Freeman whether there wouldn't "have to be a massive change in orientation" in his agency "if any real progress toward biological control is to be realized."[1]

On the positive side, the President's committee recommended that "the accretion of residues in the environment be controlled by orderly reduction in the use of persistent pesticides," with the goal being "elimination of the use of persistent toxic pesticides." It conceded also that "the variety of methods that has proven useful for biological control of certain pests, and the indication of potential value for others, lead to the conclusion that more active exploration and use of these techniques may yield important benefits for the national economy and for the protection of health." Steps have been taken by the USDA to expand facilities of the Forest Service for research in biological control of forest pests, and more extensive research by the Cooperative State Experiment Station Service on "biological or natural control factors" is promised, "with the ultimate aim to utilize them to a maximum with a corresponding reduction in dependency on chemicals."

The obligations incurred in writing a book of this kind are many. The first of all is to the authors and investigators on whose writings it is based; these are acknowledged in the text and footnotes. I am especially indebted to Dr. Irvin M. Hall of

---

[1] One suggestion resulting from the committee hearings and winning favor today is to license the sale of chemical pesticides, allowing them to be sold only when they have been "prescribed" by a biologist.

the Insect Pathology Laboratory, University of California, River-
side for his early encouragement and his valuable suggestions and
criticism; he gave up time during his sabbatical leave in New
Zealand to read the chapters on insect diseases. I owe special
thanks to Dr. D. A. Chant, Chairman, Department of Biological
Control, Riverside, who wrote the Foreword, and Dr. Paul
DeBach, Department of Biological Control, Riverside for taking
time to read the manuscript. I also wish to thank Murray G. Maw,
Dr. A. L. Turnbull, Dr. J. S. Kelleher, and Dr. B. P. Byrne,
Director of the Entomology Research Institute for Biological Control, Canada Department of Agriculture, Belleville, Ontario for
their encouragement.

Pictures are an important part of a book of this nature, and
I have many to thank for their cooperation in providing them. Of
those by Roy J. Pence, Department of Entomology, University of
California, Los Angeles, one showing free larval selection by
fabric-eating insects appeared in his article, "Control of Fabric-
Feeding Insects by Neutralizing Vitamins in Fibers" (*California
Agriculture*, February 1960); others appeared in Walter Ebeling's
Subtropical Fruit Pests (Berkeley: University of California, 1959).
Edward A. Steinhaus, Dean of Biological Sciences, University of
California, Irvine, and Gordon A. Marsh, Division of Invertebrate
Pathology, University of California, Berkeley, furnished pictures
of diseased insects; these appeared in their "Report of Diagnoses
of Diseased Insects 1951–1961" (*Hilgardia*, December 1962),
as did the one by W. Harry Lange, Department of Entomology,
University of California, Davis. Other photographs were pro-
vided by Lee Jenkins, Department of Entomology, University
of Missouri, Columbia; William A. Albrecht, Dean Emeritus, Department of Soils, University of Missouri, Columbia; Edward S.
Ross, Curator of Insects, California Academy of Sciences, San
Francisco; Harry Brevoort, Glenbrook, Connecticut; Harold F.
Madsen, Department of Entomology, University of California,
Berkeley; Leopoldo E. Caltagirone, Division of Biological Con-
trol, University of California, Berkeley; Peter Belton, Institute

for Biological Control, Canada Department of Agriculture, Belleville, Ontario; M.D. Proverbs, Research Station, Canada Department of Agriculture, Summerland, British Columbia; W. A. Reeks, Officer in Charge, Forest Insect Laboratory, Canada Department of Forestry, Sault Ste. Marie, Ontario; Charles J. Myers, Jr., Chief, Photography Division, Office of Information, U.S. Department of Agriculture, Washington, D.C.; and Theodore W. Fisher, Department of Biological Control, University of California, Riverside. The photographs of predator and parasite production facilities and techniques appeared in "Mass Culture of *Cryptolaemus* and *Leptomastix*—Natural Enemies of Citrus Mealybug" (Bulletin 797, California Experiment Station, July 1963). The photographs of vertebrates are by Karl H. Maslowski, Cincinnati, Ohio, and the drawings are by Enid Furlonger, New York City.

I am very grateful to Cecil B. Moore, Birmingham, Michigan, for his help in preparation of the index and glossary. I wish to thank Mrs. Claire Granger, Pleasant Ridge, Michigan, for the painstaking work of typing the manuscript; also John Macrae, editor of Nature and Outdoor Books, Harper & Row, for his patience and valuable suggestions. I acknowledge also the value of my wife's criticism and judgment, which I have sought on numerous occasions.

L. A. S.

Royal Oak, Michigan
San Clemente, California
April, 1964

*Man's environment is the whole natural scene, the earth with
its soil, its plants, and its animals. In many places these have
reached a natural balance which man disturbs at his peril.*

—CHARLES DARWIN

INSECTS AND THE BALANCE OF NATURE

1

The popular conception of insects assumes that they are all
villains so far as man is concerned. Our attitude toward insects
is no doubt partially due to the emphasis on destruction, but it
goes deeper than that and has perhaps been best expressed by
Maeterlinck:

The insect does not belong to our world. Other animals and even the
plants, despite their mute lives and the great secrets they enfold, seem
not to be such total strangers, for we still feel in them notwithstanding
all their peculiarities, a certain terrestrial fraternity. They may astonish
or even amaze us at times, but they do not completely upset our calcu-
lations. Something in the insects, however, seems to be alien to the
habits, morals and psychology of our globe, as if it had come from some
other planet, more monstrous, more energetic, more insensate, more
atrocious, more infernal than our own. With whatever authority, with
whatever fecundity, unequaled here below, the insect seizes on life,
we fail to accustom ourselves to the thought that it is an expression of
that Nature whose privileged offspring we claim to be. . . . No doubt,
in this astonishment and failure to comprehend, we are beset with an
indefinable, profound and instinctive uneasiness, inspired by beings so
incomparably better armed and endowed than ourselves, concentrations

of energy and activity in which we divine our most mysterious foes, the rivals of our last hours and perhaps our successors. . . .[1]

AGE OF INSECTS

Insects have inhabited this world for an unbelievable span of time—probably 200 million years before the mammals, including man, made their appearance. The richest fossil find giving a clue to the age of insects was the Baltic amber found in Germany along the coast of East Prussia some years ago. This is a fossil resin from now-extinct pine trees; the insects were caught in the pitch on the tree trunks and some 150,000 of them were preserved in perfect detail. Lumps of the amber containing a remarkable collection of ants were sent for analysis to the American authority, William Morton Wheeler, who commented as follows:

There were 9,560 specimens representing 92 species and 43 genera. My study showed conclusively that the ants have undergone no important structural modifications since the Lower Oligocene (55 to 65 million years ago), that they had at that time developed all their various castes just as we see them today, that their larvae and pupae were the same, that they attended plant-lice, kept guest-beetles in their nests and had parasitic mites attached to their legs in the very same peculiar positions as in our living species, and that at least six or seven subfamilies and many of the existing genera were fully established. Some of the species in the amber were even found to be practically indistinguishable from those now living in Northern Europe and North America. Wheeler concluded that these ants—and probably the wasps, bees, and termites—had their origin about 100 million years ago or even earlier. Since the social insects are the most recent arrivals, and the fossil records of insects extend back about 250 million years, he finally concluded that "these wonderful creatures have been living and multiplying on our planet about 300 million years."[2]

[1] G. Maeterlinck, "J. H. Fabre et son Oeuvre," *Ann. Polit. et Litt.*, April 12, 1911.
[2] From *Social Life Among the Insects* by William Morton Wheeler, copyright, 1923, by Harcourt, Brace & World, Inc.; renewed, 1951, by Adaline E. Wheeler and Ralph E. Wheeler. Reprinted by permission of the publishers.

NUMBER OF INSECTS

In this long process of evolution insects have become the dominant group of animals, far exceeding all other groups in number of species and in diversity of structure and habit. The number of described species, given by Metcalf and Flint as 640,000, is constantly growing.[3] The total *described* species was estimated by the Department of Agriculture to be 686,000 by the end of 1948. For North America north of Mexico the number was 82,500. The knowledge of just what kinds of insects are present is very meager for many parts of the world, especially the tropics where the diversity of all forms of life is greatest. Estimates of the probable number of species vary anywhere from 2½ million to 10 million.

Insects are also the most abundant of all highly organized animals. Aside from the protozoa—single-celled, microscopic animals which are found practically everywhere—and the minute crustaceans called copepods, the closest rival in numbers appears to be the earthworm. It would of course be idle to speculate as to the number of individual insects, but some conception of their abundance may be gained from actual counts made within restricted areas, and from estimates based on these. Various counts of insects occurring in and on the soil indicate a frequency of from one to ten million per acre in cultivated fields. One count of the top eighteen inches of forest soil in Illinois indicated a frequency of 65 million per acre. Earthworms would still appear to be the dominant form of animal life in the soil if we exclude microorganisms. Their numbers are normally very large and in bulk they far exceed the insects. Darwin estimated that there were an average of 53,000 earthworms in an acre of British soil and that the number might be half a million in fertile soil. Other studies have arrived at estimates of 480,000 earthworms in an acre

[3] C. L. Metcalf, W. P. Flint, *Destructive and Useful Insects,* rev. by R. L. Metcalf (New York: McGraw-Hill Book Co., 1951).

of unfertilized soil, over a million in highly manured soil, and 1,450,000 in an exceptionally fertile plot. In the air above the soil, one investigator, on the basis of trappings, concluded that in morning there might be an average of 3,000 insects in flight over an acre of soil—or 1,850,000 per square mile—and in the evening about 11,000 per acre, or seven million per square mile.

The reproductive capacity of some insects is even more astonishing. It has been calculated that the progeny of one pair of houseflies in one summer would be 191,000,000,000,000,000,000— if all the eggs hatched successfully and the young survived. But other insects (predators and parasites), together with birds, diseases, and other factors such as weather usually hold them within reasonable bounds. Some of the beneficial insects are also very prolific—the honeybee queens are capable of laying from 1,500 to 2,000 eggs in a day.[4] The most prolific of all insects are the aphids, which may produce ten or more generations a year. During the warm part of the summer they produce several generations by parthenogenesis (without mating or fertilization of the eggs). The young aphids are born alive (like mammals) and already have within them developing embryos constituting the third generation. In the fall a winged generation appears and migrates to other plants. Here they produce females that mate and lay fertilized eggs; these give rise to the new generations that repeat the cycle the following year. Winged forms may be produced at any time during the season to meet changing conditions, and appear to be prompted by overcrowding and by physiological changes in the plant. Their migrations allow them to multiply with extreme rapidity since they can thus escape from the natural enemies whose numbers on the first plant might otherwise soon be sufficient to wipe them out.

Among the most widespread and abundant insects are ants and termites. The colonies of one of our common mound-building ants are said to contain from 40,000 to 240,000 individuals. In

[4] Curtis W. Sabrosky, "How Many Insects Are There?" in *Insects: Yearbook of Agriculture* (Washington: Government Printing Office, 1952).

Brazil the population of a single mound of one Brazilian species may be from 175,000 to 600,000. Some ant colonies survive for thirty or more years, although the individual worker lives no more than three or four years. One species of South American termite is said to have colonies of up to three million.[5] The queen of some fungus-feeding tropical termites may live as long as fifty years. The queen of some Australian species of termites may lay 360 eggs in an hour, or three million in the course of a year—for anywhere from twenty-five to fifty years.

SWARMING

In some insects the occurrence of excessive numbers or swarms is usually periodic, associated with mating and the normal life cycle —as in the swarming or nuptial flights of mayflies, bees, and ants. In others it may be a cyclical phenomenon associated with the natural environment. Studies of the fluctuation of the wheat midge in England indicate that peak periods follow a five-year cycle, associated with climatic factors. The appearance in vast numbers of the periodic cicada or seventeen-year locust is associated with its life cycle; it has a longer developmental period than any other insect. This species is confined largely to the northeastern part of the United States—there is a thirteen-year locust in the southeast—and both the location of the various broods and the exact years in which they will emerge are known. As many as 20,000 to 40,000 of the adults emerge from under one tree.

Enormous congregations sometimes occur among migratory insects. Flocks of the monarch butterfly, whose larvae feed on milkweed, migrate regularly in the fall like birds. They may travel a thousand miles or more and make the return flight in the following spring.[6] Huge swarms of them may be seen in winter in southern California and elsewhere, sometimes completely en-

[5] Charles T. Brues, *Insect Dietary: An Account of the Food Habits of Insects* (Cambridge: Harvard University Press, 1946).

[6] See C. B. Williams, *Insect Migration* (New York: The Macmillan Co., 1958); also F. A. Urquhart, *The Monarch Butterfly* (Toronto: University of Toronto Press, 1960).

veloping trees. Swarming and migration may be associated with hibernation, as they are in the beneficial aphid-eating lady beetles that congregate in the mountain canyons of California where they take shelter under forest litter until the following spring. Single aggregations may amount to as much as 500 gallons, or several millions of beetles. The migratory Rocky Mountain grasshoppers have appeared at times in spectacular mass flight. Those occurring over the Great Plains during the 1870's were particularly devastating—they left only holes in the ground where plants had been, and stripped trees of leaves and bark. According to one observer, one of the invading swarms in Nebraska was half a mile high, 100 miles wide, and 300 miles long; he calculated that there were more than 124 billion grasshoppers in this one migration.

ADAPTATION

Insects are the most adaptive of all animals to changing conditions, and this may be the main reason for their survival. "The problems in insect control," says Metcalf, "are more serious in areas where the biological and physical environment is undergoing rapid changes than they are in areas where conditions have become more stable by a long and gradual development." We see this in the increasing resistance of insects to the newer insecticides. There are insects that eat poisons deadly to other animals; the drug store beetle is known to eat 45 different kinds of drugs, including opium and strychnine, as well as black pepper, ginger, and yeast. Malcolm Burr[7] tells of a hardy little beetle that is virtually indestructible except by physical violence— 1,547 survived in a bottle of casein that had been stoppered for twelve years.

How, in the face of such a formidable foe, have plants and animals been able to survive? According to E. O. Essig,

The answer lies with the insects themselves. Among all the varied species, they maintain a reasonable balance, which permits normal and sometimes even excessive populations to survive, but at a low enough level so that plants continue to propagate in what we may consider to

[7] Malcolm Burr, *The Insect Legion* (London: James Nisbet & Co., 1954).

be a normal manner. Of course this so-called balance may have been determined between insects and other related natural factors ages ago. Think of what would happen if all insects were wiped out! The interrelations between the plant-feeding insects and the predaceous and parasitic forms are exceedingly intricate and unrelenting.

Parasitism by other insects invades every species of insect—the plant and animal feeders and even the parasitic ones themselves. All forms of the host from egg to adult are subject to destruction by predators and parasites. . . .

Some of the relationships between insects and plants have become so complicated that in most instances neither insect nor plant could long exist apart.

Similar relationships exist between insects and other animals and between certain insects and others of their own kind, yet their basic existence depends on the vegetable kingdom. Although millions of insects derive their subsistence from plants, they seem not to interfere greatly with the natural development of the plant world. It is true that in special situations insects might even exterminate a species of plant in a given location, and we know too well that they are responsible for tremendous losses to crops almost everywhere. However, it appears that plants have actually occupied as much of the earth's surface as is possible despite their insect enemies.[8]

NATURAL AND BIOLOGICAL CONTROL

The predators, parasites, and insect diseases that are normally present and restrain the populations of insect pests are spoken of as "natural control." Some predators and parasites, as well as some organisms that cause insect diseases, can be reared in the laboratory or insectary in large numbers and disseminated in the fields in sufficient quantities, under favorable conditions, to control the destructive insects. This is referred to as "biological control" to distinguish it from control by means of chemicals. Most of our trouble with insect pests comes from those not native to this country, which came in accidentally on ship cargoes, without the natural enemies that held them in check in their native country. When these natural control agents have been propagated and applied, in many instances, satisfactory control has been achieved.

[8] E. O. Essig, "How Insects Live," in *Yearbook of Agriculture* (Washington: Government Printing Office, 1952).

Parasites and predators of insect pests are present and exerting some influence on the population of pest species in practically every field and habitat where insect pests occur.

—CHARLES A. FLESCHNER

INSECT PREDATORS AND PARASITES

2

Curtis P. Clausen, a leading authority on entomophagous insects (those that eat other insects), writes:

As in the case of the human race, insects are their own worst enemies, and it is to this relentless conflict that we owe a large measure of credit for the maintenance of equilibrium in the insect population at a sufficiently low level to permit the existence of plant and animal life as we know it today. The entomophagous insects comprise a very considerable portion of the total insect population, as is readily realized when we consider that the great majority of species of other food habits have one or more species of parasites or predators which live at their expense.[1]

Insects that live at the expense of other insects or animals are of two fairly distinct types: predators and parasites. Predators are those that devour their prey, generally eating more than one or a number of victims.

S. W. Frost confines the term "parasite" to "species that feed on the body of another without killing it and generally attack only a single host." He uses the term "parasitoid" to designate those

[1] C. P. Clausen, *Entomophagous Insects* (New York: McGraw-Hill Book Co., 1940).

8

insects that lay their eggs in or on an insect host, and whose larvae feed on it internally or externally but avoid the vital organs until later in their development. Thus defined, "parasitism" is rare among insects, being largely confined to a small order known as the Strepsiptera, which parasitize a few bees, wasps, leafhoppers, crickets, and bugs. Some well-known parasites are the lice, fleas, blackflies, mosquitoes, bedbugs, and horseflies, all of which live at the expense of higher forms of animals. These vary widely in their dependence on the host, some spending their entire life as parasites; some, such as the fleas, are free-living in the early stages; others, such as mosquitoes, are free-living during the whole life cycle.

Wheeler felt rather strongly that the very large body of insects that lay their eggs in or on the host insect and develop and sustain the species in this way deserve to be distinguished from the more familiar "parasites."

Species that behave in this manner [he wrote] are not true parasites, but extremely economical predators, because they eventually kill their victims, but before doing so, spare them as much as possible in order that they may continue to feed and grow and thus yield fresh nutriment just as needed. For this reason and also because, as a rule, only the larval insect behaves in the manner described, it is best called a "parasitoid." The adult into which it develops is, in fact, a very highly organized, active, free-living creature, totally devoid of any of the stigmata of "degeneration" so common among parasites, and with such exquisitely perfected sensory, nervous, and muscular organs that it can detect its prey in the most intricate environment and under the subtlest disguises.[2]

However, these distinctions in name are not generally made today, and the term "parasite" is applied to the insects that benefit us as well as to those that are harmful.

BEHAVIOR

In the adult form, parasites are mainly free-living and their source of food is different than that of the larvae. Many feed on nectar

[2] William Morton Wheeler, *Social Life Among the Insects* (New York: Harcourt, Brace & Co., 1923).

or pollen and are important pollinators. In predators both the larval and adult stages are generally free-living, and their source of food is often the same.

Parasites represent more advanced forms than the predators and are limited to insects having a complete metamorphosis—those that develop progressively from egg to larva to pupa (the resting stage) and finally to the adult. Although parasites attack mainly as larvae, they may feed on any stage of the host—eggs, larvae, pupae, or (less often) adults. One of these relatively infrequent cases is that of *Centeter cinerea,* an imported fly that attacks the Japanese beetle; another is the *Pyrgota* fly that parasitizes the adult May beetle in flight. Predators, on the other hand, more often prey as larvae, *and* as adults on the various stages of other insects. Whereas many parasites attack only one species, predators are generally less selective. The variety of insects parasitized by one species, however, can be very great; for example, a minute wasp, *Trichogramma evanescens,* attacks the eggs of more than a hundred host species and has thus been reared in great numbers for biological control. Another is *Compsilura concinnata,* a tachinid fly that was introduced from Europe, and that attacks more than 125 host species, chiefly the larvae of the order Lepidoptera (moths). It has been used in the biological control of the gypsy moth and the satin moth.

TOOLS OF THE TRADE

The predators in general have stronger and sharper mouth parts than the plant-eating (phytophagous) insects. Both sucking and chewing types are found; in the former the beaks are stronger and sharper, and in the latter the mandibles or jaws are sharper and generally have teeth. The front legs are usually designed for holding prey and are often armed with spines for grasping. The praying mantid is the outstanding example of a predator with perfect tools for the job. Some parasitic wasps, such as *Brachymeria fonscolombei,* have elaborate mechanisms on their hind legs designed for grasping their prey during oviposition.

One of our largest insect predators, the praying mantid, has long and powerful front legs, equipped with spines for holding prey. (*Harry Brevoort*)

When the larval forms are predaceous their mouth parts often resemble those of the ferocious-looking adult beetles—as in the ant lion, whose curved, pointed, and toothed mandibles are not unlike those of the male stag beetle. The immature forms sometimes have elaborate grasping mechanisms; the dragonfly nymph is one of these. In the mature dragonfly the head appears to be mounted on a highly flexible swivel joint, permitting it to be whirled around quickly in order to catch prey on the wing. The spines on the dragonfly's legs are used as a sort of basket for catching and holding its prey. Predation may occur without any special adaptation; where it does so, as in some Diptera (flies), discretion is the better part of valor—they just don't pick on anything their own size—or the disadvantages are overcome by cunning.

Generally the larvae of internal parasites are specially adapted for breathing under conditions where the oxygen supply is restricted by having thinner skins, through which gases can be exchanged more readily. Some, however, solve the problem by making contact with the tracheae or breathing apparatus of the host insect, and others obtain air through perforations in the host's skin.

EGG PLACEMENT BY THE PARASITES

The parasitic habit may call for stealth and speed where the adult of one of the larger adult insects is attacked; however, the victim is more often the inert egg or pupa, or the sluggish caterpillar or nymph. The females of most parasitic wasps whose larvae feed internally on their hosts are equipped with an ovipositor —a most remarkable device for thrusting the egg into the host. The same kind of instrument is used by the wasps that parasitize wood-boring insects—not to jab the victim itself, but simply to get through the wood. The highly developed ovipositor is a fine hollow tube, similar to a hypodermic needle, that protrudes from the posterior end of the body. The egg is worked down through the tube and into the chosen spot. (In a few species the egg passes down outside the tube.)

Stanley Flanders points out that

> The ovipositor is remarkable for the diversity of its supplemental functions. It is the sense organ by which in effect the female recognizes an object as host and by which she ascertains the suitability of the host's content for the development of her progeny. It is used as a hypodermic needle not only to inject an egg into a host but to inject paralyzing or preserving fluids prior to oviposition. Perhaps its most extraordinary use is that of food-procuring instrument. Females that need additional protein for egg production use it to tap the host's body for the nutrient fluids contained therein. If the host is concealed either within its host plant or its cocoon, the female uses the ovipositor as a mold for the construction of a pipeline through which she imbibes the host's life blood.[3]

Some wasps have an ovipositor of enormous length in comparison to their bodies. The ichneumonid wasps *Megarhyssa lunator* and *Macrocentrus gifuensis* are outstanding examples. *Megarhyssa lunator*, a large wasp—one and one-half inches long—with a tail-like ovipositor three inches long, is a parasite of the pigeon tremex, a wood-boring insect. The ovipositor is stabbed through the bark and wood of the tree, into the tunnel carved out by the borer; here the egg is deposited and the larva later comes in contact with its larval host.

The minute wasps that parasitize eggs of insects much larger than themselves, pierce the host egg to insert one of their own, and the single larva develops inside. The larvae of some larger egg parasites do not begin to feed until after the host larva has developed. Many of the Diptera (flies) also have a sharp pointed ovipositor for penetrating the body of the host.

DISPERSAL OF EGGS

Some parasites simply attach the egg to the host by means of a sticky secretion. Many of these types feed externally; others bore into the host and feed internally. Still others lay egg masses on the leaves of the plant upon which their hosts feed, so that the

[3] Stanley F. Flanders, "The Parasitic Hymenoptera: Specialists in Population Regulation," *The Canadian Entomologist*, Nov. 1962.

An ichneumonid wasp, *Megarhyssa lunator,* shown on a log preparing to deposit eggs in the tunnel of a wood-boring insect, the pigeon tremex. The extremely long ovipositor, curved over the wasp's back is drilling through the wood. (*Lee Jenkins*)

eggs are swallowed as the insect eats the plant. The larvae soon hatch in the alimentary canal, from which they bore their way into the body cavity where they develop and feed. This habit entails the laying of thousands of eggs to insure their ingestion by the host—and thus the survival of the species. The habit is common among the tachinid flies, and some wasps in the family Trigonalidae reach their hosts in the same manner.

A modification of this system of dispersal occurs in some parasites whose minute larvae are scattered by the thousands on flowers and foliage to await a free ride on the first insect that comes along. (The technical name for this is *phoresy.*) The lucky ones thus find their way to the nest or habitat of their hosts, where the process of development begins; the rest perish. The insect that

Larva of *Megarhyssa* wasp in tunnel of pigeon tremex. (*Lee Jenkins*)

provides the transportation may be either the victim or simply the means of reaching it. One of these odd hitchhikers is the *Stylops* of the order Strepsiptera, whose usual host is a certain bee. If the larva succeeds in attaching itself to the right bee, it settles down in one of the cells of the hive, where it feeds on the body juices of the developing bee—which nevertheless usually grows to maturity without being greatly harmed. As an adult the bee must continue to play host to the female *Stylops,* which remains attached to its back. Here mating with the winged male takes place, the eggs are fertilized, and the larvae develop, later to be deposited on a flower visited by the bee, where the cycle begins again. One family of Hymenoptera (the Eucharidae) parasitize the larvae and pupae of ants. The female scatters her eggs over the foliage in masses, and the larvae become attached to foraging ants which unwittingly carry them to their nests. Obviously the mortality rate of such parasitic larvae is high, and the female must be lavish in both the production of eggs and the dispersal of larvae if the species is to survive.

THE STINGER

Most of us fear the sting of a bee or wasp. In the bees, wasps, and ants that possess a stinger, it is not only an offensive or defensive weapon but also the equivalent of the egg-laying organ. Therefore if you happen to be stung you may be sure that the culprit is the female of the species. The stinger of the honeybee consists of two sharp, highly polished spears that fit together to form a fine movable tube, enclosed in a sheath that acts as a guide. At the tips of the spears are several barbs which hold the stinger in place while a further jab is made. Because of these barbs the honeybee is seldom able to remove its stinger. However, other bees, the wasps, and the ants lack them and can thus sting repeatedly. Associated with the stinger are glands that secrete a venom which is the cause of the swelling and pain when you are stung. As has already been indicated, the insect victim is killed outright when the object is to devour it on the spot or when the larvae are continuously supplied with food by the adult. In other instances, when one host is sufficient to provide the growing larva through its development, the venom serves only to paralyze the victim. In this state of paralysis the insect's vital functions continue to keep it alive for the desired length of time; dead, it would soon be attacked by microbes or scavengers. A neat bit of timing causes the feeding larva to avoid the vital organs until the last, saving them until just before it is ready to enter the pupal or resting stage in its metamorphosis.

Raimon L. Beard of the Connecticut Agricultural Experiment Station recently made an interesting study of the potency and effect of the venom secreted by a wasp of the species *Bracon juglandis*.[4] He calculated that one discharge of venom amounted to .000,000,065 milliliters (a milliliter being about 1/1000 of a liquid quart, if you can conceive of so small an amount). Experimenting with a caterpillar of the genus *Galleria*, he estimated that one part of the venom to 200,000,000 parts of the caterpillar's blood was enough to cause paralysis. Blood from a paralyzed caterpillar was sufficiently potent to cause paralysis if injected into another caterpillar, and likewise from that caterpillar into a third and from the third into a fourth. During the experiment one wasp was actually observed to sting 175 larvae. Its preference was for certain moths of the genera *Ephestia* and *Plodia*, as well as *Galleria*. Its venom is still effective when dried and dissolved in water. It was noted, however, that the larvae of certain insects such as the Japanese beetle and the European corn borer were not susceptible to the venom when it was injected into them artificially. It is believed that the venom works on the prey by breaking down the connection between muscles and nerves. It was found to have a quieting effect on caterpillars in a state of violent convulsions brought on by exposure to DDT.

MASS PRODUCTION

Normally insects reproduce by means of fertilized eggs. After mating, the female retains the sperm in a pouch (the *Spermatheca*), from which she doles it out in proper amounts as the eggs are ejected. Some insects, however, can produce normal offspring without mating or fertilization. This type of reproduction is called *parthenogenesis*, and notable examples occur among wasps, bees and aphids. Among parasitic wasps females are generally pro-

[4] "Nature's Poison Factory." *Science News Letter*, April 7, 1956.

Navel orangeworm larva (*top*) parasitized by a tiny and unusual wasp, *Holcothorax* sp., which reproduces by polyembrony. *Below*, 789 adult *Holcothorax* wasps have emerged. (*F. E. Skinner*, courtesy *L. E. Caltagirone*)

duced only from fertilized eggs and males from unfertilized eggs. A few species can reproduce for many generations without the intervention of a male. In the honeybee, fertilized eggs produce females, which become workers or queens, and the unfertilized eggs produce the male drones. The flow of sperm from the pouch of the queen is regulated with such care that she can fertilize hundreds of thousands of eggs after one mating, and the sperm held by the female are capable of fertilizing the eggs many years after mating. The economy of this process has led Brues to speculate on the grim possibility that it might be applied to *Homo sapiens*, relegating the male of the species to a role of minor importance.

A peculiar—and rare—variant of parthenogenesis, called *paedogenesis*, is found in some gall midges, in which the larvae and even the pupae may occasionally produce living young. The populations of insects capable of reproduction by parthenogenesis are likely to be very great, since the risk of frustration in the search for a mate is thereby reduced considerably. Another method of reproduction found among some parasites, which is also conducive to large populations, is that called *polyembrony*. It involves the splitting of the egg into two or more eggs, each of which develops into a new individual. In some species a single egg may develop into anywhere from fifteen hundred to twenty-five hundred individuals. One observer noted nearly three thousand parasitic wasps emerging from a single caterpillar in which not more than a dozen eggs had been oviposited. The Braconidae, and Platygasteridae, among other families of parasitic wasps, include species that are able to reproduce in this manner.

PRIMARY AND SECONDARY PARASITES

"Parasitism by other insects," according to E. O. Essig, "invades every species of insect—the plant and animal feeders and even the parasitic ones themselves. All forms of the host from egg to adult are subject to destruction by predators and parasites. The degree of parasitism or hyperparasitism may be fourfold or more."[5] A parasite attacking a particular host is said to be primary to that host—and if the latter is a pest, from our own point of view the parasite is of course beneficial. The same parasite, however, may be attacked by another which is secondary to the first host, and by the same token not beneficial. The secondary parasite may in turn be attacked by a tertiary parasite, which once again would be beneficial. Even when the secondary relationship ends in the death of the host pest—since parasites must be tolerant to the degree that the host is permitted to survive long enough to ensure their own development—there is still the loss of the beneficial parasite and a reduction of the population level. Generally the secondary parasites actually begin as primary parasites in that their eggs are deposited in the original host, from which their larvae later enter the bodies of their own hosts, the primary parasites.

[5] E. O. Essig, "How Insects Live," in *Yearbook of Agriculture* (Washington: Government Printing Office, 1952).

The process may be further complicated by multiple parasitism in which two species of primary parasites attack the same host— or by superparasitism in which two parasites of the same species attack the same host. The females, however, can generally detect the presence of the eggs already laid there, and will instinctively avoid ovipositing where potential competition threatens the survival of their offspring.

A TIME FOR EVERYTHING

There must be a proper correlation between the life cycles of the parasite and host if the former is to survive—which may explain why a species is specific in selecting its host. Brues describes a situation that illustrates the point:

A common chalcid parasite of the gypsy moth, *Anastatus bifasciatus (disparis)*, develops in the eggs of this moth. The gypsy moth hibernates in the egg state and the caterpillars hatch in the early spring. The *Anastatus* delay their emergence, however, until the eggs of the moths of the next generation have been laid in the late summer when they find fresh eggs in which to deposit their own. Upon the proper timing of its development cycle the future of this and similar parasites depends absolutely, unless as often happens another acceptable host is available to fill the gap.[6]

Imperfect coordination of the life cycles of parasite and host, with the lack of an alternate host, are frequent problems in establishing foreign species for biological control.

By far the greatest number of the insects parasitic on other insects belong to the order Hymenoptera—and of these a majority are wasps, of which, according to Brues, "well over half of the existing species are parasites of other insects."[7] Altogether the destructive members of the Hymenoptera are comparatively few, the best known being the wheat jointworm, the pearslug, the various sawflies, the currantworm, and possibly some ants— which tend in general to be more annoying than harmful. Para-

[6] Charles T. Brues, *Insect Dietary* (Cambridge: Harvard University Press, 1946).
[7] *Ibid.*

sitism in the order Diptera (flies) is more scattered but is a very important factor in natural and biological control. The order includes the large family of the Tachinidae (tachinid flies), with more than fourteen hundred species, all of which are parasitic, mostly on moths. Predation is also scattered throughout the Diptera. Of the largest insect order, the Coleoptera (beetles), almost none are parasites but many are important predators, notably the ground beetles and lady beetles.

The forces set in motion by every act of every animal and bacterium, by every inch of growth added to plant or tree, affect the lives of other creatures. The principles which govern these interrelationships are embraced in the science called ecology . . . the study of how the household of nature is kept in order.

—MONTHLY LETTER OF THE ROYAL BANK OF CANADA

PREDATORY INSECTS: THE BEETLES

3

Famed in nursery rhyme and legend, the lady beetles (family Coccinellidae) are probably the best known of all beneficial insects. Along with glowworms, they "are nearly as common in books as out of them," comments Geoffrey Taylor, the English biologist.[1] According to Frank Lutz, their name can be traced back to the medieval cult of the Virgin Mary.[2] Legend has it that these winged creatures swept into the grain fields in answer to prayers for Our Lady's help during a great insect infestation. As Taylor remarks, it argues "rather more of Divine intervention than we have a right to expect, or organs of sense finer than anything so far observed," when it is reported "that in seasons when the greenfly are exceptionally numerous—especially on Kentish hops—hosts of immigrant lady beetles will cross the Channel from the Continent and bring about the destruction which the natives were too few to ensure." Probably the familiar nursery rhyme—"Ladybird, ladybird, fly away home, Your house is on fire, your children will burn"—originated from the English

[1] Geoffrey Taylor, *Some British Beetles* (London: Penguin Books, 1948).
[2] F. E. Lutz, *Field Book of Insects of the U.S. and Canada* (New York: G. P. Putnam's Sons, 1935).

Lady beetle feeding on aphid. (*Harry Brevoort*)

custom of burning the hop vines after harvest, at a time when they were covered with aphids and feeding lady beetles, including their larvae, which were now obliged to fly or crawl as best they could to safety.

THE LADY'S NOT FOR BURNING[3]

The lady beetle family is almost entirely predaceous, feeding on aphids, mealybugs, whiteflies, scale insects and the eggs of other insects. Both adults and larvae are predators, the latter being even more voracious than their parents. Only a few of the species in this family can be considered parasitic; some that feed on the larger scale insects are parasitic in the sense that they may feed on only one individual host. The Coccinellidae are almost entirely beneficial except for a few plant feeders, confined largely to one genus, *Epilachna*. The common species in this category are the

[3] Apologies to Christopher Fry.

Lady beetle larva feeding on aphid. (*Lee Jenkins*)

notorious Mexican bean beetle, *Epilachna varivestis,* and the squash beetle, *Epilachna borealis* (which should not be confused with the squash *bug, Anasa tristis,* of the family Coreidae). The lady beetles are generally hemispherical in shape, though some —for example the convergent lady beetle, *Hippodamia convergens*—are oval and a bit flattened. The latter are sometimes mistaken for the destructive leaf beetles, such as the twelve-spotted cucumber beetle, *Diabrotica duodecimpunctata howardi.* However, although the convergent lady beetle also has twelve spots, it can be easily distinguished from the cucumber beetle by the converging marks forming a broken v between the head and body—whence its name. Another difference is in the number of segments making up the tarsi or "feet": the lady beetles have *three,* the leaf beetles four well-defined segments.

The eggs of the commoner lady beetles are yellow or orange, and oval in shape; they are usually laid singly or in small clusters on plant surfaces. They hatch in a few days, and the hungry larvae immediately start out in search of their victims—or the latter's eggs. These curious little creatures are flat and dark, with orange, blue, and black patches; the deeply segmented body is covered with spines, tapered toward the end and propelled by six long legs. Only the initiated are likely to associate the larvae with their more colorful parents. The larvae are fully grown in about twenty days and pupate after gluing the tip of the abdomen to a leaf or branch. The pupa is not enclosed in a cocoon but remains exposed on the surface of the plant. The more common species winter as adults, and some congregate in great numbers to hibernate. Some species, however—for example the Australian beetle *Cryptolaemus montrouzieri*—winter as pupae.

The reproductive capacity of some species is amazing. During a life span of a month or more, the female of the vedalia beetle (*Rodolia cardinalis*), which feeds on scale insects, may produce from five hundred to eight hundred eggs. In subtropical regions there may be eight or more generations in a year, with a life cycle from egg to adult of no more than thirteen days—two days in the egg, eight as a larva and three as a pupa—while summer temperatures prevail. The eggs, which are red in this species, are placed singly or in clusters either on or beneath the scale insect that is its prey. The larvae feed on the eggs and young nymphs, the adults on all stages of the victim.

The appetite of the lady beetles seems never to be satisfied, and they eat almost continuously. One *Coccinella californica* was observed to eat 475 aphids, or an average of twenty-five a day, during its larval development; as an adult it consumed an average of thirty-four per day during its life span. One European species, *Coccinella septempunctata*, is reported to eat 267 aphids per day. The appetites of these lady beetles are exceeded, however, by that of *Chilocorus similis*, which has been observed to eat 772 aphids during its larval development, and 791 during its life span as an adult.

Adult lady beetles vary in color from red or reddish yellow

Top, life history (egg stage missing) of the twice-stabbed lady beetle, *Chilocorus bivulnerus,* a predator of sycamore scale. *Below,* larva of same lady beetle on sycamore scale. (*Roy J. Pence*)

to tan or brown, with black spots; a few are black with red spots. The number of spots varies with different species; there are, for example, the common two-spotted lady beetle, *Adalia bipunctata;* the nine-spotted lady beetle, *Coccinella novemnotata;* and the thirteen-spotted lady beetle, *Hippodamia tredecimpunctata.* Still another species has fifteen spots; and the twelve-spotted convergent lady beetle has already been mentioned. Other common species are the red lady beetle, *Cycloneda munda;* the spotted lady beetle, *Megilla fuscilabris;* the glacial lady beetle, *Hippodamia glacialis;* and the parenthesis lady beetle, *Hippodamia parenthesis,* which is so named for two black markings at the back of the elytra. The previously mentioned destructive Mexican bean beetle has sixteen spots, and unlike most of the beneficial

Congregating convergent lady beetles. (*Lee Jenkins*)

species, it has no markings between head and body. There are in all about 350 species of lady beetles in the United States. Two interesting characteristics of the adults are worth mentioning. One is the habit, when disturbed, of rising into a vertical position and then slowly dropping back; this may be a death-feigning posture. Another means of protection is a disagreeable secretion exuded by the leg joints of an adult when it is attacked.

THE CONVERGENT LADY BEETLES

The convergent lady beetle is the species most often used for the biological control of aphids, since it is the most common of the aphid-eaters and hibernates in vast colonies which can be easily collected. Such colonies occur in hollow stumps and under rocks and forest litter in the mountain valleys and canyons of California and other western states. As many as fifty or sixty gallons may be collected in one spot, making the cost low. The beetles, which can be purchased from a number of sources in practically any quantity, are shipped by air in ventilated cartons and remain in a dormant state if kept under refrigeration. A gallon is estimated to contain about 135,000 beetles.

For many years the state of California collected these beetles by the ton and distributed them free to vegetable growers, especially melon growers, who used them extensively, until tests made in the Imperial Valley indicated that the practice was of no great benefit. It was learned that the beetles dispersed rapidly as soon as they were released, and that a population of native species was always present, which began developing as soon as the aphid population was sufficient to sustain it and allow it to multiply. The same beetles have also been used on a large scale in the eastern states in an attempt to control the pea aphid, and in the middle west to control the greenbug, a destructive pest of wheat. These projects have not been successful, apparently for the same reason; C. P. Clausen therefore cautions against relying on early spring releases, no matter what the number.[4]

MIGRATION OF LADY BEETLES

The migratory habits of the convergent lady beetle have been described by Kenneth Hagen as follows:

The ladybird beetle—*Hippodamia convergens*—has the unusual habit of congregating in large masses for hibernation in mountain canyons. The times of migration from the valleys in the early summer and the return from the mountains in the following spring have an important bearing upon the effectiveness of the beetle in controlling aphid infestations. Recent research has shed much light on the several factors influencing this migration habit. After the development of one or more generations in the field during the spring, the food supply usually becomes deficient and this provides the stimulus for migration to the mountains, which may be fifty miles or more away. On arrival in the mountains in June, the beetles feed for some time on pollen, plant exudations, and other noninsect food and their weight may be doubled during this period. They first assemble in small aggregations along creeks, and later consolidate in the forest litter into larger aggregations

[4] C. P. Clausen, *Biological Control of Insect Pests in the Continental United States* (Washington: USDA Technical Bulletin No. 1139, June 1956).

which may be as great as five hundred gallons. Here they remain from October to February, usually deeply covered by snow during the winter.

During the first warm days of February or March, when temperatures exceed fifty-five degrees Fahrenheit, the beetles again become active. These warm periods are associated with high pressure areas over the northwestern states, creating easterly winds over the Sierra. The beetles take off vertically, ascending up to several thousand feet above the point of origin, and then ride the prevailing winds to the valleys below. A specially designed trap on an airplane was used to check the flight patterns of the beetles in both directions. Catches have been made at elevations up to 3,500 feet as the beetles leave the mountains, and up to 5,000 feet as they return. It is becoming apparent that the primary destination in the migrations of *H. convergens* is governed by wind direction and temperature, and that the extended flights are triggered by nutritional factors.[5]

THE VEDALIA

The most famous of the lady beetles—or possibly of all insects for that matter—is the vedalia, an Australian species (*Rodolia cardinalis*) that was first imported in 1888 to control the cottony cushion scale, *Icerya purchasi*. Unaided, these little beetles virtually rescued the citrus industry in California from destruction. The cottony cushion scale is a small insect (family Coccidae) of great fecundity that attaches itself to leaves and twigs of citrus trees, from which it sucks the sap. In the course of fifteen years after it was first discovered in California in 1872, it had become a serious threat to the citrus groves. In most cases a foreign species that gains entry comes in without the natural checks—predators, parasites, and insect diseases—that keep it more or less within bounds in its native country, with the result that it is likely to be far more troublesome than in its place of origin. The cottony cushion scale, which had been known to exist only in Australia before it somehow gained entry into California, was no exception.

In 1888 Albert Koebele went to Australia in search of a parasite that was believed to keep the scale under control there. A tiny fly,

[5] Kenneth S. Hagen, "Migration of Ladybird Beetles," *California Agriculture,* March 1959.

Adult vedalia beetles feeding on cottony cushion scale. (*K. L. Middle-ham*, courtesy *T. W. Fisher*)

Cryptochaetum iceryae, which parasitized the scale, was found and sent back to California; but at the same time, by a stroke of good fortune, Koebele also discovered the vedalia. In all he sent back 514 beetles over a period of a few months. They thrived in their new home and quickly became established throughout the citrus areas of California, with the result that in a matter of only two years the scale was brought under complete control. The parasitic fly became established too as a valuable agent of control, but it was eclipsed by the vedalia. For an expenditure of less than $5,000, savings of millions of dollars annually have been realized. So successful was the control that it was difficult to find a single small colony of cottony cushion scale, and when one did appear the vedalia soon moved in to take care of it. This situation prevailed until the advent of DDT and the other insecticides that came in rapid succession after World War II. What happened then has been described by C. P. Clausen:

The widespread use of DDT and other even more toxic chlorinated hydrocarbons and organic phosphates in the control of crop pests has upset the balance of many associated insects and has raised them to the status of major pests. These insecticides, especially DDT, persist

The mealybug destroyer, *Cryptolaemus montrouzieri:* larvae and adults feeding on Baker's mealybug. (*Roy J. Pence*)

on the foliage for months and practically eradicate the parasite and predator populations. The general use of DDT against the citricola scale and citrus thrips in certain areas in California eliminated the vedalia beetle in those areas. As a result heavy and destructive infestations of the cottony cushion scale quickly appeared such as had not been seen for more than fifty years. Consequently, it was necessary to recolonize the vedalia after the toxic residues on the foliage had been dissipated.[6]

MASS PRODUCTION

Another important lady beetle brought in for biological control was *Cryptolaemus montrouzieri,* a mealybug predator which was first introduced in California from Australia in 1891, again by Koebele. At first the beetle did very well and was credited with checking a number of outbreaks of the citrus mealybug (*Pseudo-*

[6] C. P. Clausen, *Biological Control of Insect Pests in the Continental United States* (Washington: USDA Technical Bulletin No. 1139, June 1956).

coccus citri), but later the predator subsided, apparently because it was not able to survive the winters in the interior valleys, although it did better in the coastal regions. However, new methods developed in 1917 for rearing the insect on a mass production basis, made it possible to use the beetle to control the citrus mealybug on a large scale, whenever and wherever it was needed. Each season, whenever an outbreak occurred the beetles were released on the infested trees at the rate of ten to twenty beetles per tree.

According to Clausen the rearing of *Cryptolaemus* was "the first and still one of the outstanding examples of mass production" for biological control.[7] One of the problems in mass production of predators and parasites is finding a suitable host plant or other material for rearing the host insect—that is, the one to be controlled. The predators or parasites need plenty of food in the form of their regular diet—or a substitute when a suitable one can be found—if they are to develop in great numbers. Obviously citrus trees can't be moved into the insectary, nor can production on a large scale be controlled in the citrus grove. Rearings from the original vedalia beetles had been made by covering an infested citrus tree with a cloth tent, mass production not being required since one release of a comparatively small number of insects was sufficient to establish the beetle permanently.

The solution to this problem in the case of the *Cryptolaemus* beetle—and of some parasites—was found in the use of sprouted potatoes. The mealybug accepted this substitute for the citrus tree and multiplied rapidly on its new diet. Potatoes were sprouted in open trays eighteen inches square, and infested with mealybugs; when these matured and laid their eggs the beetles were released in the room. As many as four hundred beetles were produced from each tray. At the height of the program in the 1920's fifteen county and private organizations were cooperating in the production of millions of lady beetles for control of mealybugs in southern California. At one time Orange County alone had twenty-two buildings specially built for the purpose, which altogether turned out

[7] *Ibid.*

millions of lady beetles per day. Cost of production at this time amounted to $2.50 per thousand lady beetles.

Since this was a recurring cost, parasites were sought for permanent control, and these are now used more extensively. In some instances a combination of beetles and parasites is effective. In Ventura County about fifty million *Cryptolaemus* beetles are still raised annually, as well as millions of parasites to control the citrus mealybug.[8] Experiments were conducted in Massachusetts with this lady beetle as a control of infestations of the citrus mealybug on gardenias and chrysanthemums in greenhouses. The problem there was the fact that the beetle does not reproduce rapidly when reinfestation is light, so that when the mealybug gets a head start, considerable damage may be done before the second generation of beetles appears. Also, *Cryptolaemus* does not reproduce satisfactorily at temperatures below 70° F. Since greenhouses are maintained at lower temperatures than this during the winter months, the beetle is commercially practical only during the spring and early summer months. However, in conjunction with one or two parasites it is believed to offer possibilities.

OTHER IMPORTS

Of the ninety-five species of insects imported into this country for biological control and known to be established, fourteen have been predators and most of these are lady beetles. The principal importations besides the vedalia and *Cryptolaemus* will be covered briefly here. Black scale (*Saissetia oleae*) has long been a serious pest of citrus trees, and the search for predators and parasites of this insect has gone on relentlessly for many years. Three lady beetle predators which held some promise have become established in California as a result of Koebele's search in Australia.

---

[8] Three insectaries are operated in Ventura County by growers' cooperatives, and one in Chula Vista by San Diego County. For mass. culture techniques for these lady beetles and a parasite of mealybugs, *Leptomastix dactylopii*, see T. W. Fisher, *Mass Culture of* Cryptolaemus *and* Leptomastix, *Natural Enemies of Citrus Mealybug* (Berkeley: University of California Bulletin 797, July 1963).

The most important of these is the black lady beetle, *Rhizobius ventralis,* which produced results that were sensational at the start but rather less so as time went on. It has since proved more effective in olive groves, where it has given commercial control of the black scale at various times. The second of these imports, *Rhizobius debilis,* has persisted in the coastal regions of southern California but is not numerous enough to be very important. However, it is reported to be an important check on a scale insect (*Chrysomphalus dictyospermi*) in Louisiana. The third of these introductions, *Lindorus lophantae,* is now established throughout southern and central California and is quite numerous in some places. It has, however, turned to other hosts, such as the California red scale (*Aonidiella aurantii*) and to some of the soft scales and mealybugs. Another lady beetle imported at the same time was *Orcus chalybeus,* which is also a predator of red scales. It is currently known to exist only in the Santa Barbara region, where it is common but not numerous enough to be important. Attempts to establish *Chilocorus similis,* a valuable enemy of San Jose scale (*Aspidiotus perniciosus*) in Japan, were not successful.

A lady beetle, *Scymnus binaevatus,* from South Africa, was imported by the University of California in 1921 for mealybug control, and although it was successfully established in southern California it has not become important as an agent of control. It becomes more numerous where there are infestations of the citrophilus mealybug than in the presence of the citrus mealybug. A common lady beetle that preys on scale insects and aphids in Europe is *Exochomus quadripustulatus.* Early importations from France and Italy into Massachusetts and California failed, but a later attempt by the University of California, in 1921, was successful. It has since become an important check on the woolly apple aphid (*Eriosoma lanigerum*) and works well in conjunction with a parasite (*Aphelinus mali*) of the aphid.

The attempt to establish *Catana parcesetosa,* a lady beetle from India, to combat the citrus whitefly (*Dialeurodes citri*) in Florida was not completed owing to loss of stocks in the winter, and apparently no further attempts were made. In 1936–1939 two species, *Azya trinitatis* and *Cryptognatha nodiceps,* were brought into Florida from Puerto Rico and Trinidad for control of the coconut scale (*Aspidiotus destructor*); they were later reported established near Miami, but no further information is available. An aphid-eater, *Leis dimidiata 15-spilota,* was imported from South China in 1925 by the University of California. It was not suited to that state; but it was successfully established in Florida the following year, and for several years was an important control of aphids in citrus and papaya groves. It was at one time reported to be more numerous there than any native species, but it was later found to be adversely affected by severe winters.

The appearance of an Asiatic pest, the citrus blackfly (*Aleurocanthus woglumi*) in Cuba, the Bahamas, and Central America in 1913 was a serious threat to the citrus industry in Florida. Accordingly, the United States Department of Agriculture took steps to cooperate with the countries involved in order to reduce the possibility of its introduction here. A lady beetle, *Catana clauseni,* and a parasitic wasp, *Eretmocerus serius,* were introduced from Malaya in 1930 and quickly brought about complete control—most of the credit, however, going to the wasp. Discovery of the blackfly on the west coast of Mexico in 1935 was a threat to the citrus industry in California. Cooperative steps have since been under way using the same parasite that proved so successful in Cuba, along with some others.

GROUND BEETLES

The ground beetles (Carabidae), sometimes referred to as "caterpillar hunters," feed largely on insects and as a family are among our most valuable predatory families, probably ranking close to the lady beetles. A few species are plant-feeders, and some of the insect-feeders occasionally resort to plant food, but in neither case are they a serious problem. The larvae are wholly predaceous except for a few species that live as external parasites. The number of American species is variously reported to be anywhere from

A ground beetle. Adults and larvae of these "caterpillar hunters" are important insect predators. (*Lee Jenkins*)

twelve hundred to two thousand. The attractive adults have long, somewhat flattened bodies, some with beautifully iridescent blue and green coloring. Mostly active at night, they are enabled by their long, slim legs to run swiftly over the ground and low-growing vegetation or into trees. As a rule they lay their eggs and pupate in the soil; ordinarily development from egg to adult takes one year.

The "bombardier beetle" (*Brachinus fumans*) has an interesting protective mechanism consisting of glands opening near the anus. From these it can shoot out puffs of a fetid, irritating vapor, forming a kind of smoke screen behind which it escapes. A slight popping sound accompanies the discharge, and as many as five or six puffs in succession can be sent out without "recharging." One of the larger species in this region is the "fiery searcher," *Calosoma scrutator*—a beautiful, iridescent green beetle that consumes hairy tent caterpillars in great numbers. Its name comes from its habit of giving off a blistering fluid when alarmed.

A species common east of the Rockies is *Pasimachus depressus*, which measures well over an inch in length and is one of the largest of its family. It is black with a margin of blue around its forewings and thorax, and is found in the daytime under rocks and logs. At night it forages for armyworms and cutworms. Another of the larger species, *Harpalus caliginosus*, is common throughout the same region. Its larva digs an inclined tunnel in the soil for daytime seclusion and covers the entrance with a clod of earth. *Lebia grandis* is smaller—about half an inch long—and in its iridescent blue coloring resembles the bombadier beetle; it is common in the eastern United States and southern Canada. Like most of the other ground beetles it hides under rocks and logs in the daytime. Some species of the genus *Cychrus* are among the few predators of land snails, using their long, pointed heads and mandibles to reach into the coiled shell of their prey.

Ground beetles generally prefer to feed on moths (Lepidoptera) in the larval and pupal stages, and on the adults in other insect orders, although they are also reported to attack the grubs of scarab beetles. These ferocious predators are sometimes rather fastidious in their eating habits. Some tear their victims into small pieces before devouring them; others paralyze their victims first and inject a digestive fluid which liquefies the body contents before the feast begins. *Calosoma sycophanta*, an imported species, is less delicate in these matters, simply plunging its jaws into the side of a caterpillar and drawing out the semiliquid body contents. As a larva this species feeds day and night, consuming at least fifty full-grown gypsy moth caterpillars during a developmental period of two weeks. *Calosoma frigidum*, a native species, is much less voracious, requiring only about fourteen caterpillars during its larval development. The adult of *Calosoma sycophanta* will eat several hundred caterpillars during a life span of from two to four years. The highly prolific female has been known to lay 653 eggs in one year. This remarkable creature has played an important part in the control of the gypsy moth.

GROUND BEETLES VS. GYPSY MOTHS

Importations of *Calosoma sycophanta* from Europe to New England for biological control of the gypsy moth (*Porthetria dispar*) began in 1905. By 1910 over 4,000 live beetles had been imported, and over 2,700 had been released in the field. In addition over 14,000 larvae were reared in the laboratory and released during the same time. The original releases in 1906, in colonies of thirty to fifty beetles at several points in the vicinity of Boston, were followed the next year by releases in the entire area infested by the gypsy moth. In two years one colony had spread over eleven square miles. By 1927 over 35,000 beetles and nearly 20,000 larvae, imported and reared, had been liberated, and colonization had extended outside the infested area. The species now covers a wide range outside New England, reaching into the southern and western states. Concerning the place of this beetle in the control of the gypsy moth Clausen draws the following conclusion:

It is difficult to evaluate the effect of a predator of this type, but the abundance and general distribution of *Calosoma* in the areas heavily infested by the gypsy moth warrants the belief that it is one of the most important of the imported enemies of this pest, and the large number of larvae and pupae that are destroyed by it indicates that it contributes substantialy to reducing the infestations.[9]

Another beetle in the family Carabidae that was imported and colonized about the same time as *Calosoma* is *Carabus auratus,* a predator which feeds on the gypsy moth and browntail moth in Europe. There is evidence that it was established, some recoveries having been made in 1920, but no other information is available. Millions of parasites have also been imported and released for control of the gypsy moth. These will be treated in a later chapter.

ROVE BEETLES

The beetles of this interesting family (Staphylinidae) are largely predaceous. They somewhat resemble the earwigs in that the forewings only partially cover their long, flat bodies, and that the head and thorax are about as broad as the abdomen. They do not, however, have the cerci in the form of forceps at the "tail

[9] C. P. Clausen, *ibid.*

end" of the abdomen as do the earwigs. Like some of the ground beetles, certain species are armed with protective glands at the tip of the abdomen, from which they give off a foul-smelling vapor or fluid, curving the abdomen over the back and ejecting the secretion in the direction of attack. A few fairly large species, such as the hairy rove beetle, are scavengers; others live in ant colonies as harmless "guests" or as predators. Some very small species prey on mites; others eat the eggs and larvae of bark beetles; and a few species are external parasites on small mammals—marsupials and rodents—in Central and South America. This is a very large family of insects, comprising over twenty thousand species throughout the world and over a thousand in this country.

A minute species, *Oligota flavicornis,* that preys on mites in English orchards, has been described by B. D. Moreton.[10] It overwinters under bark or vegetation as an adult, laying its eggs on the lower parts of leaves and covering them with debris. Development from egg to adult takes about four weeks, with two generations occurring each year. The adults devour the mites completely; the larvae suck out the juices. A large species called the devil's coach horse (*Staphylinus olens*) is also common in England; both adults and larvae live almost completely on slugs. The adults are formidable creatures, able to pierce the skin of a man's hand with their jaws, and give off an odorous yellow secretion. The larvae of *Tachyporus hypnorum* attack aphids on raspberry and strawberry plants. Two British species, *Aleochara bilineata* and *A. bipustulata,* are known to attack the pupae of the cabbage root fly.

Rove beetles are also an important enemy of the cabbage maggot in this country. *Aleochara bimaculata* is a small, active insect, less than a quarter of an inch long, with shiny black wing covers. These beetles have a sort of social life, congregating in large numbers in the soil where they build a series of small chambers and interconnecting tunnels. They are parasitic in that they

[10] B. D. Moreton, *Beneficial Insects* (London: Ministry of Agriculture, Fisheries and Food, Bulletin 20, 1958).

depend on a single host for their development; but unlike those of true parasites, the larvae must search for the host. The adult female lays her eggs where cabbage plants and the maggots or larvae of the cabbage fly, *Hylemya brassicae*, are likely to be found. The brown, horny larvae of this rove beetle hatch in about ten days and immediately start in search of the fly's pupae. In a season as many as 80 per cent of the cabbage maggots in a field may fall victim to these aggressive beetles.

CHECKERED BEETLES

The checkered beetles (Cleridae), named for the contrasting color patterns on their wing covers, are almost completely predaceous in both the adult and larval stages. They show a remarkably consistent preference for the bark and other wood-boring beetles, and constitute one of the most important checks on these destructive forest pests. They are handsome insects, whose rounded bodies are covered with a thick coat of hairs. The larvae may be either flat or rounded and are also covered with hairs, with horny projections on the top of one body segment; they vary in color through several shades of red and yellow. The adults prey on adult wood-borers, and the larvae feed on the eggs and larvae. The larvae seek out the wood-borers in their tunnels but can themselves bore through dead wood if necessary. When they reach maturity they descend to the base of the trees and pupate in cells made from earth and held together by secretions from glands inside their mouths. Adult females lay their eggs near the food supply. They may produce one or several generations a year, depending on the life cycle of their prey.

The most important species belong to the genera *Thanasimus, Enoclerus,* and *Tillus.* Both the adults and larvae of *Tarostenus univittatus* prey on powder-post beetles (Lyctidae) of the genera *Lyctus* and *Xylobiops,* which infest seasoned wood products. *Enoclerus sphegeus,* occurring throughout western forests from British Columbia to New Mexico, preys on the Black Hills beetle (*Dendroctonus ponderosae*) and other bark beetles. *Thanero-*

clerus girodi is the most important natural enemy of the cigarette beetle (*Lasioderma serricorne*) of the family Anobiidae. The ant beetle, *Thanasimus formicarius,* is mentioned as a hunter of bark beetles in England; its red larvae feed on eggs and larvae in the tunnels of these beetles. *Callimerus arcufer* is an important enemy of the coconut moth in Malaya.

FIREFLIES

The flashing of fireflies (Lampyridae) or "lightning-bugs" is a familiar sight on warm, languorous summer evenings. More abdominal segments are luminous in the males than in the females, and they give a brighter light. Some doubt exists as to whether the luminescence is actually a device for bringing the sexes together, although this is generally the explanation given. In one common species, *Photuris pennsylvanica,* it may be a device used by the female to attract males of other species, for a less romantic reason—namely, in order to devour them. The female of one European species loses her luminosity after mating. The glow is explained as a chemical reaction within the cells between an enzyme called luciferase and another substance called luciferin. But as Geoffrey Taylor says, for most of us this explanation is probably "less illuminating than the glow itself."[11]

Collectively fireflies sometimes make a startling display of light. John Pursell describes a scene on Mindanao in the Philippines as follows:

. . . There were two trees about the size of apple trees and perhaps a hundred feet apart, and every evening these were filled with fireflies which flashed in synchronism, first one tree lighting up, then the other. There must have been several thousand insects in each tree, yet the synchronism was so perfect that rarely or never did a single firefly flash at the wrong time. . . . The illuminated period lasted about two or three seconds and the dark period perhaps twice as long. . . . It seemed so strange and produced so beautiful an effect that I thought it one of the most remarkable things in the Philippines, and it made a deep impression on me.

[11] *Some British Beetles* (London: Penguin Books, 1948).

Larva of lampyrid beetle ("firefly"), an important predator of snails and slugs. Adults fly only at twilight and appear not to feed at all. (*Lee Jenkins*)

This phenomenon, although rarely observed outside the tropics, is apparently not uncommon there and is associated in some way with temperature and moisture conditions.

The flashings appear to follow a rhythmic pattern. It has been observed that the male *Photinus pyralis* flashes at intervals of 5.7 seconds, and that the female responds at intervals of 2.1 seconds. Laboratory studies show that although these flashings are associated with the light intensity of the environment, they are governed by a definite periodicity. It has been found that if fireflies are kept in darkness for periods of 24, 48, 72, or 96 hours, they begin flashing when exposed to a dim light, but that they fail to do so when they are kept in the dark for periods of 12, 36, 60, or 84 hours. Another remarkable thing about this light is that it is produced with almost no heat loss. It is not a phosphorescence, since it does not depend on any previous illumination, and it continues—though without flashing—after the insect dies. It does not contain infrared or ultraviolet rays, but it can be polarized and will affect a photographic plate.

Adult fireflies are rather long and flat, the common species measuring about half an inch long, and range in color from black to brown. Some females have very short wings or none at all, and are thus almost or entirely unable to fly. This is true of two common species: the female of *Photinus pyralis* flies a little, and the female of *Photinus scintillans* does not fly at all.

The larva, the "glowworm" celebrated in romantic verse and song, has luminous organs on one or more segments of the body and glows even before hatching from the egg. Entirely predaceous, it is a flat, sturdy creature with a small head that can be extended and retracted, equipped with strong, sicklelike jaws—all of which suits the glowworm to its job of preying on snails. It climbs over the snail's back, and when the head is extended it pierces the skin with its jaws, injecting a digestive fluid that so quickly paralyzes the snail that it cannot withdraw into its shell and that reduces the body contents of the prey to a more or less liquid form—a practice that is not uncommon among predators. These beetles are valuable allies of man in controlling snails and slugs, which can become serious garden pests. In Ceylon *Lamprophorus tenebrosus* is an important check on the African or Kalutara snail, a serious pest of vegetable crops. Another species, *Lampyris noctiluca*, was imported into New Zealand from England for biological control. In the Orient still other species are also important in controlling snails which serve as intermediate hosts to flukes that parasitize man.

Owing to their predilection for snails and slugs, fireflies are most commonly found in damp places. Their eggs are laid in or on moist ground protected by vegetation. The larvae, which require from one to two years to develop, spend the winter in individual cells hollowed out in the soil. The pupae are found in individual cells constructed of earth above ground or under rocks or litter.

SOLDIER BEETLES

The soldier beetles (Cantharidae), which resemble the fireflies, are believed to be largely predaceous and beneficial. In general their food preference is for eggs and larvae of other insects. Many species of the genera *Podabrus* and *Cantharis* are known to feed on aphids. The larvae of *Cantharis rustica* feed on grasshopper eggs and the larvae of moths and beetles; and the larvae of *Chauliognathus marginalis* will enter the tunnels of the corn earworm (*Heliothis zea*) in the corn and devour the larvae. The species most commonly found east of the Rockies is *Chauliognathus pennsylvanicus.* The eggs are deposited in masses in the soil, and hatch in about a week. One or two generations occur each year. Unfortunately—as is true of many other groups of insects—this family does not appear to have been studied extensively.

TIGER BEETLES

In the preface to his book on the tiger beetles of Canada, J. B. Wallis makes the comment:

One of the world's great biologists, J.B.S. Haldane, was once asked what one could conclude about the nature of the Creator from a study of His creation. The reply was "an inordinate fondness for beetles." This remark is based upon the fact that the beetles are the largest order of living animals. Now, if the Creator was fond of beetles, He must have been especially fond of the Cicindelidae or tiger beetles, because they are formed so beautifully, colored so brilliantly, and move so gracefully.[12]

It is believed that all species of tiger beetles (Cicindelidae) are predaceous, in both the adult and larval stages. They have large heads with prominent eyes and mandibles, and average perhaps half an inch in length. The vast majority are terrestrial, though they are common along seashores, lakes, and rivers. They are widely distributed and often are seen darting in and out of woodland trails; those that prefer the sun are fast fliers and quick on the takeoff. Many are attractively colored in various shades of metallic green or purple, with or without white spots numbering up to five on each wing. The six-spotted tiger beetle, *Cicindela sexguttata,* is a common species. *Amblycheila cylindriformis,* an interesting species found in some of the plains states, is well over an inch long. It is nocturnal in habit and cannot fly since its forewings are fused together.

[12] J. B. Wallis, *The Cicindelidae of Canada* (Toronto: University of Toronto Press, 1961).

The larvae are sometimes called "doodlebugs"—a name that is also applied to antlion larvae. Indeed, there is a similarity in their tactics too. The tiger beetles dig deep burrows in the ground, where they lie in wait to snatch and drag their prey inside. Their huge spiny heads, which fill the entrance hole of the tunnel, are equipped with powerful mandibles. Yet another special adaptation for their maneuvers consists of a pair of hooks attached to one body segment about halfway down the back. This serves to anchor the beetle in place, the better to reach out and hold its victim. Tiger beetles spend the winter in the late larval stages; when they are fully grown they close the entrance holes, and pupation takes place. Since they appear to be unselective in their choice of prey, and are not numerous, their importance as a control factor is questionable.

BLISTER OR OIL BEETLES

The blister beetles (Meloidae) are so named because a crushed adult brought into contact with the human skin can cause a severe blister. The blistering agent, known as cantharidin, is a dangerous drug which—though largely discredited today—was once used as an aphrodisiac, and is still used to some extent as a counter-irritant and even, mixed with bay rum, as a hair restorer. The substance occurs in the insect's blood and, in more concentrated form, in the reproductive organs. Perhaps the best known of these beetles is the Spanish fly, *Lytta vesicatoria,* which is found throughout southern Europe as well as in Spain. *Pomphopoea sayi,* a beetle sometimes found on peaches, can cause severe poisoning, and *Diamphidia locusta* is used by African tribes to poison their arrows. Curiously enough, blister beetles are eaten by about fifty different species of birds, which do not seem to be affected by them. The name "oil beetle" comes from an oily yellow fluid exuded from the joints.

This family is one of the most common and widely distributed groups of beetles, and in its feeding habits it is perhaps more remarkable than any other. The adults feed exclusively on plants,

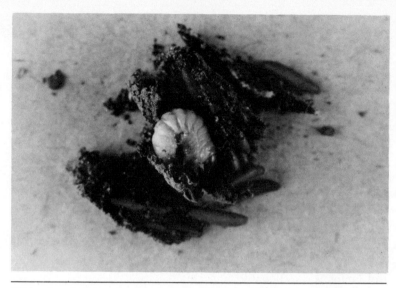

Blister beetle larva feeding on grasshopper eggs. (*Lee Jenkins*)

and some species are important crop pests; one of these, the margined blister beetle, *Epicauta pestifera,* is a pest of many crop plants, especially those of the nightshade (potato) family. The larvae of blister beetles, on the other hand, are exclusively predaceous or parasitic. The great majority of these whose food habits are known, prey on the eggs of grasshoppers (Locustidae) and belong mainly to the genera *Zonabris and Epicauta.* A somewhat smaller number of species are parasites of bees, usually those that build their nests in the soil. This combination of harmful and beneficial traits leaves the economic value of the family open to some doubt.

The adults are often more than a half inch long, with soft bodies and large heads in comparison to the thorax; some species have no wings, and others are poorly adapted for flying. The female beetles dig holes in the ground, in which they lay large egg masses —as many as ten thousand eggs at a time—and then cover them over with soil. The tiny larvae, known as triungulins, find their way through the soil to the egg pods of grasshoppers—or, if they are of the species that prey on bees (such as the *Meloe* beetle described by Fabre), they climb the stems of flowering plants and attach themselves to the flowers to await the arrival of a bee. Their heads and jaws are comparatively large and they have long legs for grasping. Some of them have spines at the end of their bodies, with adhesive pads that enable them to stand on end and latch onto the hairy body of a bee. Fabre found that *Meloe* larvae would at first grab anything offered—a piece of grass or cloth for example—but quickly learned to reject it, and would then seem wary if the same object was offered a second time. They did, however, quickly accept and cling to any insect or spider that was offered. But to complete the cycle and to perpetuate their species they must find the right bee. For the British species *Meloe proscarabaeus* and *Meloe violaceus*, the host not only must be a small bumblebee of the genus *Anthophora*, but must also be the female of the species. When the right choice has been made, the larva is transported to the bee's cell, where its first food is the egg of the host; then, after molting, it lives on the honey in the cell. Where so much depends on chance, it is no wonder that out of the ten thousand eggs laid only about two larvae survive.

NATURAL CONTROL OF GRASSHOPPERS

The part played by predators in controlling grasshoppers was brought out in a grasshopper egg survey conducted by the U. S. Department of Agriculture as a part of its Grasshopper Control Project. The survey, which involved most of the western and midwestern states and covered the years from 1938 to 1940, showed that the average annual destruction of grasshopper egg pods was 15 per cent—6.9 per cent by bee flies, 5.6 per cent by blister beetles, and 2.5 per cent by ground beetles. In several states, the average predation for many counties was much higher, however —an average of 50 per cent. Conclusions based on the survey were summarized as follows:

The beneficial effects of natural factors in reducing grasshopper infestations is generally recognized. Most farmers and workers engaged in grasshopper control have seen grasshopper populations greatly reduced by parasites and diseases; insect, bird, and animal predators;

and weather. Entomologists, including the authors, have been prone to view destruction of grasshopper eggs by larvae of bee flies, blister beetles, and ground beetles as of importance locally but of minor and unpredictable importance in reducing grasshopper populations over sizable geographical areas.

Data obtained by the Plant Pest Control Division in county surveys indicate that destruction of grasshopper egg pods by these predators was high over several extensive areas for the three years of survey, and there were few counties in which it did not occur. For example, . . . in 1938 from 25 to 49 per cent of all egg pods were destroyed in an area that included the eastern part of Montana, nearly all of North Dakota, the western part of South Dakota, the Panhandle of Nebraska, and several counties in Colorado, northern South Dakota, and western Minnesota. Within this extensive area, predatism ranged from 50 to 64 per cent in single counties and groups of contiguous counties. In many counties where the average percentage of predators was high, predatism was 80 to 90 per cent at individual survey stops and in a few counties, it was as much as 100 per cent.

Data obtained by the Entomology Research Division on smaller unit areas, but by more intensive sampling over more years, are in surprisingly close agreement with data obtained in the same counties by the Plant Pest Control Division. A comparison of data from the two sources shows that in at least four of the states subject to major grasshopper outbreaks, larvae of bee flies, blister beetles, and ground beetles destroy considerable numbers of grasshopper egg pods every year. In the counties listed, average yearly reduction approximates 25 per cent of the eggs laid.

Without destruction of grasshopper egg pods by larvae of bee flies, blister beetles, and ground beetles, and by other natural factors, the frequency of major grasshopper outbreaks over extensive areas would be greatly increased. Altogether, natural factors are so important in preventing extensive, explosive outbreaks that control by man, necessary as it is for additional population reduction and crop protection, is directed at only a small part of the potential population.[14]

HISTER BEETLES

Many of the hister beetles (Histeridae) are scavengers in both the adult and larval stages and are often found associated with dung,

[13] J. R. Parker and Claude Wakeland, *Grasshopper Egg Pods Destroyed by Larvae of Bee Flies, Blister Beetles, and Ground Beetles* (Washington: USDA Technical Bulletin No. 1165, July 1957).

decaying animal matter, and fungi; but the family also includes many members that are predaceous on various insects. Hister beetles are small and dark, with shiny forewings that don't cover the last two segments of the abdomen. The scavengers are generally more rounded and feed on the fly larvae associated with decaying animal matter. A few species attack the immature forms of leaf beetles (Chrysomelidae) and the caterpillars of moths and butterflies. Others have been found feeding on insects in stored grain. Many species in this family are tiny creatures that prey on the immature forms of bark beetles (Scolytidae) and other soft-bodied insects found under the bark of trees.

The larvae of *Plegaderus nitidus* attack the eggs of species in the genus *Dendroctonus*, while those of *Platysoma depressum*, common throughout North America, attack insects associated with the bark of oak and elm trees. *P. punctigerum* larvae are active hunters and feed on a wide variety of insects found under bark. The eggs are placed alongside those of the bark beetle, in the latter's galleries, and hatch in from ten to fourteen days. The larval development is completed in from four to six weeks and the pupal stage in from ten to fourteen days, with two generations a year. The larvae and adults of *Plaesius javanus* are important predators upon the banana borer (*Cosmopolites sordida*) in Java, and have been successfully introduced into Fiji and Australia, although similar attempts in Hawaii, Formosa, Uganda, and the West Indies were not successful. Another species, *Hister bimaculatus*, was introduced into Hawaii from Germany in 1909 to combat the horn fly.

SOME OTHER SCAVENGERS

Like the hister beetles, many of the carrion beetles (Silphidae) have forewings which do not entirely cover the abdomen. They are medium-sized, and are found mostly in decaying animal matter; many feed on a combination of decaying flesh and other insects associated with decomposing carcasses. The latter are generally flies, particularly blowflies. A European species, *Xylodrepa quadripunctata,* is associated with plants and shows a particular liking for smooth-skinned caterpillars or those with a light covering of hairs; it was once introduced into the United States for biological control of the gypsy moth. *Silpha quadripunctata* is said to be common in the oak woods in southern England, where it feeds on moth caterpillars, especially those of the winter moth and mottled umber moth. The black larvae live in the soil and do not feed among the foliage as the adults do. A European species of *Silpha* is also reported to attack snails.

The family Nitidulidae also have mixed feeding habits, but the majority are scavengers. They are minute insects with large eyes, and as in the two preceding families the forewings do not completely cover the abdomen. A few species are pests of dried fruits and stored cereals, and several genera include predaceous species. One of the latter, *Carpophilus mutilatus,* has been recorded as feeding on aphids associated with corn in the Barbados Islands. Members of this family are also reported to be an important factor in controlling bark beetles in the forests of England. An Asiatic species of the genus *Cybocephalus* that feeds on diaspine scale insects was imported from China by the University of California in 1932, and was reared in large numbers intended to control the California red scale; however, many have been found feeding on other species of these scales that infest cacti and palms, and some on the citrus-infesting purple scale. The eggs of this predator are deposited under the scale armor; the larvae feed mostly on mature female scales which (unlike the males) are wingless and remain in one place. The beetles pupate in the soil, and at summer temperatures the life cycle is completed in about twenty-four days.

The darkling beetles (Tenebrionidae) also have mixed feeding habits, most of them being partial either to dead vegetable matter and fungi or to green plants. The plant-feeders are not important pests, however, and some species prey on other insects. In size the darkling beetles vary from tiny to large, the larger ones usually being the scavengers and predators. Black, slow-moving, and nocturnal in habit, they are found under stones and dead bark in the daytime. Most of them have forewings that cover the whole body, but they can't fly because their hind wings are underdeveloped or entirely lacking. The family includes some tiny beetles with an unpleasant odor that are serious pests of stored cereals. One of these is the mealworm, *Tenebrio molitor,* which is sometimes bred as food for insect-eating pets. Another, the confused flour beetle, *Tribolium confusum,* is bred for use as an experimental laboratory subject. The darkling beetle, *Alobates pennsylvanica,* is a predatory species and hibernates under the loose bark of trees.

CLICK BEETLES

The click beetles (Elateridae) are the tumblers of the insect world. They get their name from the amusing manner in which the adult beetles right themselves when turned over on their backs. The head and thorax fit closely together against the wings, giving the beetle an almost perfectly symmetrical oval shape but tapering slightly toward the end. Just in front of the wing covers is a flexible joint that enables the beetle to arch the thorax and flip it against the ground, throwing itself into the air with a clicking sound. Click beetles lack the precision of a trained human tumbler, and more than one attempt may be necessary before the insect lands right side up. The members of the family range from small to large in size, and in color through black, gray, and brown. The larvae are known as "wireworms" and live in the soil, where they eat plant roots or soft-bodied insects. Although the majority are plant-feeders, many genera contain predatory species with a preference for the grubs of scarab beetles (Scarabaeidae). Click beetle larvae are sometimes confused with the so-called "false wireworms," the larvae of darkling beetles; however, the much shorter legs of the wireworm and the less pronounced segmentation of the body are easily distinguished.

One member of this family, *Monocrepidius exsul,* is another enemy of grubs in the Pacific islands, but it has as well the bad habit of attacking young sugar cane. In the West Indies, *Pyrophorous luminosus* is an important control of scarab beetle grubs, which attacks sugar cane. It has been imported into a number of tropical countries for control of these pests. Some species of click beetles, mostly found in tropical countries, are luminous in both the adult and larval stages. Although they resemble the fireflies, the lighting fixtures are a little different. Click beetles have two spots on the thorax that look like headlights. These spots are an opaque yellow when the beetle is at rest, but glow with a green light when it is disturbed. Inside the body is still another light, which is continuous, but remains hidden except when the opening of the wings and humping of the abdomen makes it appear to flash.

There appears to be a natural scheme of things to which
financial men would refer as diversified investment. It is the
total of all the factors, some of them very small, that maintains
the balance.

—A. D. PICKETT

PREDATORY INSECTS: OTHER ORDERS

4

The swift, graceful dragonflies and damselflies (order Odonata) are among our most valuable predators. As small children we heard them called "darning needles," and perhaps were just awed enough to keep a respectable distance away. Although similar in appearance, the dragonfly and damselfly are not difficult to tell apart. The wings of the dragonfly, a strong flier, are broader at the point of attachment than at the tip, and are held out in a horizontal position while the insect is resting. The wings of the damselfly, a weak flier, are narrow at the point of attachment; they are held upright and close together while it is resting. Also, the dragonfly's body is larger and not so delicate as that of the damselfly.

The eggs of the dragonfly are laid in or on aquatic plants or on the water; those of the damselfly are always placed *in* the stem of a plant. For this reason the latter has a well-developed ovipositor. The immature dragonfly, or nymph, is a sturdy creature with some rather strange equipment, including a peculiar lower lip (the labium) that can be extended far out to catch its prey; moreover, it breathes through tracheal gills in the rectum and propels itself

Dragonfly and damselfly: adults and nymphs (*Enid Furlonger*)

by ejecting water from the anus. Dragonflies winter as nymphs, but in some species two years or more are needed to reach maturity. The adults of both dragonflies and damselflies feed on mosquitoes, midges, and other insects, which they catch on the wing; the nymphs feed on mosquito larvae and other aquatic insects. Dragonfly nymphs consume enormous amounts of food

and will eat anything from protozoa to tadpoles and tiny minnows, and other dragonflies as well.

The fastest adult dragonflies are said to reach a speed of close
to sixty miles an hour. They can also fly long distances if it is
necessary to find a more favorable habitat—when swamps dry up,
for example. There is a record of a dragonfly migration from Australia to Tasmania, a distance of two hundred miles. The dragonflies' appetite for mosquitoes is extraordinary, and they are no
doubt an important factor in keeping mosquitoes under control.
One observer found more than a hundred mosquitoes in the mouth
of a dragonfly at one time; a dragonfly nymph to which he fed
mosquito larvae devoured sixty in ten minutes. The adults also
catch flies, beetles, moths and other injurious insects.

THE PRAYING MANTID

The praying mantid belongs to the order Orthoptera, which includes some of our worst pests—the roaches or cockroaches,
crickets, grasshoppers or locusts, and katydids—and the harmless
walkingsticks. The mantids belong to a family all by themselves,
Mantidae—which is sometimes even treated as a distinct order
(Mantoidea). They are completely predaceous, and get their
name from the posture they assume—with the fore part of body
and the spiny front legs raised in such a way as to suggest the attitude of prayer. However, there is little else to suggest piety in
their behavior, since they are probably the most ferocious inhabitants of the insect jungle. They are harmless to human beings
and can be kept as pets by feeding them insects or raw meat. They
are valuable predators, though they are guilty of attacking bees
and parasitic wasps. The female—like some female spiders—is
even likely to devour her mate; but so far as the species is concerned, this is not necessarily wasteful, since in any event the
male does not live long after mating.

Mantids have a concealing color, and although they are strong
fliers, they are most often found quietly waiting for unsuspecting
victims. Unlike other insects, mantids can turn their heads to

the side and look back, as a human being does. Their depredations on beneficial insects are believed to be minor. Young mantids are also predators, and eat small insects such as aphids. The eggs are laid in large masses and are enclosed in a sticky substance that adheres to twigs and dries to form a protective covering. A single female may lay from three to six masses, each containing anywhere from fifty to four hundred eggs. Egg cases can be purchased for colonizing; but there is no way of making sure a brood stay around if the hunting is better elsewhere.

Mantids are not commonly found north of the fortieth parallel of latitude. Our only native species, *Stagmomantis carolina,* occurs in the southern part of the United States as far west as Arizona, but seldom north of Maryland. There is usually only one generation a year, and in more northerly habitats only the eggs survive the winter. The males and some females are grayish brown with green feet; some other females are entirely green. Two foreign species have been accidentally introduced into the country: *Tenodera aridifolia sinensis* from China and Japan, whose front wings are brown with broad green margins, and *Mantis religiosa* from Europe, which is brown or green. The oriental mantid is common in southern New York state, in New Jersey, and as far west as Ohio; the European species is found as far north as southern Ontario.

Some deliberate importations have also been made for biological control. *Mantis religiosa* was introduced about fifty years ago into southern Ontario, where it has spread widely in agricultural areas. Its numbers fluctuate considerably with the severity of winters, along with other factors, according to a recent study.[1] Some species of ants are predators upon mantid nymphs, and field crickets cause some damage to the egg masses. Adult mantids and the larger nymphs feed to a great extent on Orthoptera, especially field crickets, and local populations of mantids fluctuate with them.

[1] H. G. James, "Egg Development, Hatching, and Prey Taken by the European Mantis, *Mantis religiosa* L., in Several Habitats," *Annual Report of the Entomological Society of Ontario,* 1958.

NERVE-WINGED INSECTS

Dobsonflies, lacewings, and ant lions, comprising in all fifteen families, are the best-known members of the order Neuroptera, which means "nerve-winged." These soft-bodied slowfliers with large, veined, wings gauzelike, and long antennae are largely nocturnal in habit; otherwise they would stand little chance of survival. Theirs seems to be a case of too large a propelling mechanism for the power available. The larvae are entirely predaceous, feeding on a variety of small insects. The dobsonfly (family Sialidae) is one of our largest insects—one species is five inches long—and is made still more conspicuous by its extremely long mandibles, especially those of the male. Despite this formidable equipment the adult's life is short, and it possibly does not eat at all. It lays its eggs in large masses on stones or foliage near the water. After hatching, the larvae—which are called "hell-grammites"—fall or crawl into the water, where they prey on other aquatic insects. They pupate away from the water under stones or logs. Alderflies, which belong to the same family, are much smaller and are without the long mandibles; they are active by day rather than by night.

BROWN LACEWINGS

The lacewings are found in gardens everywhere, and are quite important economically. Their voracious larvae have curved hollow mandibles for piercing their victims and sucking out the body juices, and they prey on a great variety of small insects. F. C. Bishopp says they are "among the most helpful insects of prey."[2] The brown lacewings (family Hemerobiidae) are small, fragile-looking insects whose appearance so belies their true mission in life that they might be thought of as wolves in sheep's clothing. Indeed, their larvae are sometimes called "aphid wolves"; they prey on a great variety of small insect pests—aphids, mites, thrips, scale in-

[2] F. C. Bishopp, "Insect Friends of Man," in *Insects: Yearbook of Agriculture* (Washington: Government Printing Office, 1952).

Brown lacewing adult attacking aphids on honeysuckle. (*E. S. Ross*)

sects, and leafhopper nymphs. The oval eggs are stuck to the surface of leaves and the bark of trees, singly or in clusters. The adults, which prey on aphids and mealybugs, are themselves the victims of a great variety of other predators, as well as of parasitic wasps.

GREEN LACEWINGS

The green lacewings (Chrysopidae) are similar to the brown lacewings in general appearance, but differ in color and in being considerably larger. Their lustrous eyes have earned them the poetic name of "golden eyes." Because of a protective device consisting of a foul-smelling fluid ejected from glands on the sides of their bodies, they are also called "stinkflies." The eggs are "planted" on foliage at the ends of short filaments, apparently as a means of protection—which, however, does not seem to prevent the minute trichogrammid wasps from depositing their own eggs in them. The voracious larvae of the green lacewing are also known as "aphid lions," and devour a great variety of aphids, citrus mealybugs, cottony cushion scales, red spiders, and thrips, as well as the eggs of many caterpillars. They spend the winter as pupae, in ovoid or spherical cocoons spun of silken threads, from

California green lacewing: adult and stalked eggs. (*Roy J. Pence*)

which the adult emerges in spring after neatly cutting a round, hinged lid at the top. The feeding larvae of some species pile up the discarded aphid skins on their backs, making themselves into a sort of trash heap, again apparently as a means of protection— and well they need it. Along with other lacewings, they have as enemies a number of insect predators and parasites, including certain wasps. One of these parasites is the biting midge *Forcipomyia eques* (one of the "no-see-ums"), which sucks blood from the wing veins of the green lacewing while riding on its back.

ANT LIONS

Ant lions (Myrmeleontidae) are widely distributed, and may be found in sandy, protected locations throughout much of the country. Their fat, ovoid larvae—sometimes called "doodlebugs"—trap their prey, which consists mostly of ants, by digging a cone-shaped pit in sand or light soil and partially burying themselves at the bottom, where they wait for unwary victims to fall in. These interesting little predators walk backwards, and hollow out their pits by moving in a circle, starting with a relatively wide diameter at the top and gradually narrowing it as they work their way down, tossing sand out with their heads as they go. If the ant lion fails to seize its unwary victim on the first try, there

Adult ant lion, *Hesperoleon abdominalis.* (*USDA*)

is still little chance of the ant's escaping; as it struggles to get out, the sides of the pit tumble in and the ant lion makes things harder for the ant by tossing out more sand.[3]

The ant lion larva has a pair of curved hollow mandibles with which it pierces its victims and sucks out the body juices. These implements for grasping and sucking—which are found not only in the ant lion and lacewing larvae but in other insects such as the diving beetle—have either a groove or a closed canal leading into the mouth opening or preoral cavity; the mouth is either partly or wholly closed. After a digestive fluid has been pumped into the victim its blood or body fluids are sucked into the mouth by a pharyngeal pump or by secondary "mouths" attached to the mandibles.

Some species of ant lion simply bury themselves in the soil and seize their victims as they pass by. Adult ant lions, which re-

[3] Ross E. Hutchins, *Insects—Hunters and Trappers* (New York: Rand McNally & Co., 1957).

semble damselflies, lay their eggs in the soil. The larvae spin cocoons similar to those of the green lacewings, and the adults cut their way out in the same way. They may winter either as larvae in the soil or as pupae in their cocoons.

POWDERY LACEWINGS

The powdery lacewings (Coniopterygidae) prey on aphids, scale insects, and mites, and are reported to be an important factor in the natural control of red spider mites in English orchards.[4] They differ from other nerve-winged insects in that their wings are covered with a powdery white substance and are much less veined. The small oval eggs, which are laid singly on bark or the underside of leaves, between April and June, are covered with a mealy white substance similar to that on the wings and body. A second brood of adults lay their eggs during July and August, and a partial third generation lay as late as November. These lacewings live as much as eight weeks under laboratory conditions, and probably longer under natural conditions.

The highest recorded number of eggs laid by one female is 107 in the space of seven weeks. Both adults and larvae feed almost entirely on mites and their eggs. The larvae suck the eggs as they do the body juices, and show a preference for female mites. The newly hatched larvae feed on mites of about their own size, and have been observed to consume an average of from fifteen to forty-five mites, depending on the age of the larva. Adults completely devour their prey—as many as thirty female mites in an hour—and open the eggs by biting off the tops, which are then thrown away. Introduction of cocoons and adults to various fruit trees markedly reduced the infestations of mites; but parasites that appeared the following year made them less effective.

COLONIZING LACEWINGS

Green lacewings have been shown to be effective as an agent of biological control. Experiments in California used the green

[4] B. D. Moreton, *Beneficial Insects* (London: Ministry of Agriculture, Fisheries and Food, Bulletin 20, 1958).

lacewing *Chrysopa californica* to combat the grape mealybug (*Pseudococcus maritimus*) in pear orchards, where its population had risen to injurious levels as a result of spraying with DDT and other pesticides for control of the codling moth. Since adult lacewings are highly sensitive to poison sprays and their larvae are not, eggs were used rather than the adult insects. Three carefully timed releases during the spring and summer brought the mealybugs under control and restored the balance that had been upset by the application of insecticides. This control continued through the second year without further colonizing, and apparently could be maintained by releasing eggs in alternate years. It would thus appear that insecticides and biological control are not necessarily incompatible if they are properly coordinated. Less difficulty has been encountered when such older, plant-derived insecticides as rotenone, pyrethrum, and nicotine were used since these do not persist long on plants. According to C. P. Clausen, "The portion of the natural-enemy population affected by these materials was only that which was in the active stage for a short period after treatment, and thereafter the ratio of natural enemies to the pest insects was appreciably higher than before."[5]

STYLOPS OR TWISTED-WING PARASITES

The minute insects of this strange group are so different from any others that they constitute a small order of their own—Strepsiptera. Little attention is accorded these insects, which are not generally considered important, and which are seldom encountered or noticed. Traits similar to those in the blister beetles (Meloidae) during the active first larval stage suggests that there may be a close relation between this order and the Coleoptera. They are beneficial as a whole, and especially for their depredations on planthoppers (Fulgoridae) and leafhoppers (Cicadellidae), which are serious crop pests.

[5] C. P. Clausen, *Biological Control of Insect Pests in the Continental United States* (Washington: USDA Technical Bulletin No. 1139, June 1956).

Aside from the planthoppers and leafhoppers (both of the order Homoptera), the hosts of these parasites—so far as the records show—belong largely to the order Hymenoptera, and especially to the families Andrenidae, Vespidae, and Eumenidae. (They appear to be rarely if ever associated with honeybees.) In Fiji the species *Elenchoides perkensi* has been shown to destroy as many as 70 per cent of a population of *Perkinsiella vitiensis,* a pest of sugar cane. In East Africa, *Corioxenos antestiae* has been recorded to destroy from 12 to 84 per cent (with an average of 40 per cent) of populations of the pentatomid bug, *Antestia lineaticollis,* a serious coffee pest. Attempts to use this parasite for biological control in Hawaii were not successful.

The adult male *Stylops* is free-living, and short-lived; he has stalked eyes and two pairs of wings, the front pair of which are mere stubs. The hind wings—which are extremely large, comparatively speaking—have no cross veins, and fold over the body like a fan, whence the name "twisted-wing." In most species the female never leaves the insect host. The tip of her body, head and thorax, protrudes just far enough between two segments of the host's body to permit her to mate and the larvae or triungulins, as they are called, to escape. The latter, which are born alive, are legless and wingless, without eyes, antennae, or developed mouth parts—not much more than worms enclosed in the last larval skin.

The number of progeny recorded for these small insects is scarcely believable. As many as 7,000 triungulins have been observed to emerge from a single female of the species *Stylops aterrima.* The entire process is short, generally taking place in a single day, but a female has been known to give birth to several thousand in less than a minute. They are released on plants, most often on the flowers, where they remain for hours, ready to jump when the chance presents itself. In some species jumping is triggered by the movement of a nearby object, or by its color. Those of the genus *Corioxenos* are known to be attracted by red, black, and orange. Those that parasitize the Homoptera—planthoppers and leafhoppers—find the host directly, since the plants on which they are deposited are species frequented by these pests, where they are likely to be abundant. The species of *Stylops* that parasitize wasps and bees usually, though not always, have to hitch a ride.

For the larvae of these latter the timing can be critical: they must reach the cell in which the egg of the host bee or wasp is deposited, along with a supply of food, before it is finally sealed off. In those species whose larvae are fed periodically the timing is less critical and the degree of parasitization is likely to be higher. The parasite enters the body of the host larva during the early part of its development and absorbs nourishment from it through its own abdominal wall. It emerges during the pupal or early adult stage of the bee or wasp, before the body hardens; when the host belongs to the Homoptera, it emerges in the nymphal stage.

The number of individuals that develop in a single host varies considerably. As many as thirty-one have been found in a single larva of the *Polistes* wasp, but between one and five is more usual. The effects of these parasites on their hosts are extremely interesting. If the host is a bee it will eat the available food supply more rapidly, with the result that its development is accelerated; if it is a wasp, since the food supply is unlimited its development will be retarded, and the adult will be abnormally late in emerging. Parasitization has a still more profound effect on the host in that it alters the sexual characteristics, often producing sterility—or what is sometimes called parasitic castration. Although the death of the host is not always a consequence, the nature of the long-run effect is obvious.

THE TRUE BUGS

Although the word "bug" is commonly used to refer to any insect, or even to arthropods of other classes, such as spiders and mites, the entomologist applies it only to a certain group of insects of the order Hemiptera (or Heteroptera). Most of these "true bugs" suck plant juices—a few others are parasitic on mammals—and the order is more noteworthy for its pests than for its beneficial members. There are nevertheless some very valuable predators in this group, and some families that are wholly predaceous. The forelegs of predatory bugs are generally modified for grasping and holding the prey while sucking their body juices. The metamorphosis of the bugs (and homopterans) is gradual.

STINKBUGS

The stinkbugs (Pentatomidae) include some valuable predators of moths, butterflies, and leaf beetles. Small to medium in size and shaped like a medieval warrior's shield, they are named for the disagreeable odor of a substance they exude from glands situated on the sides of the thorax. This odor is imparted wherever a stinkbug goes, and may be responsible for the occasional bad-tasting specimen you find in a box of berries. Among the better known of the pests in this family are the shield bug, the southern green stinkbug—a pest of various vegetables—and the flashy harlequin bug, a pest of cabbages and related plants. Incidentally, the English sparrow is said to keep the harlequin bug under control in some localities. One pentatomid, the Australian *Tectoris lineola*, is known to brood its eggs for several weeks, eating nothing until they are hatched. Beneficial members of this family are found in the genera *Euschistus, Apateticus, Brochymena, Acrosternum, Podisus,* and *Perillus.* The colorful *Perillus biocu-latus*—which is generally yellow or red with a black Y on its back —attacks cutworms and other caterpillars, as well as the Colorado potato beetle. *Apateticus bracteatus* preys on the larvae of the argus potato beetle, and *A. cynicus* feeds on one of the leaf-roller moths (Tortricidae) found on oak trees. Other predaceous species include *Brochymena arborea* and *Podisus serieventris.* The latter and *Apateticus bracteatus* both attack the red-headed pine sawfly.

AMBUSH BUGS

The ambush bugs (Phymatidae) are a small family of predators found on flowering plants, where they hide behind flowers or leaves and grab their unsuspecting victims as they pass. These

Ambush bug attacking skipper. (*E. S. Ross*)

grotesque bugs are about three-eighths of an inch long; although they are slow-moving, they sometimes attack insects much larger than themselves. The front pairs of legs are highly developed for grasping, as the mantids' are. They are indiscriminate in their choice of food, including some beneficial species such as bees in their diet. The ambush bug *Phymata erosa,* commonly found on goldenrod in the fall, is one of the more familiar of the twenty-five species known to occur in North America.

ASSASSIN BUGS

The assassin bugs (Reduviidae) are mostly predatory. Both adults and nymphs prey on other insects, including bees captured during visits to flowers frequented by the bugs. The adult uses its forelegs for this purpose, even though they have no special modification for grasping. The nymphs are sometimes camouflaged by debris that collects on the sticky hairs of their bodies. This family includes the so-called "kissing bugs," the most common of which

Assassin bug, *Apiomerus* sp., feeding on soldier beetle. (*E. S. Ross*)

is *Reduvius personatus*, sometimes also called the "big bedbug." Its favorite food is bedbugs—or more precisely the secondhand human or animal blood it drains from these insects.

The giant wheel bug, *Arilus cristatus*, is a well-known member of this family and a valuable predator on destructive caterpillars and on adult Japaneses beetles. Its habitat ranges over the southern states and as far north as Pennsylvania, and its prey includes the pine sawfly.

Some members of this family, of the genera *Conorhinus* and *Triatoma*, are parasites of mammals, including man, and may be vectors of a microbe that is the cause of Chagas' disease. These parasites are found mainly in the tropics, but two species occur in the southwestern United States, where they have been known to infest wood rats.

Another tropical species, the Java bug *Ptilocerus ochraceus*, has a method of enticing its victims that is diabolically suggestive of

Wheel bug feeding on tobacco hornworm. (*Lee Jenkins*)

dope peddling. This bug preys on a species of ant, *Dolichoderus bituberculatus,* that is common in the East Indies. The addiction to sweet exudations from the bodies of other insects that is a common trait among ants dupes this species into association with a predator that is in no way beneficial. On the underside of its body, concealed by a tuft of bright red trichomes or hairs, the Java bug has a gland that secretes a toxic drug along with the sweets to which the ants are attracted. What happens has been described by an observer as follows:

[The bugs] take up a position in an ant-path or ants find out the abodes of the bugs, and attracted by their secretions visit them in great numbers. On the approach of an ant of the species *Dolichoderus bituberculatus* the bug is at once on the alert; it raises halfway the front of the body, so as to put the trichome in evidence. As far as my observations go, the bugs only show a liking for *Dolichoderus bituberculatus*; several other species of ants, e.g. *Crematogaster difformis* and others which were brought together with a stranger, the bug inclined its body forwards, pressing down its head; the reverse therefore of the inviting attitude taken up towards *Dolichoderus bituberculatus*. In meeting the latter the bug lifts up its front legs, folding them in such a manner that the tarsi [leg segments] nearly meet below the head. The ant at once proceeds to lick the trichome, pulling all the while with its mandibles [jaws] at the tuft of hairs, as if milking the creature, and by this manipulation the body of the bug is continually moved up and down. At this stage of the proceedings the the bug does not yet attack the ant; it only takes the head and thorax of its victim between its front legs, as if to make sure of it; very often the point of the bug's beak is put behind the ant's head, where this is joined to the body, without, however, doing any injury to the ant. It is surprising to see how the bug can restrain its murderous intention as if it was knowing that the right moment had not yet arrived. After the ant has indulged in licking the tuft of hair for some minutes the exudation commences to exercise its paralyzing effect. . . .

In this way a much larger number of ants is destroyed than actually serves as food to the bugs, and one must wonder at the great prolificacy of the ants, which enables them to stand such a heavy drain on the population of one community. As soon as the ant shows signs of paralysis by curling itself up and drawing in its legs, the bug at once seizes it with its front legs, and very soon it is pierced and sucked dry . . .[6]

DAMSEL BUGS AND PIRATE BUGS

The damsel bugs (Nabidae) are entirely predaceous, and practically all are beneficial. Small, ovoid insects, about a quarter of an inch long, they prey on destructive caterpillars, mites, aphids, plant bugs, and other destructive members of the same order. They are found throughout the United States, Mexico, and eastern Canada. *Nabis ferus* is said to attack the redheaded pine sawfly (*Neodiprion lecontei*). The pirate bugs (Anthocoridae) are much

[6] E. Jacobson, "Biological Notes on the Hemipteron *Ptilocerus ochraceus*" (*Tijdschr. Ent.* 54, 1911; quoted in Documentary Appendix, *Social Life Among the Insects,* by W. M. Wheeler).

smaller, an eighth of an inch or less long, and are also valuable predators. They are very numerous and exercise an important check on aphids, scale insects, thrips, and other small insect pests. The insidious flower bug, *Orius insidiosus,* is an important enemy of thrips. It has also been called "the most important predatory insect enemy of the earworm eggs and small larva" in the eastern states.[7] This small, black bug, about a sixteenth of an inch long, is found on many plants but is most abundant on corn. Its eggs are deposited on the silks, and the tiny red nymphs that hatch pierce the earworm eggs with their beaks and suck them dry. Many eggs are destroyed in this way, and the total effect of this small predator is very significant; it is not uncommon to find twenty-five of these bugs on a single corn plant.

In England *Anthocoris nemorum* is reported to be abundant and to attack larvae and pupae of the apple blossom weevil, caterpillars, midges, aphids, and scale insects; it is also an important check on the red spider mite. Adults were found to suck an average of fifty red spider mites in a day, and some individuals have been known to consume between five hundred and six hundred aphids. They winter as adults under bark and leaves. Two smaller species, *Orius majusculus* and *O. minutus,* are also plentiful. The effectiveness of these bugs is all the greater since there are two generations a year, so that their work begins in spring and continues through the fall; in addition, the winter eggs of the mite are sucked not only in autumn and spring but even on warm days during the winter.

PLANT BUGS

The plant bugs or capsids (Miridae) belong to the largest family in the order. In size they range from small to very small—less than an eighth of an inch. In some species the males are long-winged and the females short-winged. The best known of these bugs are plant feeders—for example the tarnished plant bug

[7] R. A. Blanchard and W. A. Douglas, *The Corn Earworm* (Heliothis armigera) *as an Enemy of Field Corn in the Eastern States* (Washington: USDA, Farmers' Bulletin No. 1651, Nov. 1953).

(*Lygus lineolaris*), the garden fleahopper (*Halticus bracteatus*), and the green soldier bug (*Acrosternum hilare*), a pest of peaches. *Cyrtorhinus mundulus,* a species native to Australia, Java, the Fiji Islands, and the Philippines, is an efficient destroyer of eggs of the sugar cane leafhopper and has been successfully introduced into Hawaii for biological control.

Not much information was available concerning the predators in this group until after a five-year study had been made in England of the predatory insects associated with the fruit tree spider mite in both neglected and cultivated orchards. Some of the findings of the study have already been mentioned in the discussion of the flower bugs and the lacewings. Sixteen species of predators of the family Miridae (out of a total of 185 in England) were observed. In cultivated orchards the most important of these proved to be the black-kneed capsid (*Blepharidopterus angulatus*), which is so named for a black band at the base of the long joint of each leg. The eggs are laid from July to October on a variety of trees, most commonly in the little niches formed by bud scars or wounds in the younger shoots—or they may be sunk into the smoother bark, causing a swelling or "egg bump." The eggs are usually laid singly; under laboratory conditions each female produces up to fifty.

The nymphs hatch the following year, between May and July, and remain in this stage from twenty-five to fifty-three days; there is only one generation a year. Both nymphs and adults prey on small insects such as aphids, thrips, and mites. The study showed their preference to be for the red spider mite, especially the female. Nymphs consumed anywhere five to forty mites a day, according to their age; adults averaged sixty or seventy a day, and the average for one year was recorded to be 4,230. In some years the bugs are able to keep the mite population within economic levels, although this does not happen in some orchards for more than two or three years in succession. Populations vary greatly from orchard to orchard and from year to year, the variations being due in great part to spraying practices. Since the bugs hatch after the mites and produce only one generation a year, they may not be able to overtake the pest until the following year if the balance has been disturbed in the latter's favor.

The study brought out some interesting differences between neglected and cutlivated orchards—or in other words, between the sprayed and the unsprayed—"showing the effects of human interference and particularly of the insecticides regularly sprayed on to the trees."[8] In unsprayed orchards the pests are preyed on continuously and the populations of predators and pests is quite constant, with neither occurring in excessive numbers. In cultivated or sprayed orchards, on the other hand, the total number of predatory species was found to be lower—though individual populations could at times be high—and the populations were found to fluctuate violently from year to year and orchard to orchard.

A recent study made in Nova Scotia produced some interesting information concerning the importance of predators—especially certain mirids—in the control of the codling moth. The orchard selected for the study was twenty years old, consisted of 8.7 acres planted with 559 trees, and was operated under what is called an "integrated program" of chemical and natural controls—using insecticides only as they are needed and so as to preserve as many beneficial insect predators and parasites as possible. During the eleven years that the orchard had been operated in this manner, insecticides had been applied on only seven occasions. The orchard was divided into four quarters, and twelve trees in each section were selected for study. Five mirids were found to be among the most numerous predators of the codling moth: *Pilophorus perplexus, Blepharidopterus angulatus, Diaphnidia* sp. (probably *pellucida*), *Hyaliodes harti*—all predators of codling moth eggs and young larvae—and *Phytocoris* sp. (probably *dimidiata*), a predator on young larvae. (A mite, *Anystis agilis*, was also one of the most common of the predators.)

----

[8] D. B. Moreton, *Beneficial Insects* (London: Ministry of Agriculture, Fisheries, and Food, Bulletin 20, 1958).

The relatively small damage to the fruit on the twelve trees is quite surprising. A total of 958 stings were noted on 46,248 fruits, with a subsequent count of 858 deep entries (wormy fruits); infestation in dropped fruit was 2.7 per cent, and in the harvested crop it was .5 per cent of a total of 12,776. This shows a reduction of 58.5 per cent in the number of young larvae between hatching and the time when fruit injuries were noted. A further mortality of 10.4 per cent took place after the larvae entered the fruit, making a total mortality of 68.3 per cent. Predators destroyed 14.4 per cent of the larvae found, and the egg parasite *Trichogramma* sp. destroyed 2.4 per cent. The study also showed the interesting fact that during the winter 59 per cent of the hibernating larvae were destroyed—47 per cent by woodpeckers and 9 per cent by a braconid parasite, *Ascogaster quadridentata,* the other 3 per cent as a result of severe winter weather. The interesting thing here is the relatively small amount of damage caused by the codling moth after eleven years of integrated control, with only seven applications of insecticides. It would appear that the predators were mostly responsible for limiting the damage to .5 per cent of the harvested fruit.[9]

PREDATORS AND PESTICIDES

The spotted alfalfa aphid (*Therioaphis maculata*), a destructive pest of alfalfa, first invaded the western states in 1954, and by 1956 had spread to thirty states. The damage was particularly heavy in California, where alfalfa constitutes a very important feed crop for pen-fed cattle and dairy herds. By 1956, following widespread applications of parathion, malathion, and TEPP to combat the pest, it was apparent that complications had entered the picture. In many places the aphids were developing resistance to the insecticides, and in the absence of the natural enemies that were being destroyed, the resistant aphids and those migrating from other fields were multiplying in tremendous proportions

[9] C. R. MacLellan, "Mortality of Codling Moth Eggs and Young Larvae in an Integrated Control Orchard," *The Canadian Entomologist,* June 1962.

despite frequent chemical applications. Other insects present
which were not damaging to the alfalfa could also be expected to
develop resistance, and to carry this resistance with them to other
crops where they were pests.

The most important native predators of aphids in California are
the lady beetles. Next in their importance to agriculture are three
other predators, the damsel bug (*Nabis* sp.), the pirate bug
(*Orius* sp.), and the green lacewing (*Chrysopa* sp.). Tests made
by researchers at the University of California show that where
chemical treatments had allowed a fair number of these beneficial
insects to survive, they were able to destroy the aphids as they
reinvaded the plots.[10]

Observations by Canadian researchers on the predators of the
pear psylla (*Psylla pyricola*) in the South Okanagan Valley in
British Columbia also show both the importance of these predators and the detrimental effects of pesticides.[11] The pear psylla
has become "one of the chief economic insect pests on pear in
North America." Various chemicals have been used in an attempt
to control it, but it has managed to develop resistance to most of
them. In a study undertaken to determine other means of control,
two native insects were found to prey heavily upon it under normal conditions. These are the pirate bug, *Anthocoris melanocerus*,
and the green lacewing, *Chrysopa oculata*.

Both of these predators attack psylla eggs and nymphs but not
the adults, which are too large and fast for them. They will, however, attack live (but not dead) adults that are injured or caught
in honeydew. Tests showed that one of these predators was able
to suck between ten and twelve psylla eggs dry in twenty minutes
and to devour a late-stage nymph in less than five minutes. They
also have the tidy habit of cleaning the platter—or rather leaf—
before going on to the next one.

[10] Vernon M. Stern, Robert van den Bosch, and Dewey Born, "New Control of Spotted Alfalfa Aphid," *California Agriculture,* January 1958.
[11] T. K. Watson and W. H. A. Wilde, "Laboratory and Field Observations on Two Predators of the Pear Psylla in British Columbia," *The
Canadian Entomologist,* April 1963.

A three-year laboratory and field study showed that "high populations of the pear psylla have been accompanied by low populations of these predators. When either predator became numerous it proved capable of suppressing the pear psylla to very light or trace numbers only." Together they were somewhat more effective. The researchers conclude: "Orchards that had received no chemical spray applications for a number of years showed only trace numbers of both the pear psylla and its predators. Apparently when biological control of the psylla is achieved, very few predators suffice to maintain it."

EARWIGS

These odd-looking insects with a pair of curved, forcepslike hooks protruding from the rear, resemble beetles and were originally classed with the order Coleoptera; later they were shifted to the Orthoptera (grasshoppers and roaches), and finally to the Dermaptera. Both male and female have the forceps—an appendage technically known as the cerci, which takes various forms among insects; one is the "tail" of the mayfly. In the earwig it is probably a defensive weapon, since it can exert a fairly good pinch—the male a harder one than the female. Another defensive weapon is a set of abdominal glands which exude a liquid that smells like creosote.

Earwigs have been likened to the rove beetles; they are similarly shaped, and like them have two forewings covering only about half the body, leaving the hind wings partially exposed. Most of them fly very little or not at all. The female has the interesting habit of brooding her eggs (which are usually laid in the soil) and guarding her young nymphs. Earwigs are not native to North America, but came here in ship cargoes. In the Pacific northwest the European earwig, *Forficula auricularia*, was formerly something of a nuisance in households and occasionally in gardens. A tachinid parasite, *Bigonicheta spinipennis*, imported from England between 1928 and 1931, has brought about satisfactory control. Essentially scavengers, earwigs also eat other insects and snails. They are mainly objected to because of their appearance and their habit of turning up in houses and garbage pails. Two Canadian researchers, Turnbull and Chant, point out that they "have at least potentialities of being definitely beneficial by attacking many harmful insects" and that "healthy and vigorous populations should be preserved. [The parasite] seems to have accomplished this happy compromise."[12]

The name "earwig" may have come from a superstition that these insects attack people's ears; or possibly, as E. S. Ross suggests, they may actually have crawled into the ears of ancient Anglo-Saxons while they slept on the ground in huts—a theory he considers plausible in view of the Anglo-Saxon origin of the word.[13]

SCORPIONFLIES

Not much is known about these strange insects of the order Mecoptera. Their two pairs of wings, their legs and their antennae, are long; they lay their eggs in the soil. Although not important economically, they are included here because the larvae, which are primarily scavengers, have the predatory habit as well, as do some of the adult forms. One strange family native to North America are the Boreidae, the so-called "snowfleas," found in forests and sometimes seen hopping about in great numbers on the surface of the snow. Snowfleas have only vestigial wings and do not fly; in the males the wings, which look like a pair of brushes, are used to hold the females during mating. These insects are believed to be predators upon springtails and to feed on dead vegetation. More typical members of the order are the scorpionflies (Panorpidae)—such as the common scorpionfly, *Panorpa nebulosa*—in which the tip of the abdomen is swollen and turned up in such a way as to resemble that of a scorpion. Weak fliers, they are preyed on by dragonflies, robber flies, and spiders. The insects

[12] A. L. Turnbull and D. A. Chant, "The Practice and Theory of Biological Control of Insects in Canada," *Canadian Journal of Zoology*, Oct. 1961.

[13] E. S. Ross, *Insects Close Up* (Berkeley: University of California Press, 1953).

of this family bear a close resemblance to those of the family Bittacidae, commonly called "hanging flies" from their habit of hanging from vegetation by their two front legs while they snatch flies and other insects with the other four.

THRIPS

These minute, highly active insects belong to the order Thysanoptera, which means literally "bristle wings." In most species the two pairs of narrow, feathery-looking wings are fringed with hairs, have practically no veins, and fold back close to the body when at rest. In other species either the male, the female, or both are wingless. Another peculiarity of the thrips is in the foot, which is cupped and encloses a sort of bladder that can be extended or withdrawn. For this reason the order is sometimes called Physopoda, meaning "bladder-footed." The mouth parts, designed for both chewing and sucking, are also unique. Some of the thrips are predators upon mites, aphids, and the eggs of other small insects —which is the reason they are included here. However, they also include such highly destructive species as the onion thrips (*Thrips tabaci*), greenhouse thrips (*Heliothrips haemorrhoidalis*), gladiolus thrips (*Taeniothrips simplex*), citrus thrips (*Scirtothrips citri*), pear thrips (*Taeniothrips inconsequens*) and wheat thrips (*Frankliniella tritici*).

The destructive species feed on the foliage and flowers, some depositing their eggs on the plants, others in the tissues; some species reproduce by means of parthenogenesis. They are also known to transmit virus diseases. On the other hand, it is reported from England that the onion thrips, and also *Aeolothrips malaleucus,* attack immature stages of the fruit tree red spider mite. Reports from England also mention *Aeolothrips ericae, Haplothrips* sp., and *Scolothrips longicornis* as predators—the last named being believed to feed on red spider mites also. Some species are known to feed on sap, fungi, and decaying vegetation. Important enemies of thrips are the insidious flower bug, *Orius insidiosus,* the lacewing larvae, lady beetles, and toads.

Larva of windowpane fly, *Amphrale fenestralis*. About three-fourths of an inch long, this white worm is often seen in accumulations of grain and flour where it preys on small insects. (*USDA*)

PREDATORY FLIES

Even though the flies do not appear well equipped for predation, the habit is actually widespread throughout the order. More families in the Diptera include predatory species than they do those with parasitic habits; the latter, however, are more important as regulators of pest populations and are much more adaptable as agents of biological control. The importance of flies as predators, parasites, and scavengers is apt to be overlooked because they include most of the insect vectors of human diseases, and many of them are notorious tormentors of animals and man.

Some flies are easily mistaken for other insects, especially for wasps and bees. They differ from almost all other insects in having typically but one pair of wings; a few species have no wings at all. Flies are the *only* insect order with halteres—two thin stubs, each ending with a knob, that take the place of the hind wings and are believed to act as balancers during flight.

HOVER FLIES

The most important family so far as predation is concerned—and one of the largest in the order—are the Syrphidae. They are commonly called hover flies or, sometimes, flower flies, because of their hovering habits and their frequent presence around flowers. Their transparent wings move so rapidly that they are scarcely visible, and the fly looks as if it were suspended in midair. They are certainly the most attractive of the flies, with their bands of alternating black and yellow or other combinations; some are covered with black and yellow hairs and look like bees or wasps. The adults feed on nectar and pollen and are probably next in importance to bees as pollinators. The larvae of many species prey on aphids, and some on mealybugs and leafhoppers; some feed on plants; others are scavengers or live as guests of ants. As aphid-eaters they closely rival the lady beetles. Metcalf mentions a report that at a packing plant in Maryland, around the turn of the present century, twenty-five bushels of syrphid larvae were screened from peas in a matter of a few days; and they were mostly of one species.[14]

A common aphid-eating species found in some of the eastern states is *Platychirus perpallidus*. One female may deposit as many as a hundred eggs, scattering them about in an aphid colony. The larvae hatch in a few days and immediately begin devouring the aphids. A larva first punctures its prey and then lifts it into the air as if to drain it—but actually to pull it loose from the plant— before beginning to suck the body fluids. The larval stage lasts about two weeks. *Eupeodes volucris,* a species common in the West, is also a heavy feeder on aphids. The larval period for this fly is about three weeks.

BEE FLIES

Bee flies (Bombyliidae) are quite important as predators of grasshopper egg pods, but the family includes species that are parasitic on wasps and bees and on moths and butterflies as well. There are short, stout ones covered with fuzzy hairs, which closely resemble bees; others are longer and more slender, and look like wasps. They have a habit of hovering similar to that of syrphid flies. The eggs are deposited in crevices in the ground, near the egg pods of grasshoppers. As soon as the larval flies hatch, they begin

[14] C. L. Metcalf, and W. P. Flint, *Destructive and Useful Insects,* rev. by R. L. Metcalf (New York: McGraw-Hill Book Co., 1951).

Adult syrphid fly; larvae are important predators of aphids. (*Lee Jenkins*)

moving through the soil in search of the egg pods, whose contents they devour one after another. Each pod contains from twenty-five to thirty eggs.

Parker and Wakeland[15] report that *Systoechus vulgaris* and *Aphoebantus hirsutus* were the most common species found in the grasshopper egg surveys made in seven western states from 1938

[15] J. R. Parker and Claude Wakeland, *Grasshopper Egg Pods Destroyed by Larvae of Bee Flies, Blister Beetles, and Ground Beetles* (Washington: USDA Technical Bulletin No. 1165, July 1957).

Robber fly, *Erax barbatus,* feeding on leafhopper. (*E. S. Ross*)

to 1940. The conclusions of this survey have already been mentioned in connection with the blister and ground beetles. A study made in 1932 indicated that *Systoechus vulgaris,* together with blister beetle and ground beetle larvae, had destroyed 20 per cent of the grasshopper egg pods in the entire province of Manitoba, and that in some areas the figure was as high as 90 per cent. A study made in northern California in 1929 showed that bee fly larvae had destroyed 44.5 per cent of the egg pods of *Cammula pellucida,* no other predators having been found. In South Dakota a study made in 1938 indicated that 59.3 per cent of the eggs of *Melanoplus mexicanus* were destroyed by predators—35.6 per cent by bee fly larvae and 23.7 per cent by blister beetle larvae.

ROBBER FLIES

Robber flies (Asilidae) are large, powerful flies that prey on other insects, both adults and larvae. They are not easily confused with any other insect except in flight, when their loud droning might cause them to be mistaken for a bee or wasp. The head and thorax are large and the abdomen is tapered at the end. Robber flies are usually gray, and some are densely covered with hairs. They capture other insects on the wing, as do the dragonflies, and are not in the least selective—moths, butterflies, beetles, grasshoppers, wasps, bees, and flies serving as prey. The victim is pierced by the fly's beak and the body juices are sucked out. The larvae live in the soil, where they feed on grubs and grasshopper eggs. As adults they are probably not very effective in reducing pest populations, but the larvae are quite beneficial and are believed capable of reducing grub populations considerably.

Promachus vertebratus is common in the midwestern states and is an important predator of white grubs. Its eggs are laid in cracks in the soil; after hatching, the larvae move through the soil in search of grubs, which they pierce and drain of body fluids. They overwinter as larvae, but the entire life cycle is believed to be three years.

GALL MIDGES

Gall midges or gnats (Itonididae: Cecidomyiidae) are very small, delicate flies with long legs, whose antennae are ringed with short hairs. They are mostly plant feeders, many of them forming galls on leaves, stems, and other parts of plants. The Hessian fly, a pest of wheat, pierces the stem at the base of the leaf sheath and feeds on the plant juice. A large number of species,[16] however, feed on aphids, mealybugs, and mites; some prey on the larvae of bark beetles, and others are scavengers. A native species that preys on aphids is *Aphidoletes meridionalis*. The young larva feeds by piercing the underside of the aphid and drawing out the body fluids; in the later larval stage it has a most unusual habit of opening a joint in the aphid's leg and sucking the body juices from there, apparently without the aphid's being conscious of it.

Cleodiplosis koebelei, a predator upon mealybugs in Australia, was imported in 1928 by the University of California in an at-

[16] According to D. D. Jensen, 50 species of gall midges are predatory in the larval form, mostly on scale insects. They also prey on adult psyllids. See "Parasites of the Psyllidae," *Hilgardia*, Sept. 1957.

tempt to control the citrophilus mealybug. The fly was mass-produced and released at many places in southern California; it became established, but not in numbers great enough to be very effective, although it did prove quite successful in controlling the grape mealybug in greenhouses.

Aphidoletes thompsoni, a European predator upon the balsam woolly aphid (*Chermes piceae*), has been imported into Canada, mainly from Czechoslovakia, for control of this serious forest pest. Shipments have been sent from Canada to New England, the Pacific northwest, and North Carolina. So far it is known to be established only in the Pacific northwest. It is quite abundant in Europe, where it produces from three to five generations a year. The female lays her eggs in the waxy mass on the bark, where the fly larvae will eat the eggs and larvae of the aphid. The fly pupates in the soil, after overwintering there as a larva. P. B. Dowden believes that since the fly is very small and does not require much food for its development, it may be of importance as a control factor where the density of the aphid is relatively low.[17]

SOME OTHER PREDATORY FLIES

The mosquitoes (Culicidae) are well known vectors of diseases of man such as malaria and yellow fever. Some species, however, are valuable in their aquatic larval forms as predators upon other mosquitoes, and have been used for biological control. *Toxorhynchites inornatus* and *splendens* were imported into Fiji in the 1930's for this purpose, and became established there.

The snipe flies (Rhagionidae), which prey on other insects as adults and larvae, resemble the robber flies but are smaller. The larvae are entirely predaceous on other small insects; some of them are called "worm lions" because of their habit of trapping other insects, mostly ants, in the same way as the ant lions—by digging pits. They are common in the western states.

Dance flies (Empididae), common throughout this country, are

[17] P. B. Dowden, *Parasites and Predators of Forest Insects Liberated in the U.S. Through 1960* (Washington: USDA, Agriculture Handbook No. 226, July 1962).

predatory as adults and larvae. Some species feed on mites; one of these, *Drapetis micropyga,* is reported to be an important predator on the citrus red mite (*Panonychus citri*), in California. *Tachydroma minuta* has been reported to give complete control of an infestation of a leaf-miner, *Phytomyza aconiti,* by its attack upon the adults of this fly. The male of some species of *Tachydroma* and other genera of dance flies has the interesting habit of carrying one of its prey around before mating, as a gift for the female; the more fastidious male of some species first wraps the gift in a frothy web.

Another predaceous family in the adult and larval stages are the Dolichopodidae (they have no common name). In Canada several species have been observed to prey on the European red mite. Others, during the larval stage, are predators on bark beetles in forests of Europe and North America. *Medetera aldrichii* is one of the important natural control agents of the mountain pine beetle, *Dendroctonus monticolae,* in our western forests.

Two species of the family Chamaemyiidae are among four predators imported from Europe and established in the maritime provinces of Canada for control of the balsam woolly aphid, *Chermes piceae.* (The other two are beetles.) One of these is *Cremifania nigrocellulata,* which has as many as three generations a year and overwinters in the ground or bark as a pupa. This fly has been released in New Brunswick each year since 1952, and was also released in Oregon. It has been fairly abundant in places but spreads slowly. The other imported chamaemyiid fly referred to is *Leucopis obscura,* which was introduced into Canada in 1933 and has spread rapidly, spilling over into Maine. Beginning in 1954 colonies were released in Vermont, New Hampshire, New York, Washington, Oregon, and (as late as 1960) North Carolina. The fly develops rapidly where the aphid infestation is high; it requires a high density and is not likely to be found where the aphids are few. It feeds mostly on adults and so does not entirely prevent the laying of eggs; but it greatly reduces the number of later generations and of those coming in from other trees.

A *Polistes* wasp, an important predator. The larvae are fed on insects. (*USDA*)

SOME PREDATORY WASPS

The social and solitary wasps are for the most part beneficial, though the food of some includes other beneficial insects; at times they are important factors in natural control of insect pests. The spider wasps (Pompilidae), of which the so-called tarantula-hawk is one of the best known, do not appear to be a serious threat to the largely beneficial arthropods that are their prey. The valuable members of this group belong mostly to the families Vespidae and Sphecidae, which include the paper wasps, potter wasps, mud daubers, and digger or burrowing wasps. Because of their many similar habits we have included both families here, though it can be argued that the sphecids are more often parasites than predators. These wasps are usually quite specific in their food preferences, often to the point of confining their attack to a single species.

The Vespidae are the only wasp family that share with ants and termites the distinctive trait of living in societies or colonies. In color these wasps are black, yellow and black, or rust, and they may be distinguished by their habit of folding the wings straight back when at rest. Like other wasps they have two pairs of transparent (or translucent) wings, held together by little hooks that make them look like a single pair. One of the common social wasps is *Polistes*, whose small paper nest consists of a circular comb suspended by a stem glued to the branch of a tree or shrub, ceiling or eaves of buildings. The paper is made from wood chewed to a pulp. The comb is not closed in the way a hornet's nest is, so the heads of the larvae are plainly visible. They are fed on caterpillars and other insects, pre-chewed and formed into balls by the attending adults. The behavior of the queen, who does the feeding in the early stage of the colony, and later of the workers, is not entirely maternal: both obtain a secretion from the mouths of the larvae in return for the meat.

POLISTES AND THE HORNWORM

Unless molested these wasps are quite peaceful—they have neither the unpredictable aggressiveness nor the painful sting of a hornet—and deserve protection as a valuable predator. *Polistes exclamans* is important in controlling the tobacco hornworm (*Protoparce sexta*), a serious pest. By providing inexpensive shelters or nesting boxes to protect the wasp from larger predators, southern tobacco growers have found that the population of *Polistes* can be increased to the extent that moderate infestations of the hornworm are reduced to a noneconomic level.[18] This is all the more impressive in view of the fact that single nests and colonies of these wasps are not normally large, and that only the

[18] C. H. Hoffman, "Biological Control of Noxious Insects and Weeds" (An Address before the 23rd Annual Convention of the National Wildlife Federation, New York City, Feb. 27, 1959).

young queens survive the winter. (The males and young queens arrive in late summer; workers, males and the old queens die with the approach of winter, leaving only the young queens, who find shelter in cracks and crevices and under the bark of trees.)

More serious infestations of the hornworm can be controlled with the help of a disease organism (*Bacillus thuringiensis*) that is now available commercially (from certain chemical companies, what's more), and which, in a water suspension, can be sprayed on like a chemical insecticide. The bacillus is not injurious to the wasp, but enables it to survive and play a valuable role in control of the pest population. Objectionable residues on the tobacco are thus avoided. Another wasp species, *Polistes fuscatus* var. *bellicosus,* destroys many of the larger larvae of the tobacco budworm (*Heliothis virescens*) and plays an important role in the natural control of this pest. Still another, *Polistes crinitus* var. *americanus* F., is reported to control the fall webworm (*Laphygma frugiperda*) in Puerto Rico.

HORNETS AND YELLOWJACKETS

Other noteworthy members of the Vespidae are the hornets. The name "yellowjacket," though used quite loosely, is most often applied to the smaller yellow and black hornets. Native North American hornets are confined to two genera, *Vespula* and the numerous *Dolichovespula;* there is also a species introduced from Europe—*Vespa crabro,* a large yellow and brown hornet that builds its nest in hollow trees. *Vespula* and *Dolichovespula* both have either yellow and black or black and white markings. The former nests underground, the latter in the globular paper nest that is commonly seen hanging from the branch of a tree or shrub.

One of the more familiar papermakers is *Dolichovespula maculata,* a large black and white species commonly called the bald-faced hornet. The food habits of hornets are substantially the same as those of *Polistes.* The adults feed on the juices of their prey as they prepare it for the larvae, as well as on nectar

and fruit juices. Their fondness for ripe fruit makes them a
nuisance at times. The large hornets are more largely carnivorous
than the yellowjackets, and include among their prey such large
insects as robber flies and dragonflies. They are especially fond
of the larval secretions too, and the workers sometimes devour
the late brood larvae when the food supply runs short and the
colony starts breaking up.

Before the American Revolution the French settler Hector
St. Jean de Crèvecoeur, a keen observer of nature, wrote from
his farm in New York of using hornets to control flies. No doubt
he referred to a species of *Dolichovespula*. This early excursion
into the field of biological control, which was apparently successful, is best described in his own words:

> In the middle of my new parlor I have . . . a curious republic of
> industrious hornets; their nest hangs to the ceiling, by the same twig
> on which it was so admirably built and contrived in the woods. Its
> removal did not displease them, for they find in my house plenty of
> food; and I have left a hole open in one of the panes of the window,
> which answers their purposes. By this kind usage they are become
> quite harmless; they live on the flies, which are very troublesome to
> us throughout the summer; they are constantly busy in catching them,
> even on the eyelids of my children. . . . By their assistance, I am but
> little troubled with flies. All my family are so accustomed to their
> buzzing, that no one takes any notice of them; and though they are
> fierce and vindictive, yet kindness and hospitality has made them use-
> ful and harmless.[19]

SOLITARY WASPS

The Vespidae also include potter wasps and burrowing wasps.
The potter wasps have a distinctively long "waist," (known as the
petiole). Their cells constructed out of clay or chewed foliage,
usually on twigs of trees, are often skillful works of art, suggesting intricately shaped ceramic vases. Some are built in
hollow twigs or the crevices of walls. The female of *Eumenes
fraternus* constructs her clay cells on the twigs of trees and fills

[19] Hector St. Jean de Crèvecoeur, *Letters from an American Farmer* (New
York: E. P. Dutton & Co., 1957; first published 1782).

them with paralyzed cankerworms before depositing her eggs; she gives no further attention to the developing larvae. On the other hand, an African burrowing wasp, *Odynerus tropicalis,* provides her larva every day with paralyzed caterpillars, increasing the number as it develops; at precisely the time the larva is mature, she stops feeding it and seals the cell, leaving the larva to pupate and emerge later by itself. Still another variation is found in *Synagris spiniventris,* whose female first stocks the cell with caterpillars, then deposits her egg and seals it in; however, at times when caterpillars are scarce she will resort to what is called progressive feeding, in the manner of *Odynerus tropicalis* and the social wasps.

SPHECIDS

The Sphecidae are mostly solitary wasps, but they exhibit a variety of nesting and feeding habits. Mud daubers may build their nests singly or in groups. *Sphex ichneumoneus* digs a hole— it may be as much as a foot deep—in which she places one to three cells. Each cell is provided with one or more longhorned grasshoppers before the egg is deposited. Several such holes may be dug in one nesting area. The tastes of *Sphex lobatus* are different; here the female provisions her nests with crickets. Certain wasps of the genus *Podium,* common in South America, supply their burrows or mud nests in trees with a larder of cockroaches. Two species from the Philippines, *Larra luzonensis* and *Motes subtesselata,* were introduced into Hawaii in 1921 in an attempt to control mole and field crickets; against the mole cricket the former has been very effective. *Larra americana,* from Brazil, was introduced into Puerto Rico beginning in 1936. *Larra analis,* which also attacks mole crickets, is found in the southern United States. These wasps are quite specific in their choice of a host. They invade the burrows of crickets, driving them out into the open, where one by one they are paralyzed and implanted with an egg. In a short time, the cricket revives and returns to its burrow, where it is devoured by the wasp larva in a few days.

Larrid wasp, Sphecidae, and paralyzed cricket prey. (*E. S. Ross*)

Here the relation of larva to host is typically parasitic, whereas the adult in its attack on the host, which usually leads to a violent struggle, is a typical predator. The habits of *Sphex laeviventris,* which preys on the Mormon cricket, are typical of the burrowing wasps: from two to four crickets are paralyzed and placed in a burrow accommodating a single offspring.

Bembix spinolae, a burrowing wasp, feeds its larvae progressively on a great variety of flies. *Bembix hinei* provisions its burrows mostly with horseflies; in the rural areas of the South, where it is commonly seen around horses and cattle, it is appropriately called the "horseguard." It may be observed that farm animals are greatly agitated by horseflies and their buzzing, but not by the noise and gyrations of the wasps—presumably because they have learned to distinguish friend from foe.

The giant cicada-killer, *Sphecius speciosus,* is strictly solitary. The female digs a large hole in the ground and provisions it with one or two paralyzed cicadas, on each of which she lays an egg and on which the larva feeds as it develops. Though this is one of our largest wasps, it finds the prey too heavy to transport over the ground or through the air for any great distance. After capturing the cicada, the killer must have sufficient altitude to take advantage of air currents; if the capture has been made on the ground, she drags the cicada up a tree from which she takes off in the manner of a glider. Several such maneuvers may be necessary to reach the nest. For sheer industry, the female of a species of *Ammophila*—and this holds true for many of her relatives—rivals the proverbial ant. She digs a burrow several inches deep in the sand, which she painstakingly removes, a grain at a time, to a distance of a foot or so from the entrance. After paralyzing a caterpillar and imbibing some of its liquid contents, she drags it into the burrow, where she deposits a single egg. She then covers the nest carefully, sometimes tamping down the sand with a small pebble held in her jaws. Some species of *Ammophila* feed the larva progressively, caring for several widely separated nests at a time.

EGG PREDATORS

Some species of wasps lay their eggs within the egg or egg mass of the host, and the larvae eat the eggs before the host larva develops. The feeding does not end with one egg—some or all of the egg mass may be consumed or the larva may go in search of scattered eggs. The female *Scutellista cyanea*, of the family Pteromalidae, a predator upon the eggs of scale insects, inserts her ovipositor underneath the body of an adult female scale and deposits a single egg. Although the eggs of one scale insect may be enough to feed more than one wasp larva, the female never deposits more than one egg at a time. If, as sometimes happens, the egg is placed under an empty scale, or if there are not enough eggs, the larva may puncture the body wall of the adult insect and feed on it; where this happens, it may be regarded as a true parasite, since it can reach maturity while feeding on a single host.

In summer the egg, larval, and pupal stages of S. *cyanea* normally take three, eleven, and ten days respectively to develop. If host eggs are in short supply the larval stage may take several weeks longer. Under favorable conditions, several generations a season will develop on black scale, where there may be enough eggs in a single large scale chamber to rear several larvae. Five hundred eggs, or even fewer, are enough to permit one larva to reach full development; but it may consume as many as two thousand. A female egg predator lives from ten to twelve days, and may deposit twenty-five or thirty eggs.

Scutellista cyanea is not a native wasp, but was brought from Italy in 1895 to combat the barnacle scale (*Ceroplastes cirripediformis*) and the Florida wax scale (*Ceroplastes floridensis*), both pests of ornamental plants in the Gulf states. Releases were made in Louisiana, where although the wasp was observed to be well established among these scales some years later, not much is known concerning its effectiveness. A large percentage of the scales are attacked, but not all the eggs within a scale chamber are consumed—a fact that limits the value of the wasp as a control insect. In 1900 this same predator was imported from Africa in an attempt to check the black scale (*Saissetia oleae*), a serious pest of citrus groves in California. Although it attacks a high percentage of scales, especially in the coastal regions, its effectiveness is once again limited by the fact that not all the eggs in a scale chamber are consumed. Another egg predator, *Lecaniobius utilis,* was imported for the same purpose in 1934— this time from Brazil and Argentina. It has the same habits as *Scutellista* and does not appear to be very effective. It has been recovered only in a limited area and was found attacking nigra scale instead of black scale. Still another egg predator, *Tomocera californica,* abundant in California before *Scutellista* was imported, seems all but to have disappeared; it is believed that its place may have been taken by the foreign species.

Among wasps of the family Eulophidae are two Hawaiian species: one of the genus *Ootetrastichus*, whose larvae will consume all the eggs of the sugar cane leafhopper in one mass, and *Tetrastichus hagenowii*, which preys on the egg capsules of several kinds of roaches. *Macrorileya oecanthi,* of the family Eurytomidae, places an egg next to one imbedded in a plant stem by the snowy tree cricket (*Oecanthus niveus*); after consuming this egg, the larva burrows through the pith of the plant stem in search of others, consuming some ten to fifteen in all. Among the

Evaniidae, *Zeuxevania splendidula* deposits its egg inside one of the eggs in the capsule of a cockroach, *Loboptera decepiens,* as soon as it is dropped. During the later stages of its development, the larva consumes all the eggs in the capsule. In buildings with a heavy infestation of cockroaches there are likely to be a large number of the wasps that prey on them.

SOLITARY WASPS AND FOREST PESTS

The role of solitary wasps as predators upon the spruce bud-worm and associated spruce-fir defoliators has recently attracted the interest of forest entomologists in Canada. In order to learn whether there were species present that might provision their nests with these defoliators, 322 trap-nest bundles, each com-posed of eleven pierced elderberry stems, were scattered over twenty-one sites. From these, 107 nests of solitary wasps and 157 nests of bees were collected simply by pulling out the stems from the bundles, which were held together by elastic bands. More of these nests had been appropriated where the stand of trees was somewhat open, since nesting wasps and bees prefer sunlight. The stems with completed nests were taken to the laboratory for study. Three species of wasps showed promise, since their provi-sions did indeed include the spruce budworm, *Choristoneura fumiferana*—along with a variety of other pests of conifers. The peak of their first-generation nesting activity coincided with the late larval stage of the spruce budworm and other pests. With these "encouraging results," as the report[20] calls them, an attempt will be made to determine the number of defoliators taken by a particular species of wasp in relation to the total populations. It is hoped that they may prove of value in keeping these pests—particularly the spruce budworm—at non-economic levels.

Several species of vespid wasps are reported[21] to be important

---

[20] R. E. Fye, "Predation of Lepidopterous Larvae by Solitary Wasps" (*Bi-monthly Progress Report,* Canada Dept. of Forestry, March-April 1962). The three species of wasp are *Ancistrocerus catskill albophaleratus, A. tigris tigris,* and *Rygchium leucomelas* (Sauss.)

predators of the jack pine sawfly (*Neodiprion swainei*), and also vectors of a virus disease to which this pest is susceptible. The most important of these wasps is *Vespula rufa consobrina.* Others include *V. vulgaris, V. maculata,* and *V. arenaria.* A sphecid wasp, *Crabo* sp. is also an active predator upon the jack pine sawfly.

ANTS

The ants (family Formicidae) as a whole exhibit a wide range of feeding habits; but a very substantial number are predators of insect pests. In fact, ants were the first insects used for biological control. Centuries ago Chinese citrus growers are known to have placed colonies of *Oecophylla smaragdina* in their groves, and to have aided the movement of the ants from tree to tree by means of bridges between the trees made of bamboo poles. Ant gatherers—laborers of a special class—went into the hills where ants abounded, and collected them in pig or goat bladders greased inside with lard, which they stretched over the opening of the ant nest. The first published record of transferring insects from one place to another for biological control appeared in 1775, and concerns the transfer of colonies of predatory ants from the mountains to the date plantations of Yemen, in southwestern Arabia, for controlling another species of ant that was destructive to the date palms. The Japanese are said to have used beneficial species of ants to control destructive beetles on mango trees.

According to William Morton Wheeler,

All primitive ants are decidedly carnivorous. . . . That this must have been the character of the whole family during a long period of its history is indicated by the retention of the insectivorous habit, in a more or less mitigated form, even in many of the higher ants. . . . The ants belonging to the oldest and most primitive subfamilies, the Ponerinae, Dorylinae, and Cerapachyinae and also to many of the lower genera of Myrmicinae, feed exclusively on insects.[22]

[21] W. A. Smirnoff, "Predators of Larvae of *Neodiprion swainei* Midd.," *The Canadian Entomologist,* April 1961.

[22] W. M. Wheeler, *Social Life Among the* Insects (New York: Harcourt, Brace & Co., 1923).

THE VALUE OF ANTS

That ants play an important part in protecting forests and wood lots from destructive beetles and other pests, was recognized in Germany nearly a century ago. In 1880 a law was passed in Prussia protecting ants from human interference; and a new statute that replaced the older one in 1936 is still in force tbday. Some French and British forests have suffered from the raids of collectors of ant nests for eggs to be used as food for aquarium fish. In Europe today formicine and related ants are colonized and protected for their value in controlling forest insect pests.

A tropical ant that is a valuable predator albeit an unpleasant one at times—and is reputed to be the one used by the Chinese for biological control centuries ago—has been described as follows by J. D. Tothill *et al:*

An ant called the green tree ant *(Oecophylla smaragdina)* occurs in practically all the tropical lands lying between the Solomon Islands and Southern China. It is very conspicuous for the reason that it lives in various trees, including the coconut, in a conspicuous nest, sometimes a foot in diameter and composed for the most part of leaves woven together with a white, silklike material. The habits of this ant have attracted a good deal of attention. Observations by Ridley (1890), confirmed by those of Doflein (1905) and of Dodd (1916), state that the nest is built in this remarkable way: The edges of two leaves are first pulled together by a series of workers bridging the gap between the two. When the gap has been adjusted to the proper size another series of workers come up, each carrying an ant larva between its front legs. By squeezing the larva gently with the mandibles, it is made to discharge a fine thread of silk, and by moving the larva slowly from edge to edge of the two leaves, a silken web is finally constructed that holds the leaves in place. The ant has an unpleasant bite that makes it well but unfavorably known, to natives at least, throughout its range. It is carnivorous and particularly insectivorous in habits, and it is known to keep down a number of insect pests within its range. . . .

It has recently been shown . . . that this ant is the principal factor in the biological control of the coconut flower bug, *Axiagastus campbelli,* and in the event of that injurious insect finding its way to this

Colony there is no question that it would then be desirable to introduce the green tree ant.[23]

Tothill's colleague T. H. C. Taylor found a minute ant, *Monomorium floricola,* to be an important predator of the coconut leaf-mining beetle (*Promecotheca reichei*) in Fiji. Although the ant is a general predator, it concentrates pretty much on the beetle during outbreaks of that species. It enters and frequently nests inside the beetle's tunnelings, where it feeds on larvae, pupae, and newly emerged adults. It also feeds on the eggs, biting a large irregular hole in the capsule and sometimes tearing away part of it. The ant enters the excavated leaf by biting a small hole in it, and immediately proceeds to attack whatever beetles may be present. The ant that begins the operation is followed by others intent on the same mission, and in a short time the occupants, of whatever stage, have been devoured.[24]

The sorghum midge, *Contarinia sorghicola,* one of the most important pests of grain sorghums in the southern states, is preyed upon by such species as the Argentine ant and the small fire ants. These predators "destroy many midges by swarming over the sorghum heads and seizing the pupae as they work themselves out of the spikelets. They also attack the newly emerged adults before they are able to fly."[25] They are also reported to destroy the eggs and caterpillars of *Anticarsia gemmatilis,* a pest of velvetbeans, soybeans, and peanuts in the southern states. According to D. W. Morley, the cotton boll weevil can be held in check by "the encouragement of a dozen species of ant" which are capable of destroying 50 per cent of the weevil larvae. Morley also reports that in a day, a colony of 40,000 carnivorous ants will devour

[23] J. D. Tothill, T. H. C. Taylor, and R. W. Paine, *The Coconut Moth in Fiji: A History of Its Control by Means of Parasites* (London: The Imperial Bureau of Entomology, 1930).

[24] T. H. C. Taylor, *The Biological Control of an Insect in Fiji* (London: The Imperial Institute of Entomology, 1937).

[25] E. V. Walter, *The Sorghum Midge* (Washington: USDA Farmers' Bulletin No. 1566, July 1953).

a quart of insects by volume, or the equivalent of 20,000 insects every day during their active period in the summer.[26]

Ants are noted enemies of termites, on which they are an important check in the tropical countries where they abound. It is a common practice in some Asiatic countries to encourage ants to live around warehouses; in Madras, myrmicine ants were used to protect warehouses from these marauders of structural timbers. Some tropical species of ants invade and take over termite nests for themselves; in South Queensland, Australia, for example, one species of dolichoderine ants is said to occupy 80 per cent of the nests of certain common species of termites. In tropical countries it is not uncommon to find mounds that appear to be the home of termites, but are actually occupied by ants.

C. P. Clausen concludes that the predaceous ants

. . . rank high as natural control agencies, which hold many insect pests of forest trees and agricultural crops below the level of economic injury. They feed extensively on many insects that pass all or part of their lives in the soil, and have been reported to destroy a high percentage of larvae of fruit flies and house flies *(Musca domestica)*, which enter the soil for pupation. The driver and legionary ants of the tropics when on the march destroy practically all insect life in their paths that is unable to escape by flight. . . .

The species that are harmful to agricultural crops are mainly those that feed on honeydew secreted by scale insects, mealybugs, whiteflies, aphids, and leafhoppers. The injury is mainly indirect, resulting from protection given these pests from their natural enemies. The predators are driven away and oviposition by parasites is prevented. The harmful effect is especially noticeable with parasite species that require considerable time for completion of oviposition or for host feeding.[27]

THE IMPORTED FIRE ANT

The imported fire ant, *Solenopsis saevissima*, gained entry into this country through the port of Mobile, Alabama at some time

[26] D. W. Morley, *The Ant World* (Harmondsworth, Middlesex: Penguin Books, 1955).

[27] C. P. Clausen, *Biological Control of Insect Pests in the Continental U.S.* (Washington: USDA Technical Bulletin No. 1139, June 1956).

prior to 1920. First it spread slowly; by 1949 it was known to be in twelve counties in southwestern Alabama, in fourteen in southeastern Mississippi, and in two in northwestern Florida. Its spread after this—over much of Alabama and Mississippi, and into Louisiana, Texas, Arkansas, Georgia, and South Carolina—was more rapid. The first of several annual appropriations for the "eradication" of the fire ant was made by Congress in 1957, and amounted—as did later appropriations—to $2.4 million, to be matched by state and local funds. Extensive aerial applications of granular heptachlor were made, with damage to wildlife that led to a storm of protest, and that also prompted some studies of whether the damage done by the fire ant actually justified these drastic measures. These are the findings of F. S. Arant and his co-workers:

The worker ants search for food through a network of tunnels radiating as far as 66 feet from the mound. Their food consists principally of insects that they sting to death and devour. One laboratory colony killed and consumed 20 adult boll weevils within 2 hours. The ants have been observed devouring house fly larvae, boll weevil grubs, cutworms, and many other destructive insects in the field. Occasionally, they consume seed that are high in fat and protein content. Although okra, potatoes, and other crops are sometimes attacked, damage to plants in general is rare, except that resulting from building mounds. Captive laboratory colonies became cannibalistic rather than feed on growing plants they had been reported to relish. No damage to livestock has been observed. Cattle and sheep graze over the mounds and even lie down near them. Newly born livestock is rarely if ever killed.

Fire ant damage is of two principal types. The mounds interfere with the operation of mowers, combines, and other farm machinery, especially in heavy soil. The worker ants inflict stings on laborers clearing clogged mower blades, handling hay, harvesting some field crops, or performing other tasks in heavily infested areas. The sting causes a burning sensation and usually results in formation of a tiny pustule that remains several days. There is no severe or prolonged pain or after effect except in rare instances where an individual is allegeric to the sting. Allergic reactions may be severe, as is true with stings from bees, wasps, and other related insects.[28]

[28] F. S. Arant, K. L. Hays, and D. W. Speake, *Facts About the Fire Ant* (Auburn: Agricultural Experiment Station, Alabama Polytechnic Institute,

Preferred sites for nest-building are open fields, pastures, along roadsides and fencerows, waste land and islands within marsh areas, and sparsely wooded areas. Cultivation will prevent the construction of large mounds. The number of mounds varies with the availability of food. As many as 120 mounds per acre have been counted in a newly invaded area; but in a stable situation, when competition between the colonies has caused a leveling off, the number of mounds in an open area will average from 25 to 40 per acre.

It now appears that the fire ant may possibly even be turned to the advantage of medicine, as well as of agriculture, quite aside from its value as a predator. Studies at Louisiana State University have shown that the venom of the ant kills other insects and mites —and thus might be superior as an insecticide to the chemical poisons that lead to the problem of resistant insect strains—and that it contains an antibiotic that kills many bacteria and molds.[29]

ARMY ANTS

The most notorious of their kind are the army ants, also variously called driver, legionary, or traveler ants. The most ferocious of these belong to the genus *Dorylus* and are found in Africa; their counterparts in the Western Hemisphere are of the genus *Eciton,* and are found mostly in the tropics but do range as far north as California, Colorado, and North Carolina. These ants are wholly predaceous, and obtain their food by raiding. They do not build nests; their colonies, which number in the tens of thousands, and sometimes as many as a hundred thousand or more, settle only long enough for their larvae to spin their cocoons and pupate, for the queen to lay her eggs, and for the new brood of larvae to hatch.

This period varies with the species. For *Eciton hamatum* the period of the fixed bivouac is nineteen or twenty days; then the colony moves on, marching by night, pausing by day to make a

1958). See also J. L. George, *The Program to Eradicate the Imported Fire Ant* (New York: The Conservation Foundation, 1958).
[29] *Time*, March 9, 1959.

raid, and then resuming the migration. Each night's march follows one of the trails begun during the day's raiding, but with the difference that this time the larvae are carried along with the rest. In this species the colony is nomadic for seventeen days; then it bivouacs again and the cycle is repeated. During the bivouac the colony builds no shelter, but merely forms a cluster in a hollow log or tree trunk, above ground; an opening in the living mass permits the foragers returning from raids to feed the brood. By the end of the first week in bivouac the queen is swollen to about five times her normal size and begins laying eggs, the usual production being about 25,000. The larvae hatch in a few days, and by the nineteenth or twentieth day the new workers have emerged from their cocoons. Great excitement is now evident among the workers—probably in response to secretions they obtain from the newly emerged adults—and the colony is again ready for its nomadic phase. The cyclic nature of these phases of nomadism and rest is of course tied in with the reproductive cycle of the queen, and is not believed to be related to food requirements.

During the bivouac period the daily raids are carried on by a comparatively small number of workers; during the nomadic period they engage the entire colony except the queen and a few attendants, and are carried out with much greater vigor and over longer distances. Raid tactics vary; some species attack in large masses on a broad front, others in column formation. Ants of a small black species found in Mexico, called *soldados,* sometimes raid a whole village. At such times people may leave their houses, while any occupants such as cockroaches, mice, and lizards are devoured by the ants, which thereby perform a valuable santitation service. The German writer and world traveler Hans Ewers observed that in order to protect themselves from night raids of army ants, the Indians set the bedposts in pewter saucers filled with vinegar or kerosene, which the insects would carefully avoid. Apparently the ants that raid the villages do so in search of fresh meat, which they so much prefer that they will often pass up dead insects along the way. Such foods as sugar and bread don't interest them and are passed by when a house is raided.

One night in a Mexican village Ewers was "trapped" by the raiding ants as he sat writing at a table. Seeing a carpet of ants between him and the door, he panicked and tried to escape by standing first on the chair, then on the table. As the ants swarmed over the chair and table, clinging to each other to form a bridge, he tried to escape by stepping into a large pewter pitcher filled with water which was sitting on the washstand, within reach of the table. The water was not long an obstacle to the ants; they swarmed up to the edge of the pitcher and one after the other dropped into it, apparently intent on forming a bridge between the pitcher's edge and his leg. Finally he had the presence of mind to jump onto the nearby bed—where behind the protective barrier of the bowls of kerosene underneath the bedposts, he was safe.[30]

In Africa, where they are more ferocious, the raids of army ants are dreaded by the villagers. Albert Schweitzer gives a vivid description of the migrations and of a raid on the hospital at Lambarene:

On their great migrations they travel five or six abreast in perfectly ordered columns. I once observed, near my house, a column that took thirty-six hours to pass! If their course is over open ground or across a path, the warriors with their powerful jaws line up several rows deep on each side and protect the procession in which the ordinary traveler ants carry their young along. When they form protecting lanes they turn their backs to the procession like Cossacks guarding the Czar. In that position they remain for hours.

Usually three or four independent columns march along one beside the other but from five to fifty meters apart. At a particular moment they disperse. How the command is given we do not know. But in a trice a huge area is covered with a black swarm. Every living thing found on it is doomed. Even the great spiders on the trees cannot escape, for the frightful ravagers creep after them in droves up to the highest twig. And, if in despair the spiders jump down from the tree,

[30] Hans Heinz Ewers, *Wonders of the Ant World* (New York: Dodd, Mead & Co., 1931).

they fall victim to the ants on the ground. The spectacle is gruesome. The militarism of the jungle almost bears comparison with that in Europe.

Our house lies on one of the great military routes of the traveler ants. Usually they swarm at night. A scratching and a peculiar cluck-ing of the hens warn us of the danger. Now no time must be lost. I spring out of bed, run to the hen house and open it. Hardly have I opened the door when the hens rush out; shut in they would be the victims of the ants. The latter creep into the nose and mouth of the hens until they are stifled. Then they devour them until in a short time only the white bones remain. Ordinarily it is the chickens that fall victim to the ravagers; the hens are able to defend themselves until help arrives.[31]

The ants are driven away by pouring a hastily contrived solu-tion of water and lysol mixed in pails. During this endeavor the doctor and his helpers are badly bitten; the ants crawl upon them, as many as fifty at a time, and sink their jaws into the flesh so that they can't be pulled off without tearing the flesh. All this goes on in the dark of night, with the only light coming from a lantern held by the doctor's wife. In a single week they were attacked three times. The principal migrations, Dr. Schweitzer says, are at the end of the rainy season. He notes that these ants are not much larger than the red European ants, but have much stronger jaws and move much more rapidly.

One may wonder how these ruthless marauders could be of any value. Besides being an annoyance to man, they destroy beneficial insects and other animals along with the pests. Not many insects in their path escape; those that do are usually other ants equipped with repellent glandular secretions or living in large colonies which discourage attack. But, like the predatory mammals that are members of the same community, they undoubtedly have their place in maintaining a balance in the teeming plant and animal life of the jungle.

[31] Albert Schweitzer, *On the Edge of the Primeval Forest* (New York: The Macmillan Co., 1956). Reprinted by permission.

*To the ecologist, the handwriting was on the wall from the
beginning. Any control policy which completely ignores biological
balances is eventually doomed to failure.*

—A. D. PICKETT

PREDATORS OF INSECTS:
VERTEBRATES, SPIDERS, AND MITES

5

"As enemies of insects birds stand supreme among vertebrates," Harvey Sweetman asserts, because they exceed most
insectivorous vertebrates in number both of individuals and of
species, and because, being highly mobile, they are able to concentrate quickly in vast numbers where a sudden outbreak of insects occurs.[1] Though opinions differ on the over-all economic
importance of birds as biological control factors, there is no doubt
that they consume on enormous number of insects, or that in
the control of local outbreaks they are at times of prime importance, even though they may not be able to cope with severe
infestations or explosive increases of insects over a large area.

It is generally agreed that more than half the food consumed
by the more than 1,400 species and subspecies of birds in
North America consists of insects. Their food preferences vary
with the season and with what is available. Most birds feed to a
considerable extent on insects during the summer months when
they are plentiful; at other times certain species may prefer

[1] Harvey L. Sweetman, *The Principles of Biological Control* (Dubuque,
Iowa: Wm. C. Brown Co., 1958).

An eastern bluebird arriving at its nest with a grub. The nestlings of most common birds are fed on insects exclusively, and consume an enormous number of insect pests. (*K. H. Maslowski*)

seeds, fruits, or berries. The enormous quantity of food consumed by nestling birds consists mainly of insects, regardless of the food preferences of the adults—except in the case of doves and pigeons, whose young are fed on a protein secretion from the crop of the parent bird. Nestlings increase in weight by from one-fifth to one-half each day, and at some stages of their growth they require more than their own weight in food daily!

Chester A. Reed wrote that a cuckoo consumed from 50 to 400 caterpillars in a day, and a chickadee from 200 to 500 insects or up to 4,000 insect eggs.[2] He estimated that a single insectivorous bird would consume an average of 100 insects a day during the summer, and that there were no less than five insectivorous birds

[2] Chester A. Reed, *Land Birds: Bird Guide, Song and Insectivorous Birds East of the Rockies* (Garden City, N. Y.: Doubleday, Doran, 1943).

per acre in Massachusetts. On this basis, he estimated the useful bird population of that state to be 25,600,000, which in their turn would require a total of 2,560,000,000 insects per day—or figuring an average of 120,000 insects per bushel, a daily consumption of 21,000 bushels during the months of May to September inclusive. Reed estimated the consumption in winter, late fall, and early spring to be half that amount.

GULLS TO THE RESCUE

Birds can sometimes be the deciding factor in bringing about natural control of a local outbreak of insect pests. The most celebrated instance is that of the gulls that saved the small plantings of the Mormon settlers in the Salt Lake Valley in 1848, when a severe outbreak of "crickets" threatened the crops on which the success of the settlement depended. To commemorate this event a monument topped by a sculptured gull in flight, was erected on the grounds of the Mormon Tabernacle in Salt Lake City. George Q. Cannon, one of the early settlers, wrote in 1894;

> To us who lived in Utah . . . it seemed there was a visitation of Providence to save us. Seagulls came by hundreds and by thousands, and before the crops were entirely destroyed these gulls devoured the insects, so that our fields were entirely freed from them . . . I have gone along ditches in the morning and have seen lumps of these crickets, vomited up by the gulls, so they could begin again killing them.[3]

The "Mormon cricket," as the insect is now commonly called, is not a true cricket; and in the strict sense the name applies only to the species *Anabrus simplex,* although two other species, *A. cerciata* and *A. longipes,* are sometimes included in the designation. The coulee cricket, *Peranabrus scabricollis,* is a related species. All these insects are flightless katydids or longhorned grasshoppers belonging to the family Tettigoniidae; the true crickets belong to the family Gryllidae. Not being versed in

[3] Quoted by Claude Wakeland in *Mormon Crickets in North America* (Washington: USDA Technical Bulletin No. 1202, Aug. 1959).

these refinements, the Mormon settlers gave the name of "cricket" to the black grasshoppers which the Indians gathered for food, and which before the coming of the white man had constituted a major item in the diet of some tribes. The Mormon cricket is found only in North America, from the Coastal Range eastward to the north central Great Plains, and in southern Canada provinces from Manitoba westward. During their active lives the adults migrate in bands of varying size, traveling anywhere from half a mile to a mile in a day. What prompts these migrations or their direction (which is not always toward the most abundant food supply) is not known. Mormon crickets prefer range plants if these are available, but are omnivorous plant feeders; in addition, the stronger individuals are cannibalistic and may attack weak or injured members of the band. Over large areas as a whole their total damage is usually not great, but in localized areas the losses can be extreme. Occasionally a widespread outbreak will do considerable damage. The outbreak that threatened the early Mormon settlers in the Salt Lake Valley and which was brought under control by the gulls was a localized one.

NATURAL CONTROL OF GRASSHOPPERS

Gulls are at their best in cleaning up infestations of Mormon crickets where the vegetation is scattered and the insects are easily found; they do not feed extensively in heavily cropped fields or on rangeland with a heavy cover of grasses. California gulls (*Larus californica*) were credited with cleaning up a heavy local infestation of two-striped grasshoppers (*Melanoplus bivittatus*) in Montana in 1949. It was estimated that 5,000 gulls flew in for the feast, and that after five days of working the bare strips between the rows of barley they had reduced the average number of grasshoppers per square yard from twenty-five to five.

Hawks congregate in great numbers in an area infested with Mormon crickets, soaring over a band of the crickets or perching on every available fence post; they are often the means used by agricultural agents to locate cricket bands. At least nineteen species of wild birds and several species of rodents are very fond of Mormon crickets; coyotes, skunks, badgers, lizards, poultry, toads, and spiders also eat them in large numbers. Numerous scattered cavities in the soil give evidence that mice and rats have been digging for Mormon cricket eggs. The order of importance of the natural enemies of the Mormon cricket, as given by the workers in the infested areas, is roughly as follows: crows, hawks, meadowlarks, several kinds of small field birds, and the burrowing sphecid wasp *Sphex* [*Chlorion*] *laeviventris*—followed by poultry, ground squirrels, horned larks, and black widow spiders.

Birds are also important in the natural control of the high plains grasshopper (*Dissosteira longipennis*). Found only in the high plains area of the United States, this grasshopper reached outbreak proportions in parts of Colorado, Kansas, New Mexico, Oklahoma, and Texas between 1933 and 1940. By the latter year, according to Claude Wakeland, "baiting and control by natural agencies—birds, weather, animal and insect predators, and insect parasites—had checked the outbreak."[4]

Birds, chiefly western horned larks and lark buntings, are considered the most important predators of the grasshopper in New Mexico. In Colorado the desert horned lark and lark bunting are reported to be the most important bird predators; in addition, it was observed that shrikes fed heavily on the adults in late summer, that curlews provided their nestlings with adult grasshoppers, and that killdeers feasted greedily on those whose migrations took them near the moist areas inhabited by these birds.

Birds and rodents—specifically western horned larks, rats, mice, and gophers—were reported to have destroyed 15 per cent of the *D. longipennis* pods in the egg beds of New Mexico and 10 per cent of those in Texas. In New Mexico an egg bed covering five acres was reported to have been heavily worked by birds, and in

[4] Claude Wakeland, *The High Plains Grasshopper* (Washington: USDA Technical Bulletin No. 1167, January 1958).

another place they were observed to be very active in excavating eggs over an area of 150 acres. Several species of lizards, horned toads, and rattlesnakes are heavy feeders on the immature grasshoppers. At certain times skunks and coyotes feed almost exclusively on *D. longipennis* adults and to a lesser extent badgers, bobcats, and kit foxes feed on both nymphs and adults.

BIRDS IN THE FOREST

If it could be determined which single category of birds had the greatest economic value to man, the prize might well go to the woodpeckers. The value of these energetic birds in forests and in certain orchards is incalculable. From studies made between 1944 and 1951 C. L. Massey and N. D. Wygant concluded that woodpeckers were the most important predators of the Engelmann spruce beetle (*Dendroctonus engelmanni*), a serious pest of forests in the western United States. "In some areas," according to these entomologists, "woodpeckers destroyed as much as 75 per cent of the beetle population."[5] The most common species in Colorado are the Alpine three-toed, Rocky Mountain hairy, and downy woodpeckers. During the summer months the first two of these work over the infested trees in pairs with a thoroughness that is remarkable. Each pair concentrates on a small area in the infested stand, sometimes confining its activity to only a few trees for a period of several weeks. The authors report that "many of the trees are completely stripped of bark by the birds and the mortality of the brood in these trees approaches 100 per cent." A large reduction in beetle population took place even in trees only moderately worked by the woodpeckers, and in those only slightly worked the beetles were reduced almost by half. In a large sample it was found that the infested trees not worked by the woodpeckers averaged 162 beetles per square foot; those slightly worked averaged 90 beetles (or a reduction of 44 per cent), those moderately worked averaged 41 beetles

[5] C. L. Massey and N. D. Wygant, *Biology and Control of the Engelmann Spruce Beetle in Colorado* (Washington: USDA Circular No. 944, July 1954).

(a 75 per cent reduction); and the heavily worked trees averaged only four beetles per square foot, or a reduction of 98 per cent.

In a study of the food habits of these woodpeckers, the average number of insects per stomach was 27.68 for the Rocky Mountain hairy woodpecker, 26.89 for the downy, and 21.39 for the three-toed. Males did more damage to the beetles than females, the stomach contents for those of all species averaging 23.04 adult beetles as compared to 16.04 for females of all species. The same study indicated that 65 per cent of all the beetles consumed were *D. engelmanni*, 13 per cent other bark beetles of the same family (Scolytidae), 12 per cent ants, and 6 per cent wood-boring beetles of the family Cerambycidae. Red-shafted flickers were also common in the area infested with the Engelmann spruce beetle, but the study did not indicate that they had any effect on the beetle population; their stomach contents consisted entirely of ants.

Foresters in the southern pine belt consider woodpeckers to be the only effective control for bark beetles in that region, and believe that any other form of control would cost more than the timber is worth.[6] Woodpeckers are also valuable predators of the western pine bark beetle (*Dendroctonus brevicomis*), a serious pest of ponderosa pine stands. Where woodpeckers had worked over the bark they were found to have reduced the brood by about 73 per cent. Their destruction of the beetle is greatest during the winter months, when the pest is in the dormant larval stage. In Oregon and California the chief species preying on these beetles are the white-headed, Modoc, Gairdner's, Arctic three-toed, and western pileated woodpeckers, and the Williamson's sapsucker. The western pileated woodpecker appears to be the most valuable because it chisels off large areas of the outer bark, amounting to half to three-quarters of the total, on the trees where it feeds.[7]

After three years of spraying operations against the spruce

[6] Leonard W. Wing, *Natural History of Birds: A Guide to Ornithology* (New York: The Ronald Press Co., 1956).

[7] J. M. Miller and F. P. Keen, *Biology and Control of the Western Pine Beetle* (Washington: USDA Miscellaneous Publication 800, March 1960).

budworm in Quebec, J. R. Blais concluded that predators and
parasites were responsible for bringing about the final collapse
of the outbreak. (It appears that they are unable to *initiate* the
decline.) "Without the help of such factors," Blais says, "suppression of the infestation would certainly not be achieved."
Parasites were evidently the major factor, but "the action of
predators, mostly birds . . . was extremely important, especially
during the last weeks of the outbreak . . ." There was good
evidence that most of the residual population of budworm pupae
and late-stage larvae in the summer of 1962 (the last year of
these operations) were destroyed by birds.[8]

BIRDS IN THE ORCHARD

Populations of the codling moth, one of the most troublesome
pests for apple-growers to contend with, are often greatly reduced by woodpeckers in the winter months. In a Nova Scotia
orchard C. R. MacLellan found that during the winter months of
1959–1960, 59 per cent of the codling moth larvae that had hiber-
nated were destroyed, with woodpeckers accounting for 47 per
cent and the braconid parasite *Ascogaster quadridentata* for 9 per
cent, the other 3 per cent having succumbed to the winter temperatures.[9] Studies in Nova Scotia have also shown that woodpeckers
are more effective in destroying the overwintering codling moth
larvae where there is adequate bird cover.[10] E. J. LeRoux has
attributed much of the effectiveness of the modified program in
Quebec to the increased numbers of predators and parasites
that survive; "an undetermined amount" of the success of the
program is ascribed to the predation of birds.[11]

[8] J. R. Blais, "Results of Three Years of Spraying Operations Against the
Spruce Budworm in the Lower St. Lawrence Region," *Bi-monthly Progress
Report*, Canada Dept. of Forestry, Jan.-Feb. 1963.

[9] C. R. MacLellan, "Mortality of Codling Moth Eggs and Young Larvae
in an Integrated Control Orchard," *The Canadian Entomologist*, June
1962.

[10] A. D. Pickett, "Utilization of Native Parasites and Predators," *Journal
of Economic Entomology*, Dec. 1959.

[11] E. J. LeRoux, "Progress in Harmonizing Biological and Chemical Control of Orchard Pests in Eastern Canada" (*Proceedings of 10th International
Congress of Entomology*, 1958).

BIRDS IN THE CORN

Birds also play an important part in the reduction of hibernating larvae of the European corn borer *Ostrinia nubilalis*. The results of a study in Indiana in the spring of 1933, covering twenty fields with a total area of 38 square miles, are interesting and significant. In eighteen of the twenty sampled fields the proportion of bird-pecked stalks ranged from 6 to 62 per cent; in two fields no signs of bird-pecked stalks were observed, while in five fields a 50 per cent reduction of the borer was indicated. The average reduction for the twenty fields studied was 30 per cent. In a similar study in Ohio the proportion of bird-pecked stalks ranged from 1 to 50 per cent, with an average of 15 per cent for the whole area. Since the birds more often attacked badly tunneled stalks than those showing light infestation, it is probable that the number of borers consumed by the birds was actually greater than the averages indicate. The birds seen feeding on the European corn borer included downy woodpeckers, robins, crows, rusty blackbirds, red-winged blackbirds, purple grackles, chickadees, ring-necked pheasants, and starlings. The study indicated that the downy woodpecker and the red-winged blackbird had the greatest effect on the corn borer populations.[12]

At least twenty-one species of birds are known to feed on another corn pest, the corn earworm (*Heliothis zea*). The most important of these are the Brewer's and the California red-winged blackbird, the boat-tailed grackle, the English sparrow, and the downy woodpecker. The attack of the birds in their search for the earworms is sometimes so vigorous that they cause damage to the corn, especially sweet corn, by tearing open the husks.[13]

[12] W. A. Baker, W. G. Bradley, and C. A. Clark, *Biological Control of the European Corn Borer in the United States* (Washington: USDA Technical Bulletin No. 983, Dec. 1949).

[13] R. A. Blanchard and W. A. Douglas, "*The Corn Earworm as an Enemy of Field Corn in the Eastern States* (Washington: USDA Farmers' Bulletin No. 1651, Nov. 1953).

BIRDS IN CULTIVATED FIELDS

The killdeer, or plover, has been described by W. B. Barrows as "a voracious insect feeder" especially valuable to the farmer because of its fondness for grasshoppers and other insects of field crops.[14] Its nest is merely a small depression in the ground of a cultivated field, often between the young plants in a cornfield, and its food consists of a great variety of crop pests such as grasshoppers, mites, beetles, bugs, and caterpillars. According to Wing, a single family of bobwhites living in a potato patch is capable of keeping the potato beetle under control. Baltimore orioles also feed freely on potato beetles and are often found in potato patches with their fledged young. Orioles, much of whose food consists of caterpillars, have been observed to destroy an entire local infestation of tent caterpillars in an orchard. Bobolinks are exceptionally thorough destroyers of the alfalfa weevil in Utah, and in California the western meadowlark is said to be unequaled by any other bird as a destroyer of cutworms, caterpillars, and grasshoppers. According to A. C. Bent, "Few birds of the agricultural areas can claim a higher rank in its economic relations with man than does the meadowlark."[15] In 1919, just as measures were about to be taken against a severe devastation of the coulee cricket near Adrian, Washington, western meadowlarks appeared in great numbers and brought them sufficiently under control to make the program unnecessary.[16] Eastern meadowlarks—which are also efficient destroyers of cutworms, caterpillars, beetles, and grasshoppers, especially in Florida and the southern states during the winter months—are considered an important enemy of the cotton boll weevil, since by feeding regularly on the weevil at that time of the year they materially

[14] Walter Bradford Barrows, *Michigan Bird Life* (East Lansing: Michigan Agricultural College, 1912).

[15] Arthur Cleveland Bent, *Life Histories of North American Blackbirds, Orioles, Tanagers, and Allies* (Washington: U. S. National Museum, Bulletin 211, 1958).

[16] E. F. Kalmbach, "Birds, Beasts, and Bugs," in *Insects: Yearbook of Agriculture* (Washington: Government Printing Office, 1952).

reduce the number that are left to attack the cotton crop the following season. Leonard W. Wing asserts that "the insect-suppression value of birds to agriculture clearly runs into the hundreds and even thousands of million of dollars annually."[17]

DOMESTIC ANIMALS IN BIOLOGICAL CONTROL

The discussion of the Mormon cricket referred to poultry as effective destroyers of this pest. This is particularly true of turkeys. A more or less familiar practice is the use of domestic geese to control weeds—especially in California, where from 175,000 to 200,000 are used each year to control grassy annual and perennial weeds in fields of cotton and various other crops.[18]

The use of poultry as biological control agents against insects is something of a novelty. Turkeys, however, have actually been transported from one place to another for insect control—the latest application being the use of young male chicks to control flies around laying hens. The system was worked out by John Rodriguez, a technician, at the University of California in Riverside. Chicken ranchers who have tried it have found it less expensive than chemical control and also more desirable, in view of the increasing resistance of flies to chemicals and of the hazards of toxic residues to the hens and eggs. Young male chicks (cockerels), placed under the hens' cages, will eat practically all the fly larvae and pupae in the chicken droppings before the immature stages of the insect have a chance to develop into adults. Hatcheries supply the male chicks free since they are unproductive and have no other use. On one farm where the system was tried, 750 chicks were sufficient to control the flies for 35,000 laying hens; in some places it may be necessary to use as many as one chick for each ten or twenty hens.[19]

Domestic hogs used to control insects will root out white grubs

[17] Wing, *ibid.*
[18] Clarence Johnson, "Management of Weeder Geese in Commercial Fields," *California Agriculture*, Aug. 1960.
[19] "Male Chicks Help Lick Hens' Insect Problems," *Science News Letter*, Aug. 20, 1960.

from the soil, although they cannot be safely put on land heavily infested with grubs since these insect larvae may be an intermediate host for a hog parasite, the thorn-headed worm. Hogs can, however, be turned loose in a properly fenced orchard to eat the dropped fruits, which harbor the larvae of insect pests. In South Africa hogs have been used very successfully to control the Emperor moth (*Nudaurelia citheria capensis*) in plantings of introduced pines, where they root out the moth pupae from the needle litter. They are kept in by a single-wire electric fence, and are moved from one plantation to the other.[20]

FISH TO CONTROL MOSQUITOES

The value of fish in controlling mosquitoes has been known for many years, but their actual transport for biological control is fairly recent. Some use was made of carp to control mosquitoes in water tanks as long ago as 1892, and in the early 1900's minnows were placed in water containers around Havana for the same purpose. The fish best suited for larvicidal purposes belong to the order Cyprinodontiformes, and more particularly to two families, the Cyprinodontidae, which are oviparous—that is, the young hatch from eggs outside the parent's body—and the Poeciliidae, which are viviparous, the female giving birth to young hatched inside her body.

The cyprinodonts, especially those of the genus *Gambusia*, are especially effective in controlling mosquitoes, since they breed in great numbers and have a short life cycle, are small in size and so can penetrate weeds that protect the mosquito larvae, and are surface feeders, so that mosquito larvae are a major source of food. In addition, they are hardy fish that can be transported without harm and that become quickly adapted to their new environment. They spawn in shallow water, depositing their adhesive eggs on the bottom or on a bushy plant, where they hatch in anywhere from five to twenty days. In northern climates the spawning begins in April or May, and the young grow to full size in

[20] Harvey L. Sweetman, *The Principles of Biological Control.*

less than a year. In the tropics spawning continues throughout the year, and the young mature and are ready for breeding within two or three months. There may be anywhere from six to two hundred in a brood (depending on the size of the female), and six or more broods will be produced in a summer. One of the Poeciliidae, the guppy (*Lebistes reticulatus*), is even more prolific, and has been used very effectively to control mosquitoes in northern South America.

The cyprinodonts that have been the most effective larvicidal fish in North America are *Gambusia affinis* in the Mississippi Valley, Texas, northern Mexico, and along the Atlantic coast, and *Fundulus heteroclitus* in the salt marshes of the east coast. *Gambusia* has been introduced widely throughout the world—in the Near East, India, Malaya, and Australia. In 1926 it was imported from Italy for mosquito control in Sydney, Australia, and was distributed widely throughout New South Wales and other parts of the continent. Later there were introductions into Queensland, and also into New Guinea, to control disease-carrying mosquitoes. During World War II malarial control units of the Australian and United States armies undertook the collection, breeding, and distribution of *Gambusia* in creeks, swamps, bomb holes, tanks, and drains in Papua and New Guinea, and around camps in Queensland and New South Wales. The mosquito populations were materially reduced as a result. Control work of this kind was continued after the war, and in parts of Australia the fish have been able to control the malarial *Anopheles* mosquito where all other efforts had failed. Fishery authorities and anglers have been critical of these introductions, because *Gambusia* are predatory to some extent on the fry of native species. According to Frank Wilson, "Mosquitofish (and possibly other fishes) often give excellent control of mosquitoes in waters which are permanent, not too weedy, and freely accessible in all parts to the fish." He points out that their efficiency can be increased by periodic restocking of impermanent waters, and by reducing the excessive growth of weeds at the water's edge and in channels and marshes. At the same time it is necessary to drain other breeding sites—puddles, gutters, holes, and any places where water stands.[21]

Sweetman contends that fish can control mosquitoes effectively in small pools, tanks, and artificial pools by restocking annually. He cautions that the fish should be shipped in tin cans, not galvanized iron, copper, or brass containers. Subjecting the fish to sudden changes of temperature should be avoided, and a pond or tank should be ready to receive the fish, with its temperature a fraction of a degree higher than that in the tins. Enough mosquito larvae should be on hand to feed the fish for twenty four hours after their arrival.[22] Properly carried out, mosquito control with fish is cheaper, more effective, and longer lasting than artificial methods such as oiling. Insecticides, even in extremely low concentrations, are very destructive of larvicidal fish just as they are of other fish.[23]

REPTILES AS INSECT CONTROL FACTORS

So far as is known, the effect of snakes on insect populations is relatively slight. Only some of the smaller species live wholly or even partially on insects. Snakes are an important factor, however, in controlling such agricultural pests as rats, mice, moles, and gophers, and their value in this respect is not generally appreciated, least of all by the farmer. Percy Morris believes that some of the credit given to the owls and hawks for their onslaughts on rodents rightfully belongs to the snakes.[24] One of

[21] Frank Wilson, *A Review of the Biological Control of Insects and Weeds in Australia and Australian New Guinea* (Ottawa: Technical Communication No. 1, Commonwealth Institute of Biological Control, 1960).

[22] Harvey L. Sweetman, *The Principles of Biological Control.*

[23] The Endowment Foundation New Jersey Mosquito Larvicide, whose formula is based on pyrethrins, is not known to affect fish, amphibians, or warm-blooded animals (including man) when applied as recommended. It is produced by Seacoast Laboratories, Inc., New York City. (See pamphlet on Mosquito Control prepared by National Audubon Society, 1130 Fifth Ave., New York, 10028.)

[24] Percy A. Morris, *They Hop and Crawl* (New York: The Ronald Press Co., 1945).

the most familiar insect-eaters is the common garter snake, *Thamnophis sirtalis,* which eats some grubs, caterpillars, and snails, but also takes some toads and is especially fond of earth-worms. Dekay's snake (*Storeria dekayi*) is just about as common in the vicinity of towns as the garter snake. Its food is largely worms, salamanders, snails, and insect larvae. Its habits in this respect are similar to those of Storer's snake (*Storeria occipito-maculata*), sometimes called the red-bellied snake, and on the whole they are undoubtedly beneficial. Storer's snake is vivi-parous, giving birth to about a dozen little snakes in early sum-mer. The green or grass snake, *Opheodrys vernalis,* one of the most colorful and gentle of its kind, is almost entirely insec-tivorous; it is common throughout eastern North America. Averag-ing about a foot in length, it feeds on crickets, grasshoppers, grubs, and caterpillars, with an occasional slug or snail and a spider or two for good measure. The grass snake is oviparous, laying seven or so elongated eggs underneath a flat stone near the edge of a field. A closely related species, the rough green snake, *Opheodrys aestivus,* is also called by such names as green grass snake, green whip snake, and magnolia snake. Another gentle species, it lives exclusively on insects, especially cater-pillars and night-flying moths, and is valuable to the farmer and orchardist. It is often see climbing about in low bushes and trees in search of food.

Lizards are largely insectivorous and are valuable predators in some areas, but are not numerous outside the warmer regions. The little American anolis or "chameleon"—a native of the south-eastern United States—is one of the most familiar lizards. (The true chameleons have prehensile tails and are not found in this country.) The anolis is generally pale green in color; when rest-ing it is gray or brown, and when excited it becomes a brilliant green. Contrary to the popular belief, it does not necessarily change color in response to its surroundings. These small lizards live almost entirely on insects, and captive specimens do very well on a steady diet of houseflies. A widely distributed species, the

A fence lizard or common swift. Lizards are numerous and valuable predators of insects in the warmer regions. (*K. H. Maslowski*)

blue-tailed skink (*Eumeces fasciatus*), is found throughout most of the eastern United States, from South Dakota and Michigan to Texas, and from Massachusetts to Florida. About six inches long, it is shiny black with a bright yellow line down its back. The fence lizard or common swift (*Sceloporus undulatus*) is found over most of the country. The sagebush swift (*Sceloporus graciosus*) prefers the desert regions of cactus and mesquite and is very numerous in some western states such as Utah, where it is said to exert considerable effect on insect populations. The collared lizard (*Crotaphytus collaris*) is common in the southwestern states and ranges as far north as Utah and Idaho. Omnivorous in feeding habits, it lives mainly on crickets and grasshoppers, and makes a good pet. The horned "toads" (which are not toads) commonly found in the southwest are insect eaters. Unlike most lizards, which lay eggs, they give birth to live young, in broods of from six to ten. The only poisonous lizard in this country is the Gila monster, found in southern Arizona and New Mexico. It averages about eighteen inches in length, and is not quite the "monster" some would have us believe. It lives on insects, worms, centipedes, other lizards, and snakes' eggs.

Turtles are by no means confined to water or wet places; some of them range over a wide area of land. Aquatic or otherwise, they all lay eggs, and always on land. While without significance for control purposes, some turtles are insectivorous. The common box tortoise, *Terrapene carolina*, found in the eastern states, is mainly terrestrial and wanders long distances over meadows and pastures. Its food consists mostly of grubs, worms, and various insect larvae. Box tortoises (fenced in) have been used by gardeners for controlling insects to some extent and apparently with some success. They are said to keep gardens clear of pillbugs, slugs, snails, millipedes, caterpillars, and other pests.

AMPHIBIANS AS PREDATORS OF INSECTS

The amphibians, comprised of salamanders, frogs, and toads, occupy a place in the animal kingdom between the fishes and reptiles. They are almost all aquatic in the beginning but in the adult form they take on terrestrial habits in varying degrees. Toads spend a large part of their lives on land, the habits of salamanders are more aquatic though many species are partly terrestrial; the frogs are somewhere in between. All amphibians must return to the water to mate and lay their eggs. They go through a gradual metamorphosis similar to that of the higher insects, except that they do not have a resting stage corresponding to the pupal stage of insects. In the larval stage they develop a tail for swimming and gills for breathing under water; at maturity the latter are transformed into lungs for breathing air.

FROGS

All the amphibians are carnivorous—the voracious bull frogs are notably cannibalistic as well—and a large proportion of their food consists of insects. The frogs and salamanders, however, are relatively unimportant in their effect on insect populations. In the aquatic form they consume some mosquito larvae, and those that wander away from streams and wet places include a large proportion of insects in their food, but as a group they are not very numerous. The beautiful leopard frog, *Rana pipiens,* with its yellow-rimmed olive spots against a vivid green, is the best known of the frogs that incline to be somewhat terrestrial, and also the most widely distributed of all the frogs on the North American continent. It is found from the Atlantic to the Pacific coasts and from Canada to Mexico. One of our largest frogs, it may be found in almost any field or pasture. The tree frogs are interesting little creatures and live mostly on insects. The common tree frog (*Hyla versicolor*) looks rather like a toad and is mistakenly called a "tree toad." Its toes are fingerlike and have adhesive discs. Its rough skin and markings, and its ability to change its color to various tones of gray, green, and brown, are a first-rate example of camouflage.

SALAMANDERS

Salamanders look like lizards, with the important difference that their skin is smooth and moist whereas that of lizards is scaly and dry. The largest of these amphibians, the giant salamander of China and Japan, may be six feet long; the North American hellbender, a strictly aquatic species, may be nearly two feet long. The most widely distributed species on our own continent, the spotted salamander (*Ambystoma maculatum*), is six inches long, and occurs from Canada to Florida and westward to Wisconsin. It is shiny black or slate color with round yellow spots, is terrestrial in its habits, and may be found in damp places almost anywhere. It is active at night and eats grubs, sowbugs, snails, earthworms, and some spiders. The slender red-backed salamander, *Plethodon cinereus,* is about three inches in length and entirely terrestrial. An exception to the rule that the amphibians only breed and lay their eggs in water, this one lays its eggs under a stone or in some other moist hidden place. The mother broods her eggs to keep them moist, and the young pass the gill-breathing larval stage inside the egg. The diet of this species is mostly insects and worms, with some sowbugs and snails.

TOADS

Toads are of considerable economic importance as predators of insect pests and have been used successfully in biological control. The lumps or "warts" on the toad's skin contain poison glands which protect it from many animals, but unfortunately not from all; owls, hawks, crows, poultry to some extent, and above all snakes, are its enemies. The voracious toad reaches out for anything resembling an insect that may move within its range, but its victims are mostly insect pests. The prey is taken with the skill of a sleight-of-hand artist by the toad's long tongue, which is attached at the *front* of the lower jaw, has a sticky secretion on the end, and is whipped out with such speed that only the sharpest eyes can see what is happening. The most familiar and the most valuable of the toads belong to the genus *Bufo* of the family Bufonidae.

The American toad (*Bufo americanus*), the common species of eastern North America, is relatively large—from three to five inches long—and is often an important factor in controlling of crop pests. Toads of this species hibernate in groups, rather than singly, under rocks or some other shelter against the frost. In late April they gather in great numbers in ponds and marshes to mate and lay their eggs. The trilling heard at the time comes only from the males, whose throats swell to tremendous proportions as they give voice to their shrill courtship calls. One female toad will lay from four to seven thousand eggs. (Some species

Male American toad, *Bufo americanus*, with throat sac distended, singing—a valuable predator of insects in eastern North America. (*K. H. Maslowski*)

lay as many as 25,000.) The eggs hatch in from three to ten days, depending on the temperature of the water, and after about nine weeks' carefree existence as tadpoles the edge of the pond is suddenly alive with thousands of little toads not more than half an inch in length.

Toads may live to a ripe old age. A female of *Bufo marinus* lived at the experiment station of the Hawaiian Sugar Planters' Association for almost 16 years, and consumed 72,000 cockroaches during this time. James Oliver gives the maximum length of life in captivity of the American toad as 31 years. The southern toad, *Bufo terrestris*, is a large amphibian, measuring from three to four inches long, and is found in the southeastern United States. The western toad (*Bufo cognatus*) is about four inches in length and is found in the prairie states from North Dakota to

Texas, and westward to California. This toad lays up to 20,000 eggs at a time; the young toads are half grown in four months, and take from two to four years to mature. Toads feed continuously during the night. In Massachusetts an American toad was observed to eat four times the capacity of its stomach in twenty-four hours; adults of other species have been found to fill the gut once a day, and the young twice a day.

The largest of its kind, the giant toad *Bufo marinus,* is native from southern Texas to the southern extremity of South America; specimens have been found in Brazil that measure nine inches long. *Bufo marinus* has been successfully introduced into the West Indies, Hawaii, the Philippines, New Guinea, Fiji, Australia, Florida, and Louisiana, for the control of white grubs. In the sugar cane fields of Puerto Rico these grubs have been successfully controlled by the introduction of the giant toad. Since the toad's importation into Australia in 1935 to control white grubs it has become widely established in the coastal region of Queensland. It is a valuable predator upon many destructive insects, including armyworms and various scarabaeid beetle pests of sugar cane. In 1938 and 1939 the toad was introduced into the Territory of New Guinea from Queensland, and by 1940 was reported to be successfully controlling the sweet potato hawk moth (*Hippotion celerio*), a pest of the sweet potato and other crops.[25]

Toads introduced into gardens and greenhouses can be very effective in controlling many insect pests. They have a strong homing instinct, just as frogs do, but this can be overcome if they have enough food and are enclosed. Toads can also be effective in eradicating cockroaches if one or two are released in the kitchen at night—they will need a dish of water—or put in a cage with bait to attract the roaches. This will no doubt strike some people as carrying biological control a little too far.[26]

[25] Frank Wilson, *A Review of the Biological Control of Insects and Weeds in Australia and Australian New Guinea.*

[26] A sorptive dust, nontoxic to human beings or domestic animals, that kills by removing the wax or oil from the insect's waterproof outer layer, is an effective means of combating cockroaches, as well as dry-wood

A predatory snail, *Euglandina rosea*, native to Florida. A valuable predator of plant-feeding snails, used on Pacific islands for control of *Achatina fulica*, a pest of agricultural crops. (*K. L. Middleham, courtesy T. W. Fisher*)

MAMMALS AS PREDATORS OF INSECTS

Some of the small mammals are also valuable predators of insects, though they are unfortunately destructive to agricultural crops. Moles and shrews destroy great numbers of soil-inhabiting insects, principally white grubs and cutworms of various kinds, and where their burrowings are not harmful, for example in lawns, they can be useful. Studies by W. A. Reeks of the larch sawfly in the maritime provinces of Canada, at the end of an outbreak in 1942, showed that predators had destroyed 48 per cent

termites. A finely divided amorphous silica aerogel developed at the University of California, it is available in a recommended formulation under the trade name Dri-Die 67. Blown into spaces and applied on surfaces frequented by these insects, it will not only eradicate them but prevent their recurrence as well. See "Control of Household Insects and Related Pests," Circular 498 (April 1961); also *California Agriculture*, Jan. and Feb. 1959, University of California, Division of Agricultural Sciences.

of the sawfly cocoons. (The insect pupates in the ground and forest litter.) Small mammals accounted for about half the mortality and insect predators for the remainder.[27] In areas where sawfly cocoons have been abundant for several years, it has been found that 40 to 50 per cent of the cocoons are generally destroyed by small mammals; in one area of New Brunswick it was found that 80 per cent of the sawfly cocoons were opened by them. There is also good evidence that some of the late-stage sawfly larvae are destroyed before they start to spin their cocoons.[28]

Some species of shrews and mice can distinguish between sound cocoons and empty ones. The short-tailed shrew (*Blarina brevicauda pallida*) seems to have the greatest degree of sensitivity in this respect. Unfortunately they do not appear to detect the difference between a cocoon with a parasitized sawfly larva and one that is unparasitized, so it is probable that they cause about an equal loss of hosts and parasites. In tests made under caged conditions the short-tailed shrew (*Blarina brevicauda pallida*), the deer mouse (*Peromyscus maniculatus abietorum*), and the red-backed vole (*Clethrionomys gapperi ochraceus*), all showed an equal preference for parasitized and unparasitized cocoons.[29]

THE MIGHTY SHREW

The shrew is an amazing animal—a veritable dynamo of ceaseless energy. As the smallest mammal, *Sorex cinereus* has a higher rate of metabolism than any other, and one very close to that of

[27] W. A. Reeks, "An Outbreak of the Larch Sawfly (*Pristiphora erichsonii* [Htg.]) in the Maritime Provinces (Hymenoptera: Tenthredinidae) and the Role or Parasites in Its Control," *The Canadian Entomologist*, Oct. 1954.

[28] W. A. Weeks, "Establishment of *Exenterus* (Hymenoptera: Ichneumonidae), Parasites of the European Spruce Sawfly, Near Points of Introduction," *The Canadian Entomologist*, March 1952.

[29] W. A. Reeks, "Establishment of Introduced Parasites of the European Spruce Sawfly (*Diprion hercyniae* (Htg.) (Hymenoptera: Diprionidae) in the Maritime Provinces," *Canadian Journal of Agricultural Science*, Sept.–Oct. 1953.

the hummingbird.[30] The rate of metabolism varies inversely with the size of animals and can be measured by the rate of its consumption of oxygen—which is in effect to measure the intensity with which the animal lives. These small animals must consume an enormous amount of food for their size simply to stay alive. The hummingbird avoids starvation at night by going into hibernation. The shrew must eat enormous quantities of food continuously; shrews left together without sufficient food will eat one another—which explains why they are such valuable predators despite their small size. A specimen of one of the smaller shrews of the genus *Sorex* consumed 93 grams of food in eight days, or 3.3 times its weight per day. A shrew of the genus *Blarina,* which are larger, is able to kill and eat a meadow mouse two or three times its size, and where the genus abounds it probably has considerable effect on the population of mice. It is the only mammal that secretes venom and has a poisonous bite, which probably explains how it is able to overpower a mouse. (Its bite is reported to be very painful to human beings.) Its scent glands make the shrew unpalatable to most other animals except hawks and owls. Shrews have been kept in captivity for more than two years, but are believed to live less than a year under natural conditions. They are not very prolific; the size and number of litters varies with the species, but the average is probably two or three litters a year and about five per litter.[31] The average litter size for the masked shrew is reported to be 7.2

In 1958 the latter, *Sorex cinereus cinereus*—also called the cinereous shrew—was introduced from the maritime province of New Brunswick to the island of Newfoundland, where it is not indigenous, in the hope that it would supplement the complex of natural controls already operating against forest sawflies. Twenty-two shrews (10 males and 12 females) were trapped and transported to the island province. Trappings the following year

[30] Oliver P. Pearson, "The Metabolism of Hummingbirds," in *First Book of Animals: A Twentieth-Century Bestiary* (New York: Simon & Schuster, 1955).

[31] Oliver P. Pearson, "Shrews," *ibid.*

showed that the shrews were well established: of 130 shrews captured, 11 were of the original stock (according to markings), and 119 were progeny of the immigrants. Dispersal was somewhat limited, but the animals had spread to the borders of the 36-acre study plot.[32] Releases have since been made in other areas of Newfoundland, and "results indicate that the shrew is a valuable cocoon predator."[33] Shrew predation here from 1959 to 1961 has varied from 14 to 22 per cent of the total.

BATS

Bats are unique in being the only mammals that can fly, and in having an ultrasonic echo location system using the principle on which man-made radar detection systems are based. Most species of bats are insectivorous, and their echolocating cries, pitched beyond the range of the human ear, adapt them admirably to night flying and to seizing their prey on the wing. It might be expected, therefore, that a large proportion of the food of insectivorous bats would be night-flying moths; and this has been generally borne out in the limited studies that have been made of their eating habits. Their habit of reducing their victims to minute fragments makes it difficult to identify the insects by examining the stomach contents or droppings of bats, as is done with birds and other animals. Some successful studies have been made, however, by examining fecal matter. A German investigator who analyzed the droppings from a roosting place of some small species of bats, managed to identify the undigested moth scales, and concluded that their diet consisted chiefly of geometrid moths (the adult form of the measuring worm).

An observer attributed the low population of codling moths in a Massachusetts orchard, as compared to other orchards in the

[32] C. F. MacLeod, "The Introduction of the Masked Shrew into Newfoundland," *Bi-monthly Progress Report,* Canada Dept. of Agriculture, Mar.–Apr. 1960.

[33] W. J. Carroll, "Shrew Impact on Larch Sawfly" in *Annual Report* (Ottowa: Forest Entomology & Pathology Branch, Canada Dept. of Forestry, 1962).

vicinity, to a colony of between seventy-five and a hundred bats in a nearby barn. In the southwestern states remains of locusts, moths, cicadas, and beetles have been noted in fecal analyses. Attempts were made to colonize the "guano bat" (*Tadarida mexicana*) in Texas some years ago, apparently with the idea that they could control mosquitoes; there is no evidence, however, that these bats or any others have much effect on mosquitoes, which probably fly too low to be of interest to them. Microscopic examinations of the dung of these bats showed no evidence of mosquitoes; the guano under their roosting places indicated that 90 per cent of their food was moths. One observer in England, in a study of moth wings dropped by various bats, found 40 species of noctuids (cutworms), six of geometrids (measuring worms), and two of arctiids (tiger moths). An examination of the fecal remains of the big brown bat (*Eptesicus fuscus*) showed that 36 per cent of its food consisted of beetles, 26 per cent of Hymenoptera, and 13 per cent of flies, the remainder being in several other orders—but, strangely, including no moths. A considerable number of the insects identified were beneficial species. Of the beetles, the scarabaeids, including cockchafers and May beetles, were the most common.[34] The value of bats has been questioned because of their not too discriminating feeding habits, as well as the suspicion that they may be carriers of the rabies virus and that they may even transmit the pathogen without biting.[35]

Recent studies show that many night-flying moths, including the adult European corn borer, have auditory (tympanal) organs that are very sensitive to the echolocating cries of bats—which would seem to indicate that they may recognize these mammals as an enemy. Tests have shown a device for simulating this sound to be very effective in protecting a plot of corn from the borers, and thus to have practical application. Photographs using time-

[34] Glover Morrill Allen, *Bats* (New York: Dover Publications, 1962). This is a paperback reprint of the definitive work on bats.

[35] "Beware of Bats," *Time*, Sept. 29, 1961. On the other hand James Poling, in "The Baffling Bat" (*National Wildlife Magazine*, Feb.–Mar. 1963), writes in praise of the bat.

exposure techniques have shown the evasive maneuvers of moths confronted by ultrasonic sounds produced by the device. A machine for broadcasting the ultrasonic sound of bats (at 50 Kc/sec.) has been designed at the Biological Control Laboratories at Belleville, Ontario, and can be constructed at moderate cost.[36] According to its inventors, the pulse rate and amplitude of the sounds used resemble those of an echolocating bat so closely that it jars the sensory organs of the moths, causing them to change course with frantic abruptness as they come within range of the sound, as though they had struck a physical barrier. The device is strictly a repellent, of course, and does not destroy the moths.

SOME OTHER MAMMALS

Mice and skunks are important in controlling range caterpillars and grasshoppers in New Mexico. Examinations of the droppings of skunks in this region have shown that 85 per cent of their food consisted of pupae of the range caterpillars. Frequently in certain areas it was noted that up to two-thirds of the silken cocoon webs were empty—without doubt as a result of predation by skunks, mice, badgers, and to a lesser degree coyotes. Skunks belong to the family Mustelidae, and are related to the weasels, badgers, ferrets, martens, minks, and mongooses, and to the fisher —all of which destroy many rodents and other small vertebrates, as well as large insects. The little spotted skunk (*Spilogale putorius*) is common in southern and southwestern states, and is also found in some of the midwestern states; its varied diet includes grasshoppers, crickets, beetles, and the larvae of many other insects, as well as mice and other small vertebrates. The widely distributed common skunk (*Mephitis mephitis*) and others are valuable insect destroyers. Skunks have lately come somewhat into disrepute because of the discovery that they sometimes carry the rabies virus. But if the protection generally accorded these animals is lifted permanently the farmer and fruit grower will

[36] P. Belton and R. H. Kempster, "A Field Test on the Use of Sound to Repel the European Corn Borer," *Ent. Exp. & Appl.,* North Holland Publishing Co., Amsterdam, Oct. 1962.

lose a valuable friend.[37] Captive red squirrels (*Tamiasciurus hudsonicus gymnicus*) were found to have a capacity of between six and seven hundred mature budworm larvae and pupae per day. With such a potential for predation, this rodent would appear to deserve further study.[38]

The most completely insectivorous of the medium-sized mammals, according to E. R. Kalmbach, is the nine-banded armadillo which is fairly numerous in Texas, Louisiana, and Florida. Stomach examinations have shown that more than 92 per cent of its food is insects. One specimen found in Texas had eaten 87 different kinds of food, mostly insects, with a total of 3,100 individual items. Its insect diet contains many crop pests such as cutworm caterpillars and the white grubs of scarabaeid beetles.[39] The good done by the armadillo outweighs the occasional damage to plants in its energetic (if clumsy) search for soil-inhabiting insects.

SPIDERS AND MITES AS PREDATORS

It's incongruous that anything so common, numerous, and retiring as the spider should also be so feared. Spiders are timid creatures and will not attack except possibly in case of aggravation. All spiders carry protective venom but only the black widow has enough to kill a person, and only the larger spiders are strong enough to pierce the human skin with their pincerlike fangs. The bite of our largest spiders, the tarantulas, may cause considerable pain—which, however, is not likely to persist for more than an hour and is no more severe than a bee sting. Although many people are fearful of tarantulas or are repelled by their hairy shapes, they are not any more belligerent than the small spiders; indeed, the males can be easily tamed. They mostly stay hidden

[37] Kendrick Kimball, "Skunk is Master of All," *Detroit News,* July 16, 1961.

[38] R. F. Morris, "Predation and the Spruce Budworm" in *The Dynamics of Epidemic Spruce Budworm Populations,* R. F. Morris, ed. (Memoirs of the Entomological Society of Canada, No. 31, 1963).

[39] E. R. Kalmbach, "Birds, Beasts and Bugs," in *Insects: Yearbook of Agriculture* (Washington: Government Printing Office, 1952).

in their burrows or otherwise concealed except during the mating season in the fall, when the males go about in search of the females. Their enemy the "tarantula hawk," a wasp that provisions its nest with a paralyzed tarantula, is also much in evidence at this time.

The black widow is no less retiring, and although her bite is dangerous, she is much less of a threat than is commonly supposed. Between 1726 and 1943 there were 1,300 reported cases of black widow bites in the United States, every state being represented but with almost half the cases in California, with Virginia and Florida coming next. For the same period a total of fifty-five deaths from this cause are recorded, or about 4 per cent of the total; and since many less severe cases were probably not reported, the actual percentage is likely to have been smaller still. The venom of the black widow is more highly toxic than that of any other venomous animal. For example, it is about fifteen times more powerful than that of the prairie rattlesnake, but the latter kills more of its victims (from 15 to 25 per cent) because of the greater amount of venom injected with the bite.

Spiders are not insects; they have four pairs of legs rather than three, and are without either wings or antennae. They belong to the class Arachnida—and are thus called "arachnids"—along with the scorpions, the mites and ticks, and the harvestmen or "daddy longlegs." The class name comes from a character in Greek mythology—Arachne, a Lydian maiden whose consummate spinning skill made Athena, the patron goddess of weaving, so jealous that she was eventually transformed into a spider, condemned to spin perpetually. Some spiders have given up the sedentary life, with its dependence on web-spinning skill, for the roving habits of the hunter. Nor do all spiders spin with equal skill. Archne's transformation must have been into one of the orb weavers, whose webs are a mechanical marvel. One of these intricate webs can be spun in an hour, and from the outset the little spiderlings are just as skillful as the parent. Spider eggs are enclosed in a sac, whose often beautiful and intricate design is peculiar to the species. The number of eggs laid by the female varies enormously from one species to another; the largest spider, *Theraphosa blondi,* is said to lay as many as 3,000 eggs, and a large orb weaver may lay 2,200 in a single sac, whereas some small species lay very few eggs, or even only one. The average number is probably around 100; in some species they will be enclosed in more than one sac. The spiderling's first urge after emerging from the sac is to climb as high as it can and start its travels by sending out a long silk thread, which is caught up by the breeze and carries the youngster away from its place of birth. This ballooning is evidently a device to ensure dispersal and avoid overcrowding, and accounts for the wide distribution of many species over the earth's surface.

IMPACT OF SPIDERS

"Spiders are among the dominant predators of any terrestrial community," declares Willis J. Gertsch—although since definite information on their feeding habits has been lacking, it can only be assumed that "the over-all effect of such a large fauna of predators must be a very significant one."[40] Insects are the chief prey of spiders, and their method of obtaining this food is by hunting or spinning webs. What prompts the spider into action against its prey is movement, hence only live insects are taken. These unfortunately include beneficial species; this is especially true of the web spinners which trap flying insects. The hunters are in general more selective in their choice of food, and for this reason are more adaptable as biological control agents. According to W. S. Bristowe, a census taken in a field of rough grass in Sussex, England showed the late summer spider population of one acre to be two and a quarter millions. On this basis he estimated the spider population of England and Wales at two billion two hundred million, and their annual consumption of insects (figuring an average of 100 per annum for each spider) at

[40] Willis J. Gertsch, *American Spiders* (New York: D. Van Nostrand Company, 1949).

two hundred twenty billion. He reduced all this to more comprehensible terms by converting it into weight, and concluded that the weight of insects eaten annually by spiders in England and Wales was well in excess of the weight of the human population![41]

Bristowe asserts categorically that spiders consume many times the number of insects eaten by birds—contrary to popular belief, which he thinks is colored by the favorable attitude toward birds as compared to the prevalent loathing for spiders. Indeed, he suggests that the relentless pursuit of insects by hunting spiders contributed to the evolutionary development of wings by insects, and the evolution of the web spinners in turn to meet the new challenge of the flying insects. Some scientists believe that man could not live in many parts of the world if there were no spiders, and it has been suggested that their eradiction from the earth might also lead to the extermination of man himself.[42]

THE SPIDER AND THE BUDWORM

It is interesting to note that in studies of the role of predation in the population dynamics of the spruce budworm in New Brunswick forests, attention has been directed toward spiders rather than predaceous insects. The reason for this is indicated by figures on the mean population density of arthropod predators in samplings taken from balsam fir trees in June, July, and August for the period from 1950 to 1958. The average number of spiders per ten square feet of foliage on fir trees was 2.65 in June and 2.34 in July, whereas on spruce trees it was 4.81 in June and 12.48 in July. The density of mites that prey on the budworm eggs was 2.54 for August. The number of predaceous insects present on the foliage was much lower; the highest figure at any time was .24 for the lady beetles, and the total number of all insects (lady beetles, syrphid flies, lacewings, predatory bugs, and so on) was

[41] W. S. Bristowe, *The Book of Spiders* (London: Penguin Books, 1947).
[42] John Crompton, *The Life of the Spider* (New York: New American Library, 1954).

very small in comparision to that of the arachnids. What these studies show is that predators have an important effect on the survival rate of the pest at low population densities. Serological studies[43] of spiders and gizzard analyses of birds during this period show that they both take appreciable numbers of the budworms during the late larval period, when the extent of that generation's survival is determined. It has been calculated that theoretically only .46 larvae per ten square feet of foliage would need to be consumed by predators to bring about a decrease in the survival rate observed at low densities of the budworm larvae; only "one pair of breeding birds per acre along with one or two spiders per ten square feet of foliage have a feeding potential considerably in excess of this."[44]

In the Green River watershed area of New Brunswick, where part of this study was conducted, the web spinners were the most abundant forest spiders. Of a total of 54 species, representing fourteen families, 36 were web spinners and 18 were hunting spiders. Although there were considerable fluctuations, populations generally build up from early spring to late July or August. Most of the spiders were found to overwinter in the egg or in immature form; hatching of the overwintering eggs contributed to the buildup, as did the hatching of the eggs laid by the overwintering immatures after reaching maturity. "A well-marked pattern of predation throughout the season" occurred in response both to the emergence of the budworms from their mines and to changes

[43] The serological precipitin test used to detect predation is an adaptation of a test used in immunology. The presence of prey in the spider is indicated by the reaction in a serological test tube of an antigen (a protein extract from the predator, containing pest material from its gut) with an antiserum extracted from rabbits injected with the protein (antigen) of the pest. A positive test indicates that the spider has eaten budworm material, although it does not indicate when or how much of the material was eaten. Such possible limitations as the specificity of the antiserum for spruce budworm, the length of time that the budworm remains detectable in the spider's gut, and the frequency of the spider's feeding on the budworm were found, after careful testing, not to be serious drawbacks.

[44] R. F. Morris, "Predation and the Spruce Budworm," in *The Dynamics of Epidemic Spruce Budworm Populations,* R. F. Morris, ed., (Memoirs of the Entomological Society of Canada, No. 31, 1963).

in the budworm population. The number of spiders which had fed
on budworms at times reached 20 per cent. Mites were found
to be "extremely abundant during the egg-laying period"; in 1960,
24 per cent of the population sampled in the Fredericton area
had fed on budworm eggs. The most effective predators (that is,
those of which the highest percentage were found to have fed on
budworms) belonged to the family Theridiidae. Apparently these
web spinners respond more quickly than any other spiders to the
prey's movement, and they do not permit it to escape—the more
it struggles, the more tightly it is secured in the strands of silk.
Among the hunting spiders, the Salticidae were found to be important predators. The Thomisidae—also hunters—were present
in large numbers but were not as effective as the Micryphantidae,
which sometimes spin webs but also hunt. Among the natural
enemies of the spruce budworm, spiders seemed to suffer most
from the insecticide spraying operations in the New Brunswick
forests, and also "appeared . . . to recover slowly in the succeeding
years."[45]

A SPIDER COMMUNITY

In his study of the spider population in a stand of oaks in England, A. L. Turnbull found 98 species representing fifteen families.
For purposes of study he divided the community into four layers:
the ground zone (the first six inches), the field layer (six feet
above the ground), the low canopy (up to 25 feet), and the high
canopy (above 25 feet). The spiders were found to follow remarkably similar patterns of fluctuating abundance each year and
in each of the various layers. The upsurge began in mid-March
and built up to a peak in midsummer; then came a sharp decline.
The buildup was due to the hatching of the overwintering eggs,
and the decline to the dying off of the winter immatures that had

[45] B. G. Loughton, C. Derry, and A. S. West, "Spiders and the Spruce
Budworm," in *The Dynamics of Epidemic Spruce Budworm Populations*,
R. F. Morris, ed. (Memoirs of the Entomological Society of Canada, No.
31, 1963); D. R. Macdonald and L. E. Webb, "Insecticides and the Spruce
Budworm," *ibid.*

matured and laid their eggs. A lesser peak in October reflected the hatching of the eggs laid in midsummer, and a decline after this was due to the retirement of immatures to winter shelter. The number of individuals was distributed quite evenly among the ground, field, and canopy layers; but the density of the ground layer was twice that of the field layer and eight times that of the canopy layers. A marked tendency toward stratification by species in the various layers was noted, although they did extend beyond the preferred zone. However, the field zone had a rather fixed line of demarcation: spiders from the ground zone invaded this area but seldom went above, and those from the higher zones seldom went lower. Turnbull makes this significant comment:

Where field-layer vegetation grew high and dense the webs of the Linyphiinae formed a virtually continuous sheet of gauzy silk over the grass, herbs and low shrubs. In late summer it was common to find layers of sheet-webs spaced at about eight inches to one foot vertical distance apart, sometimes in as many as five or six layers. In such areas the webs present a seemingly impenetrable maze of silken lines from the soil surface to the tops of plants. At densities such as these, the Linyphiinae would seem to play a major role in the mortality of other arthropod members of the community.[46]

THE UBIQUITOUS SPIDER

From observations of the pine sawfly (*Neodiprion* sp.) on ponderosa and Jeffrey pines near Willits, California, D. L. Dahlsten concluded that the potential of spiders as predators is high. He watched a single species of spider destroy a colony of approximately 50 sawfly larvae.[47] In observations of the predators of the European pine shoot moth (*Rhyacionia buoliana*) in a reforested area in Ontario, J. A. Juillet estimated a spider population to consist of 19 individuals per pine tree (averaging seven feet in height) with a range of 4 to 56. These were mainly jumping spi-

[46] A. L. Turnbull, "The Spider Population of a Stand of Oak (*Quercus robur*) in Wytham Wood, Berks., England," *The Canadian Entomologist*, Feb. 1960.

[47] D. L. Dahlsten, "Life History of a Pine Sawfly, *Neodiprion* sp., at Willits, California (Hymenoptera: Diprionidae)," *The Canadian Entomologist*, Mar. 1961.

ders (Salticidae), sheet-web weavers (Linyphiidae-Linyphiinae), and orb weavers (Argiopidae). In an examination of 100 webs, 22 were found to have one to three shoot moths per web; it was noted that a moth hitting a web frequently escaped before the spider could reach it, but that all wandering spiders with moths succeeded in killing them.[48] During the peak of the shoot moth flight, jumping spiders and crab spiders were seen near the tips of exposed shoots, and the sheet-web weavers were seen mostly along or between new shoots—the places where the moths lay most of their eggs. Spiders are important predators of cotton pests and those of other crops in the South. Where grain sorghums are grown and the sorghum midge (*Contarinia sorghicola*) is a pest, spiders are found in great numbers on the sorghum heads while the midge is plentiful; more than twenty species have been observed feeding on adult midges.[49] A green spider (*Peucetia viridans*) is extremely common on tobacco plants in the South and is known to be an important predator of the tobacco budworm (*Heliothis virescens*).[50]

According to Tothill *et al.*, a brilliantly colored spider (*Ascyltus pterygodes*) is present on nearly every coconut tree in Fiji and is one of the most valuable predators of the coconut moth (*Levuana iridescens*). It attacks the large larvae and is said to help considerably in finally ridding the trees of the pest after it has been reduced to low levels by other factors.[51] A crab spider (*Thanatus flavidus*) is credited with eradicating the bedbug (*Cimex*) from Greek refugee camps near Athens following World War I. The refugees moved out of the barracks and so did the bedbugs; not to be denied either, the spiders followed the bugs and soon rid the camp of them. An observer noted that a single

[48] J. A. Juillet, "Observations on Arthropod Predators of the European Pine Shoot Moth, (*Rhyacionia buoliana* (Schiff.) (Lepidoptera: Olethreutidae), in Ontario," *The Canadian Entomologist*, Mar. 1961.

[49] E. V. Walter, *The Sorghum Midge* (Washington: USDA Farmers' Bulletin No. 1566, July 1953).

[50] *The Tobacco Budworm* (Washington: USDA Farmers' Bulletin No. 1531, July 1953).

[51] J. D. Tothill, T. H. C. Taylor, and R. W. Paine, *The Coconut Moth in Fiji* (London: The Imperial Bureau of Entomology, 1930).

spider destroyed as many as thirty or forty bedbugs in a day. This spider has since been used with great success to control bedbugs in animal laboratory rooms in Germany. A relative, *T. peninsulanus,* often found in great numbers in the warehouses of New York City, preys on pests of stored cereals and other products. A native of the Southwest, it was probably introduced into New York in ship cargoes.[52]

SOME PREDATORY MITES

Because many of them are important crop pests and some are parasites of animals and vectors of disease, the mites are as a group of greater economic significance than the spiders. Many mites, on the other hand, are important predators both of the destructive members of their own kind and of the eggs of insects that are many times their size in the adult stage. These tiny animals make up for their minuteness by their numbers and are often so numerous that on a plant they look like a powder rather than an assemblage of animals. Some mites gorge themselves until they are "blown up" like tiny balloons anywhere from twenty-five to fifty times their normal size. Their importance in the forests of New Brunswick has been demonstrated, and they are no doubt an important control factor in many other forests. According to one observer, "It is possible that mites are the most important biological control agent in the destruction of various species of bark beetles." They have been observed to devour from 10 to 85 per cent of the eggs of the Oregon pine engraver, the mortality varying from 52 per cent in the first generation to 85 per cent in the fifth generation, dropping to from 10 to 25 per cent in the intervening generations. Mites have also been observed to feed on the eggs of the Douglasfir beetle (*Dendroctonus pseudotsugae*), destroying 62.5 per cent of all the eggs deposited.[53]

[52] Willis Gertsch, *American Spiders.*
[53] J. A. Miller and F. P. Keen, *Biology and Control of the Western Pine Beetle* (Washington: USDA Miscellaneous Publication 800, March 1960).

The most important pest of strawberries in California is the cyclamen mite (*Steneotarsonemus pallidus*). Previous to the introduction of such newer insecticides as parathion and malathion it only occasionally did serious damage and was generally held in check by its natural enemies. Two predatory mites (*Typhlodromus bellinus* and *T. reticulatus*), when abundant, will reduce cyclamen mites to a low level and keep them there for the entire life of the planting—if they are not destroyed by chemical treatments.[54] The two-spotted mite (*Tetranychus telarius*), another pest of strawberries in California, can be controlled by a predatory mite, *Typhlodromus occidentalis*. Sometimes in spring the predator lags behind the pest, which can then build up to damaging proportions; it is less sensitive to some of the pesticides than other predatory mites, however, and can be successfully integrated with chemical control where this is needed.

The mites *Typhlodromus* and *Mediolata* were found to be mainly responsible for control of the plant-feeding mite *Panonychus ulmi* toward the end of the season in an apple orchard in New Jersey.[55] A predaceous mite (*Hemisarcoptes malus*) attacks the purple scale (*Lepidosaphes beckii*) in California, but is generally associated with the scale only when an infestation is heavy; this is because *H. malus'* power of locomotion is poor and its searching ability is thus extremely limited. Sometimes the mite overcomes this limitation by hitchhiking on the legs and elytra of a lady beetle (*Chilocorus* spp.)—one of the so-called "heavy-density feeders"—from which it drops onto the scales of a suitable host.[56]

[54] William A. Allen, *Strawberry Pests in California: A Guide for Commercial Growers* (Berkeley: California Agricultural Experiment Station, Circular 484, Nov. 1959).

[55] H. A. Thomas, H. B. Specht, and B. F. Driggers, "Arthropod Fauna Found During the First-Season Trial of a Selective Spray Schedule in a New Jersey Apple Orchard," *Journal of Economic Entomology,* 52 (1959): 819–820.

[56] Paul DeBach and John Landi, "The Introduced Purple Scale Parasite, *Aphytis lepidosaphes* Compere, and a Method of Integrating Chemical with Biological Control," *Hilgardia,* Dec. 1961.

Ecological principles are basic to two approaches to biological control: the introduction of natural enemies of pests into new areas; and the manipulation of the environment to increase natural enemies already present. The third approach is to use biotic agents in the same manner and for the same purposes as chemical insecticides.

—BRYAN P. BEIRNE

INSECT PARASITES: THE BRACONIDS

6

The parasitic wasps that belong to the great order Hymenoptera are pre-eminent among insects in their effect on populations of insect pests; in other words, they are what Stanley Flanders calls "specialists in population regulation."[1] All animals are directly or indirectly dependent on plants for food, and parasitism is simply a refinement of predation—a specialized means of obtaining plant food "predigested." Whereas the predator requires several individual plant-feeders to satisfy its needs, the parasite needs only one or a fraction of one; and in some cases, as where many parasites develop on a single host, the fraction may be very small indeed.

Populations of plants and animals, as Darwin and Malthus pointed out many years ago, tend to increase geometrically, the extreme limit being dictated by the available food supply. Left

[1] This analysis of the host-parasite relationship is based for the most part on a paper by Stanley E. Flanders of the Department of Biological Control, University of California (Riverside), entitled "The Parasitic Hymenoptera: Specialists in Population Regulation," which appeared in *The Canadian Entomologist,* Nov. 1962. See also the chapter on "Biological Control" in *Subtropical Fruit Pests,* by Walter Ebeling (Berkeley: University of California Press, 1959).

to themselves the plant-feeding insects would naturally regulate their own populations through "intraspecific competition" for the available food. "The regulation of plant-feeding insect populations by parasites and predators," Flanders points out,

precludes the plant feeders from regulating their own populations. This preclusion is highly important from the standpoint of the subsistence of man. It is quite unlikely that man could successfully compete with the hordes of other plant-feeding species constantly oscillating under feast or famine conditions in a world lacking natural enemy regulation of plant feeders. However, the parasitic Hymenoptera, in conjunction with other parasitic insects, were on the job regulating densities of plant-feeding insects long before man and the other mammals evolved. Quite possibly it was the conservation of plant life thus ensured at fairly steady densities which permitted the evolution of mammalian forms of life.

HOST-PARASITE REGULATION

The populations of plant-feeding insects are regulated by predators and parasites as long as they are able to produce successive generations at a faster rate than their hosts; the predator-parasite rate of growth is dependent on the density of the host populations. This relation between host and parasite is essentially "symbiotic," or mutually beneficial, since it ensures the survival of both host and parasite. The interaction is similar to what prevails among mammals in their natural environment. No doubt the latter relation was forced on mammals by the evolutionary process just as it was on insects.

The ability of a parasite to regulate a host population has been demonstrated in an interesting experiment conducted during the past five years on the Riverside Campus of the University of California, using a host-parasite situation that can be operated within an enclosure and that is subject to observation and manipulation. The host used is the Mediterranean flour moth (genus *Anagasta*) and an ichneumonid wasp (genus *Exidechthis*), whose larvae are internal parasites of the flour moth larvae. The moth and wasp are commonly found wherever grain is stored.

The moth is kept supplied with rolled wheat, which is replenished at regular intervals, and into which the larvae burrow as they feed. The wasp adjusts its developmental period to that of the moth, which produces a new generation every forty-eight days. The relation between host and parasite can be altered at will by changing the depth of the grain; the deeper the moth larvae, the more difficulty the female wasps have in finding them and in laying their eggs. The situation can be adjusted from one in which the parasite maintains the host at a given density to one in which both host and parasite are completely eliminated. When the populations are regulated by the parasite, both host and parasite are scarce.

SEARCHING ABILITY

In the long evolutionary process a majority of the estimated 200,000 species in the order Hymenoptera have become parasitic. To quote Flanders again,

> The development of extraordinary instincts and psychological responses which accompanied this speciation was correlated in the adult female with the enlargement of the cerebral ganglia, a correlation which, as fossil remains indicate, paved the way for the subsequent evolution of the honey bee and the ant. Darwin considered the hymenopteran brain to be "one of the most marvelous atoms of matter in the world, perhaps more so than the brain of man."

Their remarkable instinctive responses and unique reproductive mechanism have enabled the female wasps to play a major role in the regulation of insect pest populations, and consequently in biological control.

The most important attribute of a predator or parasite for effectively controlling pest populations is searching ability—the capacity enabling it to find its host, even when the latter is scarce; otherwise it cannot maintain itself at low densities. The reproductive capacity of the parasite does not determine its effectiveness. Rather, the searching ability of the female hymenopteran is in inverse proportion to her productive capacity; those species that lay the fewest eggs are the most effective searchers and most capable of maintaining the host at low density. Searching ability also tends to increase as the host population becomes scarce.

Walter Ebeling lists the following as being the most important factors in determining the searching ability of a hymenopterous parasite: (1) its power of locomotion, (2) its ability to perceive its hosts, (3) its power of survival, (4) its aggressiveness and persistence, (5) its ability to use its ovipositor, (6) its ability in egg deposition, (7) its ability to produce females in place of males, (8) its ability to develop more rapidly than the host, and (9) its ability to occupy host-inhabited areas. Most of these apply equally to predators. In a study of the searching capacity of three predators, Charles Fleschner found *Chrysopa* (a lacewing) outstanding because of "its relative freedom from tropic limitations" —the directional movements of the others were affected by light— and "its greater speed and area of perception." Perception in this case is not visual but consists of tactile responses.[2]

Ability to maintain an equilibrium in the numbers of the host does not make a parasite an effective regulator; it must maintain this level at low density, where the damage is of noneconomic proportions. The per cent of host population parasitized is not a measure of effectiveness; the level of density at which the parasite can maintain the host population is what counts.

The fact that the searching is done by the gravid female means that these parasites are better searchers than the predators; and the fact that the development of the larvae is limited to one host means that they are better able to subsist at low densities of the host. Predators are generally more effective against colonial hosts, such as the cottony cushion scale, mealybugs, and aphids. They are at a disadvantage compared to the parasite in needing more than one host, since in their larval stage they can't fly in search of another host. The vedalia (*Rodolia cardinalis*)—the example par excellence of biological control—was effective against the

---

[2] Charles A. Fleschner, "Studies on the Searching Capacity of the Larvae of Three Predators of the Citrus Red Mite," *Hilgardia*, October 1950.

cottony cushion scale because of the latter's colonial habits, and because the beetle larvae found sufficient food within the large egg sacs of the scale to maintain themselves at low densities of the host. On the other hand, *Rhizobius ventralis* failed to control the black scale because of the tendency of the black scale nymphs on which its larvae fed to scatter and thus not to be available to the predator when their density was low. *Aphycus helvolus*, a parasitic wasp, proved highly effective against the black scale and in some groves brought about complete control within a year. Parasites are generally more effective where the host is scattered.

Specialization of the Female. The effectiveness of hymenopterous parasites as regulators of pest populations is due to their extraordinary structural, physiological, and instinctive traits. Significantly, all these traits relate to the female, whose functions have relegated the male to a relatively obscure position.

Probably the most important of these is the ovipositor, a highly sensitive instrument which serves several important functions. In those hymenopterans that insert their eggs *into* their hosts, it is used like a hypodermic needle. The egg is sometimes larger in diameter than the ovipositor, and therefore must be compressed and elongated as it is forced from the female's body —an action that occurs without the aid of any movement within the ovipositor, which is entirely without muscles. Nevertheless, this versatile instrument is able to drill through scale armor, plant stems, wood, and like substances in order to convey the egg or larva to the host.

The ovipositor also serves to inject fluids for paralyzing or preserving the host, and for constructing a feeding tube. Although adult parasites feed mostly on pollen, nectar, and other plant exudates, the female requires some protein for egg production. This she dervies from the body fluids of the host as they are exuded from a puncture wound made with the ovipositor; this may take place after oviposition, or the puncture may be made solely for feeding. The feeding tube procures these body or egg fluids while the host is hidden in a plant stem, underneath scale

A braconid egg parasite, *Phanerotoma flavitestacea*, ovipositing in egg of the navel orangeworm. (*F. E. Skinner*, courtesy *L. E. Calta-girone*)

armor, or within a rolled leaf or cocoon. The ovipositor serves as a kind of mold for a waxy secretion that flows down outside it and solidifies to form a tube. The ovipositor is then withdrawn and the body fluids are imbibed as they rise to the top of the tube.

The ovipositor is also the sense organ by which the parasite determines whether or not the body contents of the host are suitable for the development of her progeny. (This is another matter entirely than locating the host.) Considerable probing and exploring of the host through the puncture wound often precede actual oviposition and may be necessary to determine whether the egg to be deposited will be fertilized or not—that is, whether the progeny is to be male or female.

For some female parasites of this order another highly important attribute is an ability to regulate the disposal of their eggs as they become mature, through either ovarian absorption (in the case of yolk-replete eggs) or uterine storage (in the case of yolk-deficient eggs). Not being under pressure to oviposit, the female may be more discriminating in selecting a host; the period in which she can respond to oviposition stimuli is prolonged and the reproductive material is conserved.

SEX REGULATION

The parasite's effectiveness as a host regulator is also enhanced by its ability to produce proportionately more females at low densities; this means an increase in the total searching ability of the progeny. With many Hymenoptera the sex of the progeny is controlled by the female in response to certain environmental stimuli associated with oviposition. The receptor of these stimuli is the spermatheca, in which—as in most insects—the sperm received from the male is stored. In addition to the capsule for storing the sperm, it consists of a spermathecal gland, a sperm duct, and associated muscles. The Hymenoptera differ from other insects in that the spermatheca is adapted for sex control and not merely for storing and conserving the sperm. The release of the sperm into the ducts and vagina is prompted by certain chemical reactions that occur as a result of external stimuli at the time of oviposition.

Among the Hymenoptera, sperm is not required to produce the male, which normally develops by parthenogenesis from an unfertilized egg, and is therefore said to be "uniparental." Only females are produced from fertilized eggs; females so produced are therefore "bi-parental." Most families in the order, however, contain some species that are strictly uniparental, the male and female both being produced without the female's mating at all. In some rare cases the male seldom or never appears. Uniparental species can still be host-regulative, but most species of Hymenoptera that have this ability are biparental and the females predominate at low densities. Where the biparental and uniparental types compete under natural conditions, the biparental forms are usually dominant.

As has been explained, Hymenoptera capable of host regulation tend to produce more females at low host densities, so as to enhance the total of their host-finding ability. Low host densities may also favor production of females by causing the size of the host to increase, since the female is more apt to use the stored sperm when ovipositing on large insects. Fertilized eggs are placed on preferred hosts, the unfertilized eggs on less desirable hosts. This is believed to be the reason why, in the eastern states, the imported *Tiphia popilliavora* does not control its host, the Japanese beetle; the host-searching *Tiphia* population occurs when only the undesirable stages of the beetle larvae are available, with the result that mainly male parasites are produced. *Aphycus helvolus,* the black scale parasite, also favors large hosts for fertilized eggs. The tendency of high host densities to favor production of the male parasite may be due to rapid egg disposition and fatigue of the spermathecal gland.

SOME BRACONID WASPS

The large family of wasps called the Braconidae are among the most important parasites because of their regulatory effect on the populations of insect pests. According to Clausen, they are almost entirely beneficial, very few of them being hyperparasites; the only exceptions are certain species of *Perilitus* that parasitize lady beetles. The braconids include many species that have been used effectively in biological control of insect pests. Moreton states that there are some 900 species of this family in Britain.

The braconids are mostly parasitic on the larvae of Lepidoptera (moths and butterflies) and Coleoptera (beetles), but also among their prey are many Diptera (flies) and Homoptera (mostly aphids in this group), and a few Hymenoptera and Hemiptera. They may be internal or external in their feeding habits. Internal parasitism is more commonly found where the host is free-living —for example, in aphids and leaf-eating caterpillars—and external parasitism where the host is confined to burrows, tunnels, and leaf rolls. The braconids are generally much smaller than the closely related family of ichneumons, seldom being as much as half an inch in length.

The adults feed mostly on honeydew and plant exudates, but in many species the female feeds from the puncture wound made by the ovipositor, living wholly or in part on the body fluids of

"Mummies" of parasitized aphids: note exit holes made by wasps after completing their larval and pupal development inside the bodies of the aphids. (*Roy J. Pence*)

the host. In instances where the puncture is made expressly for feeding rather than oviposition, it may result in the death of the host—a case of the parasite's acting like a predator. The reduction of the pest population as a result of this habit is at times quite significant. As explained, where the host cannot be reached directly (when it is in a burrow, pupa, or plant stem, for example) the female constructs a feeding tube around the ovipositor as it is inserted in the host, withdraws the ovipositor, and feeds on the body contents exuding from the end of the tube. In some cases the male feeds on the fluid with her.

The braconids that are external parasites usually paralyze the host permanently before ovipositing; where the parasites are internal the host is seldom paralyzed. Egg production is quite often large and the life cycle short, thus allowing time for several gen-

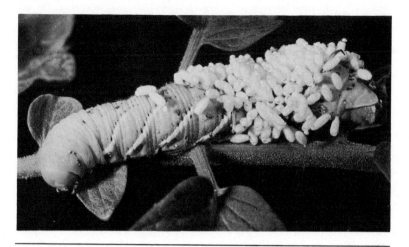

Tobacco hornworm, *Protoparce sexta,* with cocoons of parasitic wasp, *Apanteles congregatus.* Larvae of parasite emerge from host, spin cocoons, and emerge from cocoons as adults: note exit holes. (*Lee Jenkins*)

erations a year. They may winter as larvae, as pupae, or—less often—as adults. Their hosts include some of our worst pests, such as the gypsy moth, satin moth, browntail moth, codling moth, oriental fruit moth, strawberry leaf roller, and sugar cane borer, as well as various tent caterpillars, cutworms, and aphids, and numerous beetles.

THE VERSATILE APANTELES

One of the more familiar parasites of the braconid family is *Apanteles congregatus,* which parasitizes the catalpa sphinx (*Ceratomia catalpae*) and the tomato hornworm (*Protoparce quinquemaculata*). Anyone who has a garden has probably seen these large, green worms with their backs almost covered with small, white, elongated objects that look like eggs. These are usually the pupae of the parasites which have emerged from the body of the hornworm after feeding on the tissues and completing their development as larvae; or they may be the emerging larvae with some in various stages of cocoon formation—many eggs having been previously inserted in the worm by the female wasp. Need-

Southern cabbageworm, *Pieris protodice*, and cocoons from which parasitic wasps (probably *Apanteles glomeratus*) have emerged. (*Lee Jenkins*)

less to say, by this time the worm is either dead or harmless. H. E. Jaques counted over five hundred braconid larvae in the body of a seemingly healthy tomato hornworm.[3] The gardener who picks these worms from his plants would do well to leave any that are parasitized.

Apanteles glomeratus, an internal parasite of the cabbageworm (genus *Pieris*), was the first insect intentionally introduced into this country for biological control. The first attempts, begun in 1875, were unsuccessful; but in 1884 several releases and subsequent recoveries of cocoons imported from England were made around Washington, D.C., and in 1891 others were made in Iowa and Nebraska. The spread of this parasite has been phenomenal; in a matter of a few years it has become established from coast to coast, wherever the host is found. The female parasite oviposits fifteen to thirty-five eggs at a time in the cabbageworm larvae when the latter are one or two days old; the eggs float freely in the body cavity and hatch in a few days, the time lapse depending on the temperature. The full larval development takes about thirteen days, and all the larvae emerge at one time, to pupate

[3] H. E. Jaques, *How to Know the Insects* (Dubuque, Iowa: Wm. C. Brown Co., 1947).

in a mass on the leaf. Curiously enough, the host cabbageworm does not succumb immediately from the injuries caused by their feeding and emergence; it may live from two to four weeks, but is not able to pupate. The complete life cycle of the parasite takes not more than twenty-three days, so that several generations are possible in a season. The egg production of the female is very high; as many as a hundred larvae may develop in a single host.

BIOLOGICAL CONTROL OF THE SATIN MOTH

Another valuable braconid, *Apanteles solitarius*, is a parasite of the satin moth (*Stilpnotia salicis*), a pest of shade trees. The wasp is an imported species, and has been very effective in bringing about biological control of this pest. The seasonal cycle of the wasp is quite complex; it is able to overwinter either as a young larva in the host caterpillar or as a mature larva in the host cocoon. Each of the broods produces a second generation during the summer. The older brood attacks the moth larvae as they come out of hibernation in May, and the younger brood attacks the moth larvae that hatch in June; both broods attack the moth larvae that hatch in July. Some wasp larvae remain in the live host through the winter; others mature and form overwintering cocoons. This parasite was first imported from Hungary in 1927; the original stock of 55 adult parasites emerged from 105 satin moth cocoons and served as the nucleus for field colonizations. Adult parasites and infested satin moth larvae were liberated in five Massachusetts localities and one each in New Hampshire and Washington. In New Hampshire one colony spread fifteen miles the first year, and after two years a colony of 267 adult wasps liberated in Washington had spread over most of the state. Samplings have shown that 60 per cent or more of the overwintering moth larvae are parasitized by *solitarius*. It is the most important of a complex of parasites that maintain effective control of the satin moth in the New England states and in Washington.

Meteorus versicolor—a part of this satin moth complex—also

Cocoons of braconid wasp on caterpillar of *Hemileuca* moth: cocoons are open and wasps have emerged. (*E. S. Ross*)

parasitizes the gypsy moth and browntail moth in Europe. First imported in 1906 for control of the browntail moth in New England, it became established with later importations and is now widespread throughout the region. Later importations were made to control the satin moth in New England and Washington; the parasite did not adapt to the satin moth in the East but it became abundant through feeding on this pest in Washington. It remains as a parasite of the browntail moth in New England but is not by itself an important factor in pest control.

BIOLOGICAL CONTROL OF THE BROWNTAIL MOTH

The programs for biological control of the satin moth, browntail moth, and gypsy moth are intimately bound up together since many of the parasites form a complex association with all three of these pests. Seven species of imported parasites on the browntail moth (*Nygmia phaeorrhoea*) have become established, the most important of which are the tachinid fly *Townsendiellomyia nidicola*[4] and *Apanteles lacteicolor*, a solitary internal parasite of several Lepidoptera. *A. lacteicola* was imported from Europe during the period from 1906 to 1916. From 1911 to 1918 liberations totalled 255,000. First colonized in Massachusetts, it took quickly to the new environment, spread rapidly, and became generally well established within the areas of infestation in New England and Canada. In addition to being one of the most important factors in the control of the browntail moth, it contributes to control of the gypsy moth by attacking the young larvae. The average field parasitization of the browntail moth by *A. lacteicolor* has been 25 to 30 per cent. The female deposits her eggs in the body cavity of early-stage moth larvae. The egg hatches in about three days; the host larva succumbs seven to twelve days after the parasite begins feeding and just as it emerges. The parasites overwinter within the host larvae.

Since the establishment of the parasites of the browntail moth this pest has presented no problem in New England. The early outbreak spread into the Canadian provinces of New Brunswick and Nova Scotia, reached its peak there in 1913 and 1914, and completely disappeared by 1927. The program for control closely followed that in New England, but the parasites' present status is obscure. The tachinid *Compsilura concinnata,* imported for control of the gypsy moth, parasitizes many Lepidoptera and is also an important factor in control of the browntail moth. The moth is also subject to a fungus disease, a suspension of whose spores in water for use as a spray, has been tried as a control measure, together with the release of diseased caterpillars. Under certain conditions the fungus will cause very high mortality of the moths.

BIOLOGICAL CONTROL OF THE GYPSY MOTH

A serious pest of forest and shade trees, the gypsy moth (*Porthetria dispar*) was brought to Bedford, Massachusetts in 1869 by a French astronomer and amateur naturalist who was interested in

[4] Discussed under tachinid parasites (Chapter 8).

experimenting with silk production by various caterpillars. The spread of the moth throughout New England was quite rapid. The program for the biological control of this pest, begun in 1905 and renewed at various times, is the largest of its kind ever undertaken in the United States. More than forty species of parasites and predators have been imported, and of those nine parasites and two predators have become established. By 1927 over 92 million parasites had been released. The most important species are *Apanteles melanoscelus* and two tachinid flies.[5]

Apanteles melanoscelus, an important enemy of the gypsy moth in Europe, was imported during 1911 and 1912, chiefly from Sicily where it was most abundant. The wasp has two generations each season, overwintering as a mature larva in its own cocoon. The first brood emerges in May, and when her development is complete each adult female oviposits a single egg in a young moth larva. The period required for the development of the first brood is considerably shorted than for the second. The host caterpillars are not immediately killed but cease to feed. From about 160,000 cocoons imported for colonization and rearing, the parasite has become well established throughout New England, and ranks as the third most important larval parasite of the gypsy moth. Samplings show that parasitization of the moth by this species alone may be from 20 to 30 per cent or even more.

Two egg parasites, *Anastatus disparis* and *Ooencyrtus kuwanai*, have also been important factors in control. The first of these is well established throughout New England, and the other is mainly effective in the southern part of the host range. At times the combined infestation of these egg parasites has been from 20 to 27 per cent.[6]

As was noted earlier, the most important predator—and an important factor in over-all control—is the ground beetle *Calosoma sycophanta*. The gypsy moth is also subject to the so-called "wilt

[5] *Blepharipoda scutellata* and *Compsilura concinnata*. They are discussed under tachinid parasites (Chapter 8).
[6] Both species are discussed further under egg parasites (Chapter 8).

disease," a virus infection which at times has a devastating effect
on moth populations. Such epizootics develop rapidly and, according to E. A. Steinhaus, may result in a 30 to 70 per cent reduction
of the moth population in a single outbreak.[7] Studies of population
levels in ten sites in the town of Glenville, New York during the
four-year period from 1958 to 1961 show that disease and desiccation (the drying up of the larvae) were the primary causes of
sudden reductions of the population levels. At high population
levels one generation could be reduced by as much as 98 per cent
as a result of disease alone. It is believed that more gradual reductions of population, from levels that have not caused a strip-
ping of the trees, are also brought about by disease.[8]

Field tests were made in Vermont in 1960 to compare the relative value of chemicals and of the bacterial disease organism
Bacillus thuringiensis in controlling the gypsy moth. The chemicals and a suspension of the bacterial spores in water were applied
from an airplane to several seventeen-acre plots having similar
stands, where there were gypsy moth infestations ranging from
one to five caterpillars per leaf. Control of the gypsy moth with
B. thuringiensis was found to compare favorably with the chemical treatments.[9] Tests conducted in New York in 1962 also showed
the bacillus to be effective against both the gypsy moth and the
cankerworm. This has led to a clamor from conservation groups
for the use of the bacterial spray, which is harmless to wildlife
or to beneficial insects, instead of DDT, the standard treatment
prescribed by pest control bodies, both federal and state.[10]

According to a USDA leaflet (1959) on the gypsy moth, infestations which for many years had been held to reasonable levels

[7] E. A. Steinhaus, *Principles of Insect Pathology* (New York: McGraw-
Hill, 1949).

[8] R. W. Campbell, "The Role of Disease and Desiccation in the Population Dynamics of the Gypsy Moth *Porthetria dispar*," *The Canadian Entomologist*, April 1963. Part of thesis for a doctor's degree at the University
of Michigan.

[9] G. E. Cantwell, S. R. Dutky, J. C. Keller, and C. G. Thompson, "Results
of Tests with *Bacillius thuringiensis* Berliner Against Gypsy Moth Larvae,"
Journal of Insect Pathology, June 1961.

[10] *Bridgeport Post*, Sunday, Feb. 24, 1963.

and within the bounds of New England "have broken away and threaten to spread down the Allegheny and Appalachian mountains into 100 million acres of our most valuable hardwood timber resources. . . . Altogether, since 1945 about 9½ million acres of forest have been treated with DDT for control or eradication of the gypsy moth." In spite of this program, "some seasons over one-half million acres of trees have been defoliated and, in one season—1953—nearly 1½ million acres of trees were stripped of their leaves." Two successive defoliations usually result in death of the tree.

In evaluating the biological control program for the gypsy moth before these spraying operations became widespread, C. P. Clausen observed:

It is exceptionally difficult to determine the influence of natural control factors on an insect such as the gypsy moth, which is subject to wide and frequent changes of population levels. It is believed, however, that the combined effect of the parasites and predators has given appreciable control. Instead of occurring frequently in epidemic form and for extended periods, the gypsy moth outbreaks are now reduced so that they are comparable in range and severity to those occurring in Europe.[11]

A later appraisal by P. B. Dowden was as follows: "Generally speaking there is an excellent sequence of insect enemies operating against the gypsy moth in this country, but the almost universal use of insecticides when defoliation occurs complicates an evaluation of the long-term results of this work."[12]

ASCOGASTER AND THE CODLING MOTH

Ascogaster quadridentata (*carpocapsae*) is a braconid parasite of the codling moth (*Carpocapsa pomonella*), probably the most serious single pest of apples. Though the wasp is an internal parasite of the moth larva, the female does not deposit her eggs in

[11] C. P. Clausen, *Biological Control of Insect Pests in the Continental U. S.* (Washington: USDA Technical Bulletin No. 1139, June 1956).

[12] P. B. Dowden, *Parasites and Predators of Forest Insects Liberated in the U. S. Through 1960* (Washington: USDA Agricultural Handbook No. 226, July 1962).

the larva of the host, but places them singly in the egg, where they develop in the cytoplasm without disturbing the embryo and thus permit the host larva to develop. The wasp's egg hatches in two or three days, but its larva develops slowly, giving the codling moth larva time to hatch, enter the fruit, and complete its feeding there.[13] The host is weakened by this time, however, and although it leaves the fruit and spins a cocoon, it rarely pupates; the parasite emerges from this cocoon about two or three weeks later. If it is still in the host at the time of hibernation, the parasite larva overwinters in the first larval stage. Mating begins as soon as the adult wasps emerge; each female parasite lays several hundred eggs, several generations being possible in a season. This wasp, a native of North America, has been widely introduced into the apple-growing areas of the West. Foreign introductions of other species for control of the codling moth have not been successful because they are prevented from ovipositing by the moth larva's penetration into the fruit—a disadvantage which *Ascogaster* circumvents by ovipositing in the egg. A strain of this wasp parasitizes the pea moth (*Laspeyresia nigricana*) in England, and was imported some years ago into Canada, where it became established and has proved to be an important factor in control of this pest. Some authors distinguish the pea moth parasite, under the name *A. quadridentata,* from the codling moth parasite, to which they give the name *A. carpocapsae.*[14]

Though *Ascogaster* is now common in most of the apple-growing areas, it has not generally been very effective owing to the secondary parasites that attack it—which may explain why the codling moth is less of a problem in Nova Scotia, where these

[13] Codling moth eggs are laid on the upper side of leaves, twigs, or fruit spurs, near the apple clusters, anywhere from two to six weeks after the trees have bloomed. They hatch in six to twenty days, depending on tenperature and rainfall. They feed only slightly on the leaves and usually enter the apple from the calyx cup at the bottom end, gradually working their way into the core.

[14] J. W. McLeod, *A Review of the Biological Control Attempts Against Insects and Weeds in Canada,* Part I (Farnham Royal, England: Commonwealth Agricultural Bureaux, 1962).

secondary parasites are not present. Many parasites of the codling moth have been recorded, but as yet no really effective parasite or combination for biological control has been found. Mass releases of the egg parasite *Trichogramma minutum* in Georgia apple-growing areas some years ago were not considered successful. During the winter, birds—especially woodpeckers—find large numbers of the overwintering larvae in cocoons under the bark and feed on them. Ryania, a plant-derived insecticide, has come into general use in Nova Scotia in place of DDT and parathion to combat the codling moth. This is a more "specific" insecticide and causes much less damage to beneficial insects.[15] It is nontoxic to birds and other warm-blooded animals.

BRACON AND THE WHEAT STEM SAWFLY

The wheat stem sawfly (*Cephus cinctus*) is a serious pest of wheat in the plains states and in western Canada. In the native grasses of the prairie provinces it is attacked by several species of wasps; but only one, *Bracon cephi*, has been able to control it effectively in cultivated fields. The degree of control varies, however, and a recent study has shown that weather, moisture—natural or the result of irrigation—and cultural practices account for this variation.[16] The sawfly has one generation a year and overwinters as a mature larva in the stubble just below the ground. The adults emerge late in June or early in July and the eggs are deposited in the stem of the host plant. The larva spends its developmental period in the stem; when the wheat ripens, it cuts the stem at ground level and moves to the stub below ground.

The parasite has two generations a year and overwinters as a larva above ground in the uncut stems. Only limited parasitization takes place in the stubble. The larvae are protected from the cold in the same way cars are protected with an antifreeze: high con-

[15] See A. D. Pickett, "Utilization of Native Parasites and Predators," *Journal of Economic Entomology*, Dec. 1959.

[16] N. D. Holmes, W. A. Nelson, L. K. Peterson, and C. W. Farstad, "Causes of Variations in Effectiveness of *Bracon cephi* (Gahan) as a Parasite of the Wheat Stem Sawfly," *The Canadian Entomologist*, Feb. 1963.

centrations of glycerol lower their freezing point and ensure survival—even if they do freeze! The adults of the first generation emerge about the same time as the sawfly, and those of the second appear early in August. The female wasp goes through a pre-oviposition period of approximately two weeks and does not deposit her eggs until the sawfly larvae are advanced enough in their development to provide food for the parasites. The second-generation females lose no time in getting their eggs deposited before the sawflies cut the stems; many of the mature eggs at the time, however, remain in the female, unlaid, for lack of a host.

A curious thing happens at high densities of the sawfly; reversing the roles, the host becomes a predator, with the result that the percentage of parasitization may decrease even though the total is high. When more than 60 per cent of the wheat stems are infested with sawflies, and more eggs are deposited in each stem, the earliest hatch of sawfly larvae remedy the crowded condition by eating the eggs and each other until only one larva per stem remains. This is damaging to the parasite since its larvae, normally one to a stem, are also eaten. The degree of parasitization by wasps of the second generation is directly related to the amount of moisture provided either by rainfall or by irrigation. The sawfly does not cut the stem until the moisture content is less than 50 per cent; a delay in cutting therefore gives the second-generation wasp more time to oviposit. If ripening is delayed, heavy parasitization occurs regardless of the level of parasitization by the first generation; if ripening is early, parasitization is low except when the first-generation level has been high. The same effect can be achieved through the timing of seeding; by delaying it, thus bringing about a delay in ripening, heavy parasitization is encouraged. Since most of the parasites overwinter in the uncut stems, a delay in ripening of the wheat will also increase the number of wasps that survive the winter and thus the level of parasitization by the first generation the following year. Differences in the amount of parasitization among different varieties of wheat

(and also as compared to barley) are related to their comparative resistance to the sawfly and to the respective rates at which
they mature. The percentage of parasitization is usually higher
in the wheats that are susceptible to the sawfly. The results of
this useful study suggest the possibility of adjusting cultural
practices to favor heavy parasitization of the sawfly.

Bracon lissogaster, a close relative to *B. cephi,* is an important
parasite of sawflies that attack grasses in the prairie states but is
not so effective against the pest in wheat. It is an external parasite
of the sawfly larva, and may be either "solitary" or "gregarious"—
that is, one parasite may develop on a single host or three or four
may develop on a single larva. The wasp produces two generations a year and overwinters as a larva in a silken cocoon within
the wheat stem. It pupates the following spring, and the adult
wasp emerges late in June after cutting a circular hole in the
plant stem. The manner of oviposition by this female wasp is
described by H. W. Somsen and Philip Luginbill as follows:

To locate a larva for oviposition, the female *B. lissogaster* walks up
and down the wheat stem, occasionally touching the stem with her
antennae. When the larva is located she stops, raises her body to leg's
length, and stands perfectly rigid as if listening or feeling for larval
movement. Before ovipositing, her abdomen is tipped slightly forward
so that the ovipositor is perpendicular to the stem. It is very common
for her to remain in this position for several hours. As the ovipositor
is inserted into the stem and larva, it is guided by a pair of black
pads. After penetration, the ovipositor is withdrawn almost out of
the stem and then driven back with a pumping motion. The host larva
is paralyzed to some degree in this manner before oviposition takes
place.

Eggs are deposited on or near the sawfly host larva. If the larva is
not completely paralyzed and continues to crawl, the eggs, being sticky
adhere to the integument of the larva. One to four eggs are laid by each
female before she moves to another stem. After completing oviposition
the parasite either remains on the same stem and preens herself, or she
flies to another stem and oviposits again.[17]

[17] H. W. Somsen and Philip Luginbill, Jr., Bracon lissogaster *Mues., A
Parasite of the Wheat Stem Sawfly* (Washington: USDA Technical Bulletin
No. 1153, December 1956).

A curious thing about *B. lissogaster* is that it does not take well to cultivated grains. In wheat seeded in an uncultivated field it parasitized nearly 30 per cent of the sawfly population, and in volunteer wheat growing in a barley field it parasitized 85 per cent of the sawfly larvae; in large fields of wheat, however, parasitization averages less than 1 per cent.

Importations of parasites for sawfly control have not been successful so far. *Collyria calcitrator,* an ichneumon wasp that parasitizes the wheat stem sawfly in Europe, was introduced from England into western Canada between 1930 and 1938. This parasite is one of the few ichneumons with the same habit as our friend *Ascogaster,* the parasite of the codling moth, of depositing its eggs in those of the host. *Collyria* parasitized from 2 to 9 per cent of the wheat sawflies in the years when it was released, but did not become established.

Closely related to the parasites of the wheat stem sawflies is another *Bracon,* which attacks the lima bean pod borer. *B. piger* was imported from France into California between 1936 and 1938 and was quickly established; it was found to parasitize about 20 per cent of the pod borers. Its habits in many respects are similar to those of the other members of this family. It is a gregarious external parasite, and up to fifteen eggs may be deposited by one female on the host larvae in the pods; from there the wasp larvae —from two to eight on a single host larva—spread over the host and consume it in about four days. The host is permanently paralyzed at the time of oviposition and the female constructs a feeding tube from which she feeds on the liquid contents of its body.

A PEACH PEST AND ITS PARASITES

The oriental fruit moth, *Grapholitha molesta,* the most important pest of peaches, first came to the United States from Japan around 1913, probably in nursery stock. It was first found near Washington, D. C. and in neighboring parts of Maryland and Virginia; from there it spread rapidly into all peach-growing areas. By 1925 it had reached Texas, the midwestern states, and Canada, and in

1942 it was discovered in California. The moth larva attacks a wide variety of cultivated tree fruits but is mainly a pest of peaches. The first generation of the season attack the succulent young peach twigs, boring into the tips, eating downward through the pith, and causing each leaf along its path to wilt as it passes by. It may enter either another twig or the fruit to complete its development. Lead arsenate, a stomach poison used in orchards at the time, was not effective because of the caterpillar's habit of discarding the surface material it chews off to gain entry into the twig or fruit. The pest's destructiveness prompted extensive importation of its natural enemies from Asia and Europe; between 1930 and 1939 more than twenty species of parasites were imported. Although some were effective during the year of release, only one became established—a failure apparently due to the lack of a suitable alternate host to accommodate the parasites over the winter. *Agathis diversa,* one of the importations from Japan, was later found to be established in New Jersey as a parasite of the moth larvae in the fruit but not those in the twigs—a change from its habit in Japan which accounts for its not having been recovered earlier.

Unlike most pests introduced from other countries, the oriental fruit moth has been parasitized by native species wherever it has become established. During the period of these foreign introductions a survey of its parasites became a major project of the U. S. Department of Agriculture's oriental fruit moth investigations at Moorestown, New Jersey. The area surveyed extends from Massachusetts to Georgia and west to Illinois, Kansas and Texas, including twenty-five states in all. The major study was supplemented by more limited surveys from 1940 to 1957. The results of the investigation have been reported in detail by H. W. Allen.[18] More than ninety species of parasites attacking the eggs or larvae of the oriental fruit moth in the eastern states have been found. About 130 species are known to attack this pest in the United

[18] H. W. Allen, *Parasites of the Oriental Fruit Moth in the Eastern United States* (Washington: USDA Technical Bulletin No. 1265, October 1962).

States and Canada; these are mostly in the braconid and ichneumonid families of wasps, but includes some trichogrammatid
(egg parasites) and some in the family of tachinid flies.

NATURAL CONTROL

Allen reports the effect of the parasites of the oriental fruit moth
as follows:

In the United States many of the species reported as attacking the
oriental fruit moth seem to do so only rarely. A much smaller number
are abundant and relatively effective over a restricted part of its
range or during some years. Only a few species attack the fruit moth
heavily over a wide area each season. Although many of the species are
unimportant, their combined effect may be considerable in reducing
moth populations. This is particularly true of the cocoon parasites.

In orchards that have been thoroughly sprayed for control of the
oriental fruit moth, few parasites will be found, since the insecticides
greatly reduce the number of possible host insects and they also kill
adult parasites moving about over the sprayed trees. However, all the
parasite species have alternate hosts, which are frequently abundant
on plants not sprayed and which may occur in large numbers in close
proximity to sprayed peach orchards. So, despite heavy spraying in
bearing peach orchards, parasites of the oriental fruit moth continue
to be abundant and they serve to reduce moth populations in areas
that are not sprayed, such as young peach interplanted with truck
crops, abandoned peach, or apple orchards.

The fruit moth larvae of the first and second generations that infest
peach twigs are heavily attacked by parasites, of which the more important species are *Macrocentrus ancylivorus* Roh., *M. delicatus* Cress.,
M. instabilis Mues., *Glypta rufiscutellaris* Cress., *Pristomerus euryptychiae* Ashm., and *Cremastus minor* Cush. In the eastern states these
six species account for more than 90 per cent of the total parasitism
of twig-infesting larvae. The three species of *Macrocentrus* are crepus-
cular (active in twilight) or nocturnal in habit and are delicately
formed. In size and body conformation they are somewhat like mosquitoes and are amber to yellowish in color. The other three species
are diurnal (active in daytime). *G. Rufiscutellaris* is black with reddish
legs, *P. euryptychiae* has a prominent spine on the hind femur, and
C. minor is light brown with a long slender abdomen and short wings.
These six parasites attack larvae in infested twigs and emerge from the

cocoon stage. In unsprayed orchards they frequently destroy 85 per cent or more of the twig-infesting larvae.

Trichogramma minutum Riley, a widely distributed parasite of insect eggs, is a common parasite of oriental fruit moth eggs. Parasitized eggs become coal black before the adult parasite emerges. Rates of parasitism by this species are highly variable. At times more than 50 per cent of the eggs may be parasitized."[19]

The cocooned larvae and pupae of the oriental fruit moth are attacked by many parasites. One study made in eight eastern states between 1931 and 1945 showed that twenty species of parasites had an average of about 15 per cent parasitization of the moth. In some orchards parasitization was as high as 100 per cent; and in six Virginia counties it averaged 32 per cent in one year. No one species appeared to be predominant. Field mice often destroy large numbers of cocoons on the trunks of the trees, and lacewing larvae consume large numbers of the moth eggs and the larvae. In Canada, where the lacewings are numerous and the aphids scarce, these beneficial insects have been observed to destroy from 20 to 60 per cent of the moth eggs.

THE MACROCENTRUS PROGRAM

Macrocentrus ancylivorus is by far the most important parasite of the oriental fruit moth, and had become the most important vehicle of control before the chlorinated hydrocarbon and phosphate compounds came into use as insecticides. It is distinctly a North American species, first discovered as a parasite of the strawberry leaf roller (*Ancylis comptana fragariae*), and attempts to introduce it outside the continent have been unsuccessful. It is known to have fourteen hosts—mostly stem borers, fruitworms, and leaf rollers—and it takes readily to the oriental fruit moth. These hosts serve as important reservoirs for the parasites outside the peach orchards. The life cycle of *M. ancylivorus* is similar to other parasites of twig-infesting pests. The adults mate soon after emerging from the cocoons; the females oviposit for about

[19] H. W. Allen, *The Oriental Fruit Moth* (Washington: USDA Agriculture Information Bulletin No. 182, June 1958).

two days and have a life span of less than two weeks. They attack very young to nearly mature larvae during the day and night. The larvae parasite matures after the host pupates, forming its own cocoon inside that of the host, and issues from the host cocoon by cutting out a circular cap. At summer temperatures the total cycle of this parasite, from egg to adult, takes about one month when the host is the oriental fruit moth.

Between 1929 and 1935 an extensive program for the distribution and release of *M. ancylivorus* was carried on by the Moorestown laboratory in cooperation with the state agencies. According to Allen, "This effort was highly successful, and very shortly the parasite was well established in scores of districts where it had not previously occurred as a parasite of the oriental fruit moth. . . . [A study] showed that in Niagara County, New York, parasitism, due to the introduction of *M. ancylivorus,* increased steadily from 1928 to 1933, and during the same period injury to peaches decreased from 18,900 injured fruits per acre in 1929 to 4,500 in 1933." Fruit injuries were often reduced by 50 per cent, and in many areas the total loss of fruit was reduced to 10 per cent the season following the release of the parasites.

MASS PRODUCTION OF MACROCENTRUS

In 1944 a very successful method of mass producing *M. ancylivorus,* using the potato tuber moth (*Gnorimoschema operculella*) as host, was worked out by entomologists of the University of California Citrus Experiment Station at Riverside, California.[20] This made possible a continuous and unlimited supply of parasites at a greatly reduced cost.

Potato sprouts had been used very successfully for mass culture of mealybugs, making it possible to produce the lady beetle *Cryptolaemus montrouzieri* in huge quantities at low cost for control of the mealybug. The moth was often unintentionally produced in

[20] The technique is described in detail by G. L. Finney, S. E. Flanders, and Harry S. Smith in "Mass Culture of *Macrocentrus ancylivorous* and Its Host, the Potato Tuber Moth," *Hilgardia,* August 1947.

large quantities in connection with that program—which gave Harry S. Smith the idea of using it as the host for mass production of *M. ancylivorus*. Potatoes punctured to facilitate the entrance of a maximum number of tuber moth larvae are poured onto trays made of half-inch hardware cloth. These are stacked (without allowing the layers of potatoes to touch) so as to conserve floor space. Infesting of the potatoes and parasitizing the larvae of the tuber moth takes place in closed boxes or incubator units, closely stacked, where the loaded trays are kept for eight days—the time required to complete infestation and parasitization. The potatoes are infested by covering them with sheets on which the adult moths have deposited their eggs uniformly, and which are placed (egg side down) over the racks of freshly punctured potatoes in the incubator unit a day or two before they are due to hatch. By one or two days after the eggs begin to hatch the potatoes are well infested, and the egg sheets are withdrawn through openings made for this purpose. The next step consists of laying honey strips on the trays through the same openings. At this stage the mated female parasites are introduced, at a rate of five per pound of potatoes. The honey keeps the parasites alive during the parasitization period of about three days, after which the trays are removed from the incubator units and stacked on racks, and the adult parasites are allowed to disperse through the room. The incubator units are dismantled one day before the larvae begin to leave the tubers—usually on the ninth day after the placing of the egg sheets on the potato trays. Placed under the racks containing the stacked trays, and extending slightly beyond them, are containers for catching the larvae as they drop from the trays above. These containers are made of plywood; to their sides, which are two inches high, is attached a hot-wire barrier, heated electrically to a temperature of 180° F. Cocooning plates—sheets of thin plywood a little wider and longer than the potato trays—are carefully placed in the containers and within the barrier, after having been spread with lateral strips of dry sand. These strips are about two inches wide, half an inch thick and half an inch apart, and soon become matted with dropping cocoons. The cocooning plates are removed daily, and for one day are placed over the stacked potato trays to permit any larvae to return to the fresh trays. The next day the cocooning plates are removed and set aside in stacks for a period of six days. During this time the parasite larvae leave the host larvae and spin their own cocoons within those of the host. On the seventh day after cocooning, 75 per cent of the parasites on the trays will have pupated. These are run through a sodium hypochlorite–alcohol separation process to obtain parasite larvae free from moths. After a minute or less in the bath the host cocoons dissolve, leaving the parasite cocoons and the larvae and pupae of the host. The mortality of the parasites while in the cocoons, after washing and drying, amounts to from about 5 to 25 per cent, for an average of 18 per cent.

HARVESTING THE PARASITES

Unparasitized eggs, larvae, and pupae intended for moth breeding stock can be processed three days earlier than the parasitized material. They are placed in wire baskets which are set in a gastight emergence cabinet. The handling of the moths is facilitated by anesthetizing them with a mixture of ether and carbon dioxide. Egg deposition boxes or trays, made of wood and measuring an inch and a half deep, are covered with bleached muslin held taut. These are stacked one on top of the other in a cabinet or humidity chamber. Each tray has a hole with a cork, so the moths can be anesthetized each day before removing the egg sheets.

Parasite cocoons to be used for propogation purposes in the insectary are placed in wire baskets similar to those used for the moths. These baskets are placed in light-proof emergence cabinets, where they remain for about ten days, until emergence is completed. About 85 or 90 per cent of the cocoons will yield parasites if reared on healthy stock and properly handled. With a sex ratio of one to one, 1,000 cocoons should yield about 400 females. Keeping the cabinet dark causes the wasps to spread about evenly, so that contacts are minimized; but there is sufficient contact for mating, which increases in frequency with the intensity of light. Under normal field conditions a female will mate only once. Under insectary conditions she is more likely to mate several times— which tends to inhibit impregnation (since it prevents the storage of the sperm in the spermatheca) and to prolong the oviposition period. An unimpregnated female produces only male offspring; once-mated females produce more females, the likely ratio being about one male to two females.

When the female mates she receives the sperm in a large spermatophore, which must be discarded, and the sperm transferred to the sperm capsule, before ovipositing can take place. The process at an 80-degrees temperature in the insectary requires six hours; the time can be shortened by slightly raising the temperature. Once-mated females may not oviposit for twelve hours because of the presence of the spermatophore. Of the multiple-mated females, containing anywhere from two to ten spermatophores, half may produce only male offspring. The pre-oviposition period for these females may be prolonged several days because of the added time required to discard the excess spermatophores. If the time allowed for oviposition in the incubation in the insectary units is less than the time required to discard the spermatophores, these females will have no progeny.

Each day the emergence cabinet is rolled into the collecting room and the wasps are allowed to escape. They fly to the window, where the females needed for propagation purposes are collected by suction into a glass tube. In this container they can be kept under refrigeration for four days and also shipped, although rather expensive shipping cartons are required. The latter problem has been solved by the host-parasite separation process, which allows shipment of the parasite in the cocoon, and over longer distances. The cocoons are poured into bags with a capacity of about a thousand, and a loose wad of excelsior is then placed at the top in preparation for shipping. In the orchards where the parasites are to be released, a bag is hung from every tenth tree, after the excelsior has been pulled up to keep the top open; the wasps are able to rid themselves of their cocoons as they crawl through the excelsior. Kept at a temperature of 82°, *Macrocentrus* emerges from the cocoon five days after the separation process. It may continue to emerge for a week or more in the field, depending on the temperature.

BIOLOGICAL CONTROL OF THE ORIENTAL FRUIT MOTH

Alarm over the discovery of the oriental fruit moth in California prompted the most intensive program of rearing and release of *Macrocentrus* ever undertaken. This was spurred on by the efficient method of parasite production that had been worked out as has been described above. For the years 1944 to 1946 the production of these parasites in California averaged about nineteen million annually, at an average yearly cost of about $15,000. The object was to prevent the spread of the moth rather than to eradicate known infestations, and to this end colonies were placed in every orchard regardless of the degree of infestation. Cocoons were placed in the field at the rate of two thousand per acre per week. Whether wholly as a result of this program or not, the oriental fruit moth infestation subsided in California; but *Macrocentrus* did not become permanently established.

As late as 1954 *Macrocentrus ancylivorus* was available comercially, and a Farmers' Bulletin recommended its use as follows:

In the region in which *Macrocentrus ancylivorous* is known to be most effective—roughly Massachusetts to Michigan and southward to eastern Missouri, Arkansas, and northern Georgia—growers who are not equipped to spray can prevent nearly half the damage caused by the oriental fruit moth by making liberations each year when second or first and second-brood worms are present. In southern New Jersey the most favorable period for first-brood liberations is usually about May 20 to June 10, and for second-brood liberations June 25 to July 15. Southward it is earlier, and northward or at higher elevations it is somewhat later.

If liberations are concentrated against second-brood worms, release six females per tree, preferably five times at 4-day intervals. Start releases as soon as the first wilted twigs caused by this brood are observed. When liberations are to be made against both the first and second broods, use half the total of parasites against each brood. Scatter the parasites widely over the orchard by walking slowly about carrying the shipping containers and opening them to permit the parasites to fly away.[21]

C. P. Clausen sums up the value of *Macrocentrus* releases as follows:

Even in orchards that already have a considerable parasite population, the release of 500 additional adults per acre at the proper time results in an appreciable reduction in the proportion of fruit that becomes infested. In New Jersey such liberations have brought about a reduction of 50 to 80 per cent in fruit injury. This practice may also be of special benefit during seasons when outbreaks occur in sections where control is usually satisfactory.[22]

According to H. W. Allen, it has been shown "that mass liberations of *M. ancylivorus* in combination with a reduced number of spray applications were as effective as a larger number of spray applications without the parasites." Today, however, parasites have given way to pesticides, and so far as we know *Macrocentrus* wasps are no longer being mass produced for commercial use. The oriental fruit moth investigation at the Moorestown laboratories came to an end in 1958.

In their estimate of biological control projects carried out in Canada, Turnbull and Chant rate that concerned with the oriental fruit moth as a "partial success," though heavy applications of chemicals are now generally resorted to. (For Ontario orchards in 1959, five annual applications were recommended, including DDT, methoxychlor, parathion, guthion, and sevin.) These investigators state that between 1929 and 1948 "biological control agents were reasonably successful in controlling the peach moth" in the southern fruit belt of the province. Most important of these

---

[21] O. I. Snapp, *Insect Pests of the Peach in the Eastern States* (Washington: USDA Farmers' Bulletin No. 1861, February 1954).

[22] C. P. Clausen, *Biological Control of Insect Pests in the Continental U. S.* (Washington: USDA Technical Bulletin No. 1139, June 1956).

were the egg parasite *Trichogramma minutum* and the ichneumonid *Glypta rufiscutellaris* (both native species) and *Macrocentrus ancylivorus* (first imported from New Jersey in 1929 and released annually until 1934). *G. rufiscutellaris* was the dominant
parasite prior to the introduction of *M. ancylivorus*, and parasitized up to 70 per cent of the second generation moth larvae. The
introduced parasite, since it was especially effective against the
first generation, filled the gap, and the two complemented one
another nicely. Mass releases of *T. minutum*, which chiefly attacks
the third generation, gave added protection but were discontinued
because the parasites did not maintain themselves at high densities.

The loss of fruit in 1948 was severe, and spraying with DDT
began. It is pointed out that the "heavy applications of chemicals
do not in themselves provide the desired degree of control . . .
in the absence of appreciable parasitism." It appears that *M.
ancylivorus* survives by parasitizing the fruit moth or other hosts
in surrounding fields and gardens or nearby orchards that have
not been sprayed, and is thus still able to provide the necessary
supplement to the sprays. *G. rufiscutellaris*, on the other hand,
has been completely eliminated by the sprays.[23] We are told that
this nearly complete extermination of the fruit moth annually is
necessary because the consumer demands "an extremely high
grade of fruit." We would add that the agricultural agents are
also insistent on this, and it is almost as difficult to say which
started insisting first as it is to settle the question of the chicken
and the egg.

[23] A. L. Turnbull and D. A. Chant, "The Practice and Theory of Biological Control of Insects in Canada," *Canadian Journal of Zoology*, October
1961.

The earth is peopled by organisms which have been through such fiery test for an unimaginable length of time. Host and parasites have survived only because they have developed the ability to live together.

ICHNEUMONID PARASITES

7

Ichneumonid wasps—sometimes referred to as ichneumon flies—are practically all parasites. They are generally small to medium in size, though there are some minute forms as well as some of the largest of the parasitic wasps. The majority attack the larvae of Lepidoptera (moths and butterflies) but they are also important parasites upon certain harmful Hymenoptera—including some of the worst forest pests, the sawflies.

These wasps may be internal or external parasites—although they are more commonly the former—and may deposit their eggs in, on, or near the host. The external parasites oviposit in the cocoons, burrows, leaf rolls, or galleries of the host; those attacking wood-boring pests often have long ovipositors capable of penetrating deep into the wood; an example is *Megarhyssa lunator*, a parasite of the pigeon tremex. Those that place the eggs in or on the host usually sting and paralyze the larva either temporarily or permanently. The solitary external parasites will destroy the eggs or newly hatched larvae of any competitors. There may be anywhere from one to ten or more generations, although two or

[1] *Deserts on the March* (Norman: University of Oklahoma Press, 1947).

three are more usual; the number varies to some extent with climatic conditions. Hibernation is usually as a mature larva in the cocoon of the host. Very few of these wasps are restricted to a single species of host.

FEEDING HABITS OF ICHNEUMONID ADULTS

The adults feed on plant materials or exudates such as pollen and nectar; feeding from the oviposition puncture wound is also very common, and the puncture is sometimes made solely for that purpose. Robert W. Campbell found this to be true of several ichneumonids in his study of the gypsy moth (*Porthetria dispar*), and showed that the trait can conceal the real value of the parasite. In woodland study plots in the town of Glenville, New York he found four ichneumonids[2] attacking the gypsy moth.

Results from rearing [he writes] indicated that these species were of no appreciable value as enemies of the gypsy moth, since only ten ichneumonids were recovered from 2,739 pupae and pre-pupae that were collected and reared during 1958 and 1959. Actually, however, these parasites were among the most important agencies operating against dense populations in Glenville. This is because they stung as many as 250 host pupae for each pupa that was parasitized successfully (success here meaning the development of an ichneumonid offspring within the host to a size where it could be identified by field dissection).[3]

It appears that the attacks by these parasites on the gypsy moth are mostly for food rather than for oviposition and that their effectiveness as parasites can't be measured by the percentage of parasitized hosts. This is probably why it has been accepted as a "fact" for years that ichneumonids are not valuable gypsy moth parasites. Of the more than 22,000 gypsy moth pupae field-dissected in Campbell's study, only 232 contained ichneumonid parasites, and none of these belonged to the species *Itoplectis conquisitor*, the most numerous of those studied—which is all the more remarkable

[2] The four species are *Itoplectis conquisitor, Pimpla pedalis, Theronia atalantae,* and *Theronia hilaris.*

[3] Robert W. Campbell, "Some Ichneumonid-Sarcophagid Interactions in the Gypsy Moth *Porthetria dispar* (L) (Lepidoptera: Lymantriidae)," *The Canadian Entomologist,* April 1963.

considering that 5,000 of the 22,000 gypsy moths examined were stung by ichneumonid wasps. Another interesting observation made in this study was that about half of the hosts stung by the wasps were later occupied by sarcophagid maggots (larvae of a family of flies that are scavengers or parasites of injurious insects). The maggots use the puncture wounds for entrance to the gypsy moth larvae.

EXENTERUS AND THE SPRUCE SAWFLY

Several species of ichneumonid wasps in the genus *Exenterus* have played an important part in biological control of the European spruce sawfly (*Diprion hercyniae*), which at one time was a serious threat to the spruce stands of eastern Canada and the New England states. One of the most important of these is *Exenterus claripennis*, a larval parasite first imported into Canada in 1933. Like its host, it has one complete generation and a partial second one in a year. The overwintering generation emerges in late June or early July—around ten days or two weeks after the sawfly. After a pre-oviposition period lasting several days, the female parasites are able to attack the sawfly larva. The eggs are laid on those in the late larval stage of the sawfly and normally hatch within its cocoon. The adults emerge in August, following a period of larval development that lasts about thirty days for those that don't remain in diapause (resting stage) until the following summer (as about half of them do). The parasite commonly overwinters in the late larval stage, but may do so as a younger larva or even as egg. Field populations are about evenly divided between male and female. The species became well established in the Gaspé in a short time after only two small releases—140 at one point and 110 at another.[4]

Other species of *Exenterus* introduced and established in the maritime provinces between 1934 and 1949 were *vellicatus, amic-*

[4] W. A. Reeks, "Establishment of *Exenterus Spp.* (Hymenoptera: Ichneumonidae), Parasites of the European Spruce Sawfly, Near Points of Introduction," *The Canadian Entomologist*, March 1952.

torius, and *tricolor.* The seasonal history in each case is similar to that of *E. claripennis.* Both *claripennis* and *amictorius* are dependent on high host densities. *E. vellicatus* appears to be one of the most efficient of the introduced species because of its ability to survive at low host densities. Its spread has been quite remarkable—a single colony consisting of sixty-five male and female adults were sufficient to establish it in one location; recoveries indicate it is widely distributed in the maritime provinces. Although *E. amictorius* has not been important as a control factor in the spruce sawfly outbreak, its recent recovery from the European sawfly (*Neodiprion sertifer*), and others of the same family, augurs well for it.

E. tricolor has not been an important factor in control of the spruce sawfly; however, the releases were quite small. The effect of moisture on the development of this parasite is interesting. The adult female oviposits without paralyzing the host; the egg is imbedded in the host tissue by means of a disc which holds it in place while the host larva molts and sheds its skin. In a dry environment the skin hardens and does not split easily enough to allow the egg to pull through the skin, with the result that the egg is pulled off. The success of the parasite therefore depends on the degree of humidity during incubation of the eggs.[5]

OTHER IMPORTATIONS

Numerous releases of *Exenterus abruptorius,* an important parasite of the European pine sawfly in Europe, were made to control the spruce sawfly during an outbreak. Large releases of the parasite were made in Canada and the United States against both the spruce sawfly and the pine sawfly; recoveries, however, have been limited mostly to the latter. The wasp became established in New Jersey, but spraying has now reduced the host drastically. *E. abruptorius* produces one generation a year. Active in early summer,

[5] W. A. Reeks, "The Establishment of Introduced Parasites of the European Spruce Sawfly (*Diprion hercyniae* (Htg.) in the Maritime Provinces," *Canadian Journal of Agricultural Science,* Sept.-Oct. 1953.

Ichneumonid wasp, *Aptesis basizonia*, depositing an egg in a cocoon of the European pine sawfly. (*D. C. Anderson,* courtesy *W. A. Reeks,* Canada Department of Forestry)

the female embeds her eggs under the skin of the advanced larvae or prepupae. The larva, which does not hatch until the host larva has spun its cocoon, spins its own cocoon within the host cocoon after reaching maturity, and overwinters in this stage.

Exenterus confusus became widely established in New Brunswick and was the predominant species of *Exenterus* there until the decline of the spruce sawfly to low levels. Although it is primarily a parasite of the spruce sawfly, it is still present in Canada. Colonies of *Exenterus* were made available for release in the United States against the European spruce sawfly, but few attempts have been made to recover them in this country since the collapse of the outbreak.[6]

Aptesis basizonia, another ichneumonid wasp imported against the spruce sawfly, shows a peculiar phenomenon in rearing. Although normally the female paralyzes the host larva prior to oviposition, in breeding cages the parasite gradually loses this ability and the active larva ingests or crushes the parasite's egg. This trait

[6] P. B. Dowden, *Parasites and Predators of Forest Pests Liberated in the United States Through 1960* (Washington: USDA Agricultural Handbook No. 226, July 1962).

is overcome in the laboratory or insectary by exposing the cocoons to heat. Attempts to rear laboratory-bred parasites on cocoons in the field failed, but recoveries from field-collected cocoons indicate that they can develop successfully on sawfly cocoons under normal conditions. Where the female lacks the ability to paralyze the host larva, it is believed that successful attacks are made on the less active pupal stage. In 1941 and later this parasite was released at various points in Ontario against the European pine sawfly; recent recoveries from other sawflies hold promise for the parasite. *A. basizonia* releases were also made in New England, New York, and New Jersey from parasites supplied by the Canadian Department of Agriculture, but no recoveries have been made from the spruce sawfly. It was established in New Jersey, however, and recoveries have been made there from the European pine sawfly.

BIOLOGICAL CONTROL OF THE EUROPEAN SPRUCE SAWFLY

An outbreak of the European spruce sawfly (*Diprion hercyniae*) was first noticed in the Gaspé Peninsula of Quebec in 1930, and after a few years heavy infestations had developed in the rest of Quebec, New Brunswick, northern Maine, and parts of Vermont and New Hampshire. The discovery caused great alarm and resulted in what is perhaps the largest biological control program ever undertaken anywhere. According to B. M. McGugan and H. C. Coppel,

At least 27 different entities involving 890 million specimens were released between 1933 and 1951 at many points in eastern Canada. Nine species became established with variable effects. Some were recovered only in small numbers shortly after release, others became commonplace during the height of the sawfly outbreak, and two have persisted as important mortality factors through the post-outbreak period.[7]

[7] B. M. McGugan and H. C. Coppel, *A Review of the Biological Control Attempts Against Insects and Weeds in Canada,* Part II (Farnham Royal,

The principal parasites among the ichneumonid wasps involved in this program have already been discussed. Two other parasites —a wasp, *Dahlbominus fuscipennis* (Eulophidae), and a tachinid fly, *Drino bohemica*—have also been important in the program.

Dahlbominus fuscipennis is a gregarious external parasite, attacking the full-grown larvae, prepupae, or pupae of sawflies in their cocoons. There are up to three generations a year, depending on the weather; overwintering takes place in the host cocoons as mature larvae, prepupae, or pupae. The adults of various generations are present from mid-June to October, and are most active in open stands and at higher temperatures. They are poor fliers, however, and are largely restricted to crawling. One female may lay as many as two hundred eggs, though the average is much less. Twenty or more eggs are laid with one insertion of the ovipositor on a single host after it has been partially paralyzed by stinging. The period of development from egg to emergence as an adult ranges from 26 to 50 days, depending on the weather, and averages 31 days. Part of the first summer generation go into diapause and do not emerge as adults until the following summer. The average number of individuals developing in a single cocoon is thirty-four, although as many as one hundred have been observed; they all emerge from a single hole in the cocoon. The average number of progeny per female is less than one hundred, and females greatly outnumber the males, the ratio being as high as nine to one.

This parasite had been observed in southeastern Europe and was introduced into Canada "with great expectations," in a "massive program of introductions, propagation, and saturation releases" that has never been equalled in Canada or anywhere else. In all, 882 million parasites of this one species were released in eastern Canada against the European spruce sawfly, and nearly 4 million more were released against other sawflies, chiefly the

England: Commonwealth Agricultural Bureau, 1962). *Drino bohemica* is discussed further under tachinid parasites (Chapter 8).

European pine sawfly. Many millions of parasites were imported from Czechoslovakia, Holland, Poland, Estonia, and Hungary but most of those released were reared at the Institute for Biological Control in Belleville, Ontario, where very successful techniques for mass production had been developed. Between 1935 and 1939 several million parasites were sent to the United States by the Canadian Department of Agriculture; a portion of these were liberated against the spruce sawfly and related species, and the balance were used for mass rearings by the Bureau of Entomology and Plant Quarantine of the Maine Forest Service and the New Jersey Department of Agriculture. By the end of 1939, about 226 million parasites had been liberated against the spruce sawfly in Maine and another 30 million in New Hampshire, Vermont, and New York. About 13 million were released against the European pine sawfly in New Jersey. Releases were made in 1941 in Alabama, Michigan, South Dakota, and Tennessee where infestations of native species of sawflies were present.

COLLAPSE OF THE OUTBREAK

About 1940 the sudden appearance of a devastating virus disease caused sawfly populations to decline rapidly. Where the disease came from is not definitely known; it may have been brought in with the material from Europe. In the opinion of F. T. Bird and D. E. Elgee,

The parasites, which were increasing rapidly, might have been capable of bringing the "average" generation mortality above 97.8 per cent before scarcity of foliage and dying trees added the factor of starvation. The disease, however, accomplished this before the potential value of the parasites could be realized and it destroyed so large a proportion of the population that other factors became negligible.[8]

Exenterus vellicatus and the tachinid *Drino bohemica* have

[8] F. T. Bird and D. E. Elgee, "A Virus Disease and Introduced Parasites as Factors Controlling the European Spruce Sawfly, *Diprion hercyniae,* (Htg.) in Central New Brunswick," *The Canadian Entomologist,* August 1957.

emerged as the most important of the established species and are
responsible for control of the spruce sawfly at low densities after
1942. *Dahlbominus fuscipennis* is only effective at high host densities of the spruce sawfly; there are no records of its parasitizing
the spruce sawfly in Canada after 1945. It has, however, become
established as a parasite of the European pine sawfly (*Neodiprion
sertifer*) and the jackpine sawfly (*Neodiprion swainei*) in Ontario,
although thus far the percentage of parasitization has been low.
A virus disease imported from Sweden has given good control of
N. sertifer in southern Ontario plantations of Scots pine. The percentage of parasitization by *D. fuscipennis* in the United States is
generally low except in local plantations, according to Dowden.
There it has been present in up to 47 per cent of *N. sertifer* cocoons in the top litter—on one plantation in New Jersey in 1943
—and in 25 per cent of those of *Diprion frutetorum,* the nursery
pine sawfly, for three successive years on a plantation in Connecticut.

Studies show that small mammals are also an important factor
in controlling sawfly populations. Cocoons scattered about in the
litter of the forest floor are exposed to the depredations of shrews,
voles, and mice. In some areas these animals account for 50 per
cent of cocoon mortality. In one instance it was found that they
had opened about 80 per cent of the sound sawfly cocoons. Some
shrews and mice are able to distinguish between sound sawfly
cocoons and empty ones, including those from which the parasites
have emerged. It appears, however, that about 50 per cent of the
cocoons opened by these mammals are parasitized, so that there
is some reduction of the parasites along with the pests. Birds are
also important predators of sawflies. Ralph B. Swain wrote that no
less than 30 species of birds eat sawfly larvae;[9] and dissections
show that it is not uncommon to find from 50 to 100 sawflies in the
stomach of one mockingbird.

[9] Ralph B. Swain, *The Insect Guide* (New York: Doubleday and Company, 1952).

BIOLOGICAL CONTROL OF THE LARCH SAWFLY

An ichneumonid, *Mesoleius tenthredinis,* has played a major role in controlling the larch sawfly (*Pristiphora erichsonii*) in Canada. The latter is a serious pest of conifers and has periodically defoliated large stands of larch and tamarack. The parasite feeds internally on the host larva and seems to be specific to this one sawfly. It produces one generation a year, overwintering as a late-stage larva in the cocooned larva of the host. In the spring the larvae resume feeding, and when mature they pupate within the sawfly cocoons. They emerge as adults between late June and early August; after mating, the females deposit their eggs internally in the host larvae, the eggs hatch in seven to ten days, and the young larvae feed until they hibernate.

A native of Europe, the parasite was first imported from England into Canada in 1910. Early liberations followed in Quebec and Ontario, and a little later in Manitoba. The first attempts to colonize it in the maritime provinces took place in 1927, but more extensive releases were made between 1935 and 1942. The parasite is credited with being a very important factor in bringing about the collapse of serious outbreaks in the eastern provinces during this period. A native parasite, the tachinid *Bessa harveyi,* has played an important part also. A study made in New Brunswick at the final stages of the last outbreak showed that about 48 per cent of the old cocoons had been destroyed by predators— insects and small animals—and that about 48 per cent of the sound cocoons were parasitized, indicating that each of these factors was about equally effective. A more recent outbreak of the larch sawfly, commencing in 1955, has occurred among larch stands in Quebec and tamarack stands in Nova Scotia.[10]

Some of the early parasite material was provided for a small release in the northern peninsula of Michigan in 1911. In 1953

[10] W. A. Reeks, "An Outbreak of the Larch Sawfly (*Pristiphora erichsonii* Htg.) in the Maritime Provinces and the Role of Parasites in its Control," *The Canadian Entomologist*, October 1954.

several colonies were liberated by the U. S. Forest Service in northern Minnesota, and smaller releases were made in New Hampshire and Massachusetts. Large releases of *Dahlbominus fuscipennis* were made against the larch sawfly in New York in 1939 and 1940, and in Wisconsin in 1953.

HOST RESISTANCE TO A PARASITE

During the recolonizing period from 1934 to 1942, releases of *M. tenthredinis* were made in British Columbia with considerable success, and eventually the parasite became firmly established all across Canada. But after 1940 a strange thing happened in the central provinces of Manitoba and Saskatchewan: there was a marked decrease in the effectiveness of this parasite. It was suspected that the larch sawfly in this region had developed immunity to the parasite, but the nature of the immunity was not clear until a study had been made by J. A. Muldrew. He found the resistance to be due to a mechanism, as yet not fully understood, whereby the parasite egg becomes encapsulated in the host larva. Within three or four days after oviposition the development of the egg is halted, and it becomes surrounded by a coating or capsule which is believed to be produced by phagocytes—a defense mechanism possessed by most animals against invading bacteria or other foreign bodies. Encapsulation does not immediately kill many of the parasite eggs, but merely inhibits their growth. Eggs were found viable after removal from the capsules; some survived in the capsules far beyond the normal incubation period.[11]

In British Columbia the degree of encapsulation is very small by comparison, and only a few cases have been found in the eastern provinces. Nevertheless, the phenomenon has not been dismissed as a possible explanation for the present low parasitiza-

[11] J. A. Muldrew, "The Natural Immunity of the Larch Sawfly (*Pristiphora erichsonii* Htg.) to the Introduced Parasite *Mesoleius tenthredinis* Morley, in Manitoba and Saskatchewan," *Canadian Journal of Zoology*, August 1953.

tion in some eastern areas.[12] Recent studies in Manitoba show that various strains of the parasite, from different localities, have had varying success in parasitizing the resistant sawflies. Parasites from Austria and Bavaria are more effective than those from central Canada. Combinations of Bavarian females with Canadian males were very successful in parasitizing resistant sawflies; Canadian females mated with Bavarian males, however, were only slightly superior to the all-Canadian strains.[13]

BIOLOGICAL CONTROL OF THE EUROPEAN PINE SHOOT MOTH

For centuries a pest in Europe, the European pine shoot moth (*Rhyacionia buoliana*) first came to North America at some time before 1914. It is found in most of the northern states and of the Canadian provinces, but the focal points of infestation are the large pine plantations of New York, Michigan, and southern Ontario, where the host trees are mainly Scots pine, Austrian pine, red pine, and the dwarfed mountain pine. Extensive importations and releases of parasites that attack the moth in Europe have been made in the United States and Canada. Between 1928 and 1958 twelve species were imported and 86,000 individual parasites were released in Canada; fifteen species and over 300,-000 parasites were released in Massachusetts, Connecticut, New York, New Jersey, and Pennsylvania from 1931 to 1938. Four species became established in Canada and three in the United States. Infested pine shoots were shipped by air from England, Belgium, Germany, Austria, Sweden, and Finland, and the parasites were reared from these in cages.

Orgilus obscurator, a braconid wasp, has become the most abundant and widespread of the imported parasites. It produces

[12] D. F. Bracken and R. Martineau, "A New Outbreak of the Larch Sawfly in Quebec," *Bi-monthly Progress Report*, Canada Dept. of Agriculture, Nov.-Dec. 1960.

[13] J. A. Muldrew, "Immunity of the Larch Sawfly to *Mesoleius tenthredinis* Morley." in *Annual Report,* (Ottowa: Forest Entomology & Pathology Branch, Canada Dept. of Forestry, 1962).

one generation a year, overwintering as a young larva in the hibernating larva of the host. When its development is complete it leaves the host larva and cocoons within the larval mine in the pine shoot. It is prolific, and the sexes are produced in about equal numbers. It has high searching ability, but where there is multiparasitism other species are dominant. The wasp is now common in the northeastern states and southern Ontario, and has been found in Michigan, though no releases have been made in this state. In one area of Ontario where concentrated releases were made, parasitism reached more than 14 per cent. An ichneumonid, *Temelucha interruptor*, that has about the same seasonal cycle as *Orgilus*, became established readily but is now generally scarce. *Tetrastichus turionum* (Eulophidae) became established initially, but later recoveries were rare, probably owing to the severity of the winter. A gregarious parasite, the female deposits about twenty eggs in each host pupa.

The ichneumonid *Pimpla turionellae* became established initially in Canada but later recoveries were few, and none has been made in the United States. Several native external larval parasites are common and important but, like the imported species, are handicapped by a lack of alternate hosts. Canadian investigators believe that lack of success in some cases has been due to the small quantity of parasites released, and to their failure to synchronize with the host's seasonal cycle; improved techniques in handling these parasites, together with further study of selected species, may improve their efficiency. The difficulty in North America arises mainly where there are large plantations of pure, even-aged stands, as contrasted with the mixed, uneven-aged forests commonly found in Europe.[14]

PROTECTIVE SUBTILITY

Because the larvae are sheltered within the needle sheaths and buds, the pine shoot moth is difficult to control with insecticides.

[14] A. P. Arthur and J. A. Juillet, "The Introduced Parasites of the European Pine Shoot Moth, *Rhyacionia buoliana* (Schiff.), with a Critical Eval-

Field tests have indicated that the disease pathogen *Bacillus thuringiensis*, used as an insecticidal spray, was not effective against this pest; the reason was not fully understood until a recent interesting discovery was made in Ontario.[15] It was found in laboratory studies that the pine shoot moth larvae spin a web, and as they bore into the bud within the shelter of the web the first bites from the bud scales and green bud tissues are not eaten but incorporated into the web. Although the bacillus was found to be toxic to the moths, they escape much of the infection by not eating the contaminated plant surface.

BIOLOGICAL CONTROL OF THE EUROPEAN CORN BORER

Discovery of the European corn borer in the United States in 1917, and in Canada in 1920, set in motion a major biological control program in both countries. During the twenty-seven years in which the Canadian project was active, twenty species of parasites were imported and a total of nearly 5 million were released in the five eastern provinces from Manitoba to Nova Scotia. Three species became established—*Lydella grisescens, Horogenes punctorius,* and *Sympiesis viridula.* The large-scale importation program in the United States ended in 1938, but small collections of certain species were brought in from Europe during the following ten years. The program in this country has been summarized as follows:

In the course of investigations during the years 1919-1940, on the utilization of natural enemies of the European corn borer (*Pyrausta nubilalis* (Hbn.)) as an aid in its control, over 23 million larvae from Europe and 3 million from the Orient were collected and brought to the United States for rearing their natural enemies contained therein. Other parasites were also collected and forwarded to this country in

uation of Their Usefulness as Control Agents," *The Canadian Entomologist,* April 1961.

[15] P. J. Pointing, 'The Effectiveness of a Microbial Insecticide Against Larvae of the European Pine Shoot Moth, *Rhyacionia buoliana* (Schiffermuller)" *Journal of Insect Pathology,* Dec. 1962.

the cocoon or pupal stages. Of 24 species included in these importations, 22 were sufficiently numerous to permit extensive colonization
over the borer-infested area in this country. The number of parasites
from this source available for colonization exceeded 2½ million. This
supply was augmented by laboratory breeding and by domestic field
collections, the field releases from all sources during this period totaling
almost 6½ million adults.

The adults were released at selected localities over the entire infested
area where the borer was sufficiently abundant to support a parasite
population. Field surveys were maintained at these points to determine
which species became established, and to obtain needed information
on their biology and environmental requirements as an aid in increasing
their distribution within previously colonized areas and in colonizing
areas newly infested by the natural spread of the borer. The species
known to have become permanently established in this country as a
result of these introductions are *Lydella stabulans grisescens* R.D.,
Horogenes punctorius (Roman), *Macrocentrus gifuensis* Ashm.,
Eulophus viridulus[16] Thoms., *Chelonus annulipes* Wesm., and *Phaeogenes nigridens* Wesm.[17]

These established species, representing three families of wasps
and one of flies, are interesting because of their widely differing
habits.

SOME ESTABLISHED IMPORTS[18]

Horogenes punctorius, an ichneumonid wasp, is an internal
parasite of the corn borer larva that produces one or more generations a year, depending on the seasonal cycle of the host. It
overwinters as a young larva in the body cavity of a fully grown
corn borer larva. The adults emerge in late June and in July, and
oviposit on the young host larvae; development from egg to
cocoon requires about 25 to 36 days. In the eastern states, where
two generations occur, parasitization by this wasp has been as
high as 50 per cent, although it has not persisted at this high level.

[16] Also called *Sympiesis viridula.*
[17] W. A. Baker, W. G. Bradley, and C. A. Clark, *Biological Control of
the European Corn Borer in the United States* (Washington: USDA Technical Bulletin No. 983, December 1949).
[18] *Lydella stabulans grisescens,* one of the successful parasites, is discussed under tachinid parasites (Chapter 8).

Ichneumonid wasps (females), parasites of the European corn borer: *left, Horogenes punctorius*, an internal parasite of the host larvae; *right, Phaeogenes nigridens*, which attacks pupal stage of the host. (*USDA*)

Phaeogenes nigridens, another ichneumonid, is common as a parasite of the corn borer in Europe and is especially abundant in Italy. It is an internal parasite of the host pupae, and overwinters as an adult female in sheltered areas. Its seasonal cycle varies considerably in different localities; there may be one or two generations, and in some areas even a third or fourth on an alternate host. The adult female attacks the host pupae as soon as they are sufficiently developed. She enters the tunnel made by the borer, chews a hole in the cocoon, and stings the pupa. Development from egg to pupa requires about three weeks, pupation taking place in the pupal shell of the host. The wasp has a low reproductive capacity and total parasitization has been generally low.

Sympiesis viridula (Eulophidae) is a gregarious external parasite of the corn borer larvae. The female stings and completely paralyzes the larva before oviposition; eggs are placed haphazardly on the host. The number of individuals developing on one host larva averages twenty-eight in the summer and about three times that number in the overwintering colonies. Once their development has begun, they will consume the host in four or five days. There are several generations in a year and the sex ratio is two females to one male. The species became widespread in Ohio, Míchigan, and Iowa, sometimes parasitizing 15 per cent of field populations of the corn borer.

Macrocentrus gifuensis is a braconid wasp common in Europe, where the parasitization of the corn borer may be as high as 40 per cent in some areas; it is also important in Japan and Korea. This wasp is of special interest in that it reproduces by the method known as polyembrony—the division of one egg several or even many times to produce new individuals. Its seasonal cycle is synchronized with that of the host, and there may be from one to three generations each year, depending on the area. The adults emerge in June or July, and the females deposit their eggs in the young larvae of the corn borer. Each insertion of the ovipositor releases one tiny egg into the body cavity; there may be one or several insertions in a single larvae. After the complex process of division, ten or more larvae develop from each single egg; these feed and pass through the same four stages of development as any other braconid. The parasite larvae emerge from the larvae of the host after their third molt and complete their feeding externally within a day or even a few hours. Each larva then spins its own cocoon, although these are bound together in a mass in the host's tunnel. The parasites overwinter as embryos in the body cavity of a full-grown host larva; in April their embryonic development is completed and the individual larvae appear. As many as forty adult parasites may emerge from a single host, but the average is about twenty-one—originating either from a single egg or from several. Generally there is not enough food for so many parasites, and cannibalism takes care of the excess. A colony may be composed of one or both sexes. With each female capable of producing two or three hundred eggs, and with an average of ten progeny per egg, it is plain that the reproductive capacity of this parasite is very high. It has been the dominant species in southeastern Massachusetts, where parasitization in some areas is as high as 25 per cent.

RESULTS OF THE PROGRAM

C. P. Clausen's estimate of the program for biological control of the European corn borer is as follows:

The extensive federal-state cooperative program initiated in 1943 and covering mainly the north central states has permitted much more intensive colonization and recovery studies than has previously been possible. The entire biological control program, which has now been under way for more than 30 years, shows much more promise than was thought possible 15 years ago. The figures for field parasitization, especially in the north central states, indicate the possibility of substantial results in control of the pest. Definite decline in the infestations in several areas appears to be correlated directly with the establishment and increase of introduced species.[19]

NATURAL CONTROL OF THE CORN BORER

Twenty-nine native species of insects are known to parasitize the corn borer, but they are not sufficiently numerous to control it. Mass rearing of *Trichogramma minutum,* an egg parasite of the corn borer and of many other insects, for release when first and second generation borer eggs were available, was tried but did not meet with much success. Parasitism in the immediate vicinity of the releases was as high as 30 per cent, but the parasite did not spread beyond one hundred feet of the release points.

No predators of the corn borer have been imported, but insect predators are an important factor in control. Studies made in 1938 near Toledo, Ohio showed that 17.8 per cent of the borer eggs laid on corn were destroyed by insect predators; in 1939 the figure was 11 per cent. The predator largely responsible for egg predation in this area was the lady beetle *Ceratomegilla fuscilabris,* which appears early in the season and destroys 50 per cent or more of the eggs. This same lady beetle is reported to feed on borer eggs in New Jersey also. *Hippodamia convergens* and *H. tredecimpunctata* (the thirteen-spotted lady beetle) attack the eggs during the

[19] C. P. Clausen, *Biological Control of Insect Pests in the Continental U. S.* (Washington: USDA Technical Bulletin No. 1139, June 1956).

later period of the host's egg deposition. Both adults and larvae of the lady beetles attack borer eggs and also small borer larvae. Red spiders and lacewings have likewise been observed to attack borer eggs.

Birds remove large numbers of corn borer larvae and egg masses from some fields. The most active are the red-winged blackbird and the downy woodpecker. In 1933 an extensive study of twenty fields, comprising 38 square miles, in Indiana showed that the average borer reduction by birds was 30 per cent. (Stalks showing bird pecks were the basis for this figure.) A similar study in Ohio put the general average of corn borer reduction by birds at 15 per cent. Rodents probably account for some reduction also.

DISEASES OF THE CORN BORER

Baker *et al.*, in their summary of the biological control project for the corn borer, write that "*Beauveria bassiana* is the only disease organism that has been observed in the United States to kill the corn borer in the field, and then only under circumstances directly traceable to artifically imposed conditions." This fungus disease came with a shipment of parasites from Manchuria; tests showed it to be effective in proportion to the concentration of spores in the spray or dust application, but the difficulty of producing the material appeared to make it impracticable.

Field tests made in 1929 and 1930 by Metalnikov and others in Yugoslavia showed the disease organism *Bacillus thuringiensis* to be very effective against the corn borer. Similar results were obtained by other investigators in Hungary. E. A. Steinhaus has commented:

If we are to judge from the published accounts of these investigations, certain bacteria are among the most effective agents known for controlling the corn borer. For some reason, which the writer is unable to ascertain with certainty, these successful reports cease shortly after 1930, and one is left in the dark as to why the bacterial method of control did not blossom into general use.[20]

[20] E. A. Steinhaus, *Principles of Insect Pathology* (New York: McGraw-Hill Book Co., 1949).

It was first established in 1951 that the corn borer is subject to a disease caused by the organism *Glugea pyraustae*. In a study of the disease begun by the Illinois Natural History Survey, investigations made in twenty-three counties of the state between 1954 and 1957 showed that 52 per cent of the corn borer larvae entering hibernation in the fall, and 19 per cent of the population surviving in the spring, were infected with the pathogen. The study also showed that the infected borers were more sensitive to extremes of heat and cold than those not infected; of those that perished from the rigors of winter, 91 per cent were infected with the disease.[21] Studies by J. P. Kramer have also shown that the females transmit the pathogen (via the egg) to no less than half their offspring, and that only 14 per cent of those congenitally infected reach maturity. The disease also reduces egg production, often to zero. From this it appears that *Glugea [Perezia] pyraustae* is an important factor in suppressing corn borer populations.[22]

[21] J. P. Kramer, "Observations on the Seasonal Incidence of Microsporidiosis in European Corn Borer Populations in Illinois," *Entomophaga* 4, 1 (1959).

[22] J. P. Kramer, "Some Relationships between *Perezia pyraustae* Paillot (Sporozoa, Nosematidae) and *Pyrausta nubilalis* (Hubner) (Lepidoptera, Pryalidae), *Journal of Insect Pathology*, May 1959. The microorganism is now called *Glugea pyraustae*, and the corn borer is now referred to as *Ostrinia nubilalis*.

CHALCID AND TACHINID PARASITES

8

The word "chalcid" refers to a large group of Hymenoptera,
the super family Chalcidoidea, which consists of many families
and many thousands of species. Most of these insects are very
small, and many are tiny—not more than 1/32 inch long. Many
of them are black with a metallic sheen; others, the "golden chalcids," are yellow. The great majority of the chalcids are parasites
or hyperparasites, and as a group they are even more important
than the ichneumonid and braconid wasps in the natural control
of insect pests and in their application to biological control. Egg,
larval, and pupal forms of insect pests are attacked; feeding of the
parasite larva is usually from within the host, although some feed
on it externally. Most chalcids do not construct a cocoon; they
usually pupate close to the remains of the host.

The Lepidoptera (moths and butterflies), Homoptera (scales,
mealybugs, aphids, and so on), and some Diptera (flies) and
Coleoptera (beetles), are the preferred hosts. That the Coccidae
(scales and mealybugs) are more severely attacked than any
other family of insects is largely due to the chalcids—especially
those of the genera *Aphytis, Coccophagus, Aspidiotiphagus,*

192

Prospaltella, and *Aphycus.* The adult chalcids feed on plant exudates and honeydew secretions by their hosts; many also feed directly on body fluids exuded from the ovipositor puncture wound, or by constructing a feeding tube. Some species are "arrhenotokous" in their reproductive behavior—that is, the females are produced biparentally (from fertilized eggs) and the males by parthenogenesis, or uniparentally (from unfertilized eggs). The chalcids include two families of minute wasps, the Mymaridae and Trichogrammatidae, that are exclusively egg parasites—the latter of which are used extensively in biological control.

Paul DeBach declares that the results achieved in biological control of coccids exceeds that of any other group of insects, and that 40 per cent of the successful cases of biological control have been with coccids. He points out that successful biological control of these pests has been achieved with at least thirty-eight species in fifty different countries; he rates nine of these instances as "complete" control, sixteen as "substantial" control, and the remainder as "partial." Parasites alone were responsible in twenty-three of the cases, and predators alone in twelve others. He gives as reasons for this success the ease with which these pests spread, and the consequent demand for attention; the economic value of the crop involved; the difficulty of control with chemicals; and the amenability of the pests to biological control.[1]

APHYTIS AND THE PURPLE SCALE

One of the most serious and universal pests of citrus is the purple scale (*Lepidosaphes beckii*). It is believed to have come into the United States on lemons shipped from Bermuda to Florida in 1857, and to have been transferred from there to California on nursery stock. It thrives where there are moderate temperatures and fairly high humidity, such as characterize the coastal region

[1] Paul DeBach, "Biological Control of Scale and Mealybugs (Coccidae)," in *Handbook on Biological Control of Plant Pests* (Brooklyn Botanic Garden, 1960).

of southern California. According to DeBach and John Landi, the purple scale has been the only hindrance to "general biological control" of orange pests in the coastal region of southern California. Their studies have indicated that

satisfactory biological control of most orange-tree pests other than purple scale might be obtained in coastal areas, where a complex of natural enemies capable of controlling them generally occurs unless upset by unusually adverse climatic or cultural conditions. Although purple scale had been attacked in California for many years by several native or accidentally introduced enemies, none of these gave evidence during our earlier studies of being capable of restricting the scale to satisfactorily low population levels.[2]

It appeared to these investigators that the best solution to the problem would be an "integrated" or "modified" control program, with some chemical spraying done in such a way, and only to the extent, that predators and parasites were preserved and remained capable of holding other potential pests to noneconomic levels. The balancing factor on the biological side of the equation, which permits a very substantial reduction of spraying, is the parasite *Aphytis lepidosaphes*. The department of biological control of the Citrus Experiment Station at Riverside, California received shipments of this parasite from China and Formosa in 1924 and 1925 and began mass breeding of the wasp at the Riverside insectary.

MASS PRODUCTION

Lemons or seed potatoes are used as the host plant for growing the scale. (Citrus melons or banana squash are also satisfactory.) The lemons are placed in wire trays and held in cold storage until needed. When ready for scale infestation, the trays are transferred to the scale development room, where they are placed on racks. Temperature and humidity are carefully controlled. Infestation may be achieved by direct contact with lemons having crawler-producing mother-scale, or by spreading egg-producing scales

[2] Paul DeBach and John Landi, "The Introduced Purple Scale Parasite, *Aphytis lepidosaphes* Compere, and a Method of Integrating Chemical with Biological Control," *Hilgardia* Dec. 1961.

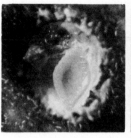
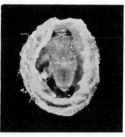

Chalcid wasp, *Aphytis proclia* (*diaspidis*), a parasite of latania scale: *left*, adult wasp; *center*, larva of parasite feeding on ventral side of female scale's body (the scale's armor has been removed); *right*, pupa of parasite under female scale armor (the scale has been turned over). (*Roy J. Pence*)

scraped from old host lemons. In the insectary about two months are needed for a generation of scales to develop on lemons. When the scales have reached the development stage preferred by the parasites for oviposition, they are transferred to sleeve-cages in parasite culture rooms. As soon as the trays on the bottom of the cages have produced their complement of parasites, they are removed and the others are moved down to make room for the new one at the top. The glass top of the cage is daily streaked with honey, which serves as food for the newly emerged parasites. These are periodically drawn off by suction (aspirated) from the upper glass surface and doled out in waxed cardboard cartons streaked with honey, for shipment and distribution in the field.

Aphytis lepidosaphes is a solitary or gregarious external parasite with a "specific" host preference—namely for the purple scale. It is arrhenotokous: females are produced from fertilized eggs, males from unfertilized eggs of either a virgin or a mated female. Mating occurs soon after emerging, and females normally mate only once. They feed on the body juices of the host through a specially constructed feeding tube, thus obtaining the protein they require for sustaining egg production; the scale is usually drained dry, and host mortality from this cause is quite high. Although often only one egg is placed on a host, this parasite is gregarious. In California an average of about two parasites de-

velop on one scale, though the number may reach five or six; in
Florida more than 50 per cent are solitary. Under laboratory conditions females average about 32 eggs in a life span of seventeen
days. Under field conditions in California about 80 per cent of
the progeny are females, whereas in Florida only about 60 per
cent are females. Under laboratory conditions the development
from egg through the pupal stages takes about three weeks.
Adults emerge from the scale after one has chewed a hole
through the covering; the rest of the colony exit through the same
hole.

COLONIZATIONS

Colonizations of *Aphytis lepidosaphes* began in 1949, and by
1953 over 580,000 parasites had been distributed. The parasite
established itself quickly and has dispersed over the entire coastal
area. Shipments from Riverside to other states and countries have
been very productive. The parasite quickly brought the scale
under control in Texas and Mexico, and is established in Chile.
According to a report from Florida,

At the present time purple scale infestations are being held at extremely
low levels by this parasite [so] that effective biological control of
purple scale and Florida red scale[3] exists in Florida citrus groves. At
the present time, parasites are maintaining low non-economic scale
populations in unsprayed groves and should continue to do so unless
this biological balance is disturbed by extremes of temperature or
moisture.[4]

Sulphur used as a miticide and fungicide is the most disturbing
element.

INTEGRATED CONTROL

To determine the best method of integrating chemical with
biological control for purple scale in California, a nine-year study

[3] *Chrysomphalus aonidum.*
[4] M. H. Muma and D. W. Clancy, "Parasitism of Purple Scale and Florida
Red Scale in Flordia Citrus Groves," *Proceedings*, Florida State Horticultural Society, Oct. 31–Nov. 2, 1961.

was conducted, using strip oil treatments. By treating strips rather than the whole orchard at one time, reservoirs are set aside for the conservation of beneficial insects, which can continue to control other potential pests. In the first trials, a six-month alternate strip treatment was used. Test plots of ten acres were divided into areas of six rows each, and the first pair of rows in each area were treated; six months later the second pair of rows were treated, and so on, so that each row was treated once every eighteen months. The results were very successful, and indicated that the treatments might be extended with equally satisfactory results. In the second trials a twelve-month alternate strip treatment was used, which meant that every other pair of rows was treated each year. Each year the rows not treated the year before received treatment, so that each row received a treatment once every two years. Under this system, the cost of pest control was reduced to less than half the cost of the usual treatment and "control was as good or better than usually obtained."

INTEGRATED CONTROL OF PURPLE SCALE

It was concluded from these trials, and from studies of other plots during this period (1949 to 1959), that the parasite *Aphytis lepidosaphes* can be helpful in the oil spray control of the purple scale, and will give temporary biological control under favorable conditions, although it requires "judicious integration" with chemicals for "consistent and reliable control." The case for natural and biological controls in this area is nevertheless an impressive one. According to DeBach and Landi, it has been shown that "in citrus groves in Orange County which had received no insecticidal applications for from three to ten or more years, satisfactory natural control of most pests usually resulted." These investigators cite the following pests as having lost economic status in this area through biological control:

CITRUS RED MITE	*Panonychus citri*	Using predators
CALIFORNIA RED SCALE	*Aonidiella aurantii*	Using parasites: *Aphytis chrysomphali, Aphytis lingnanensis*

Good natural control exists for the following:

LONG-TAILED MEALYBUG	*Pseudococcus adonidum*
CITROPHILUS MEALYBUG	*Pseudococcus gahani*
CITRUS MEALYBUG	*Pseudococcus citri*
BLACK SCALE	*Saissetia oleae*
COTTONY CUSHION SCALE	*Icerya purchasi*
BROWN SOFT SCALE	*Coccus hesperidum*
APHIDS	*Toxoptera aurantii*
	Aphis spiraecola
ORANGEWORMS	*Pyroderces rileyi*
	Argyrotaenia citrana
	Holcocera iceryaeella

It is pointed out that control of the Argentine ant (*Iridomyrmex humilis*) and the minimizing of dust deposits on the trees are necessary for maximum efficiency of beneficial species, especially the parasites, in untreated groves.

COMPERIELLA AND THE YELLOW SCALE

Red scale (*Aonidiella aurantii*) and yellow scale (*Aonidiella citrina*) have long been among the most destructive pests of citrus. For quite some time these two scales were considered to be simply two strains of the same species. According to Harold Compere, the yellow scale "was present in the San Gabriel district of southern California as early as 1872" and red scale was believed to have been brought in around 1877, probably from Australia on citrus stock.[5] The search for the natural enemies of these pests began in 1891, when the state of California sent Albert Koebele (the collector famed for his discovery of the vedalia lady bettle) to Australia. The first introductions were mostly of predators from Australia, including the lady beetles *Orcus chalybeus* and *Lindorus lophantae*, which later became established. Later importations came from China, India, South Africa, and South America. In all, about thirty species of predators and parasites

[5] Harold Compere, "The Red Scale and Its Insect Enemies," *Hilgardia*, Nov. 1961. This is an account of the biological control of the California red scale from 1879 to 1948, and of the political factors that were sometimes involved, as well as of the early explorations for natural enemies of insect pests.

have been imported. Four of these became established—*Comperiella bifasciata, Habrolepis rouxi, Aphytis lingnanensis,* and *Prospaltella perniciosi.* The most important of these were *C. bifasciata* on yellow scale and *A. lingnanensis* on red scale.

C. bifasciata is a solitary internal parasite of yellow scale, whose attacks are mostly on the female. The female parasite will deposit as many as 135 eggs during her active life. The development from egg to adult may require anywhere from twenty to forty days, depending on the stage of the host attacked. The female parasite feeds on the host by puncturing the scale, but her eggs are seldom deposited with the same puncture. Females of *C. bifasciata* also have the habit of "mutilating" host scales—destroying them by extensive thrusts and probings of the ovipositor, without either feeding or ovipositing. This considerably increases the mortality of the scales. The parasite has been able to control the yellow scale in a substantial part of the citrus-growing areas of California.

THE GOLDEN CHALCIDS AND THE RED SCALE

Aphytis chrysomphali, an effective parasite of the red scale, is believed to have been accidentally introduced into California along with the scale itself. In the early 1900's it was reared in southern California and made available to growers for colonization. These early efforts were not very effective and red scale continued to be a serious pest. Mass production techniques were worked out at the Riverside insectary of the Citrus Experiment Station, and in the spring of 1950 these parasites of the red scale were available in commercial quantities. It was estimated at the time that an insectary employing two men and operating at a cost of $50 a day could produce 100,000 to 500,000 parasites per day.[6]

Aphytis lingnanensis and *A. chrysomphali* are quite similar in habits to *A. lepidosaphes,* the parasite of the purple scale. *A. chrysomphali* is uniparental, however, and does not produce males.

[6] Stanley F. Flanders, "Mass Culture of California Red Scale and Its Golden Chalcid Parasites," *Hilgardia,* May 1951.

In spite of this considerable advantage, A. *lingnanensis* is superior to A. *chrysomphali* because it has a shorter life cycle and produces more eggs; it also destroys more eggs in feeding on the host. *Aphytis chrysomphali,* like the yellow scale parasite C. *bifasciata,* has the habit of "mutilating" host scales. It does not restrict this activity to the host, moreover, but sometimes attacks immature larvae and pupae of the parasite itself.

In 1948 studies were begun to evaluate the enemies operating against the red scale in southern California.[7] Unsprayed orchards were selected for study to eliminate the factor of insecticides. It soon became apparent that where the red scale infestations were light, the fact was due almost entirely to the golden chalcid A. *chrysomphali.* Where control was not maintained because of un-favorable physical factors, it was thought that periodic coloniza-tions might restore the balance and increase the efficiency of the parasites. It appeared that the key to successful execution of this plan was *Aphytis lingnanensis* because of its superiority to A. *chrysomphali* for mass culture and in the field.

Preliminary studies indicated that for certain groves 400,000 *Aphytis lingnanensis* per acre (or 4,000 female parasites per tree) each year, released at regular intervals from March to November, would provide enough stock to overcome any adverse conditions that might arise. This prescription was for the intermediate zone between the coastal areas—where natural control existed without colonizations—and the interior valleys, where biological control is difficult to achieve because of climatic and other factors. It was reasoned that if these parasites could be provided and colonized for not more than $40 per acre, the method could compete with chemical methods on a purely economic basis.

ECONOMICS OF PARASITE PRODUCTION

To achieve the desired efficiency required the development of new parasite production techniques. The innovations included the use of banana squash as a host plant for scale crawler production;

[7] Paul DeBach and Ernest B. White, *Commercial Mass Culture of the California Red Scale Parasite* Aphytis lingnanensis (Berkeley: California Agricultural Experiment Station Bulletin 770, March 1960).

the use of the more efficient oleander scale (*Aspidiotus hederae*) as parasite host (it reproduces uniparentally, without males; the development of new oviposition or "sting" chambers (for better control), and the shadow line method of collecting the photo-trophic crawlers (scale crawlers are attracted toward a light and collect themselves at the shadow line); the utilization of the same parasites for both "sting" and field colonization (newly emerged parasites oviposit one day in the insectary and are collected for colonization); the use of the same scales for production of crawlers and parasites (maintaining "mother" stocks of parasites and scales thus becomes unnecessary).

With the new production technique it was estimated that a two-man insectary serving 441 acres could be operated for about $17,000 a year, or $38 an acre, and that a three-man insectary serving 735 acres could be operated for about $23,800 a year, or $32 an acre. A two-man insectary can produce over 176,000,000 parasites per year. The figures include cost of distribution, which would be carried out by the same personnel. An easy and efficient method of releasing the parasites was worked out by dividing the grove into nine-tree blocks, in the central trees of which 4,000 parasites were released each month from March to November. Since no tree is more than one tree removed from the central tree where the parasites are released, they are dispersed equally to all trees. In this way each tree gets 4,000 parasites per year; with 100 trees to the acre, each acre gets 400,000 parasites per year—which was the stated objective.

BIOLOGICAL CONTROL OF THE RED SCALE

One of the more recent importations against the red scale is a parasite from India and Pakistan, *Aphytis melinus,* that was brought to California in 1956 and 1957. Nearly three million parasites of this species were released from 1958 to 1960. It is believed that this parasite will do better in the interior citrus-growing areas where the other parasites are quite vulnerable to temperature extremes and to dust. A still later arrival, *Aphytis coheni,* was imported from Israel in 1960.

It is interesting to note that surveys conducted in southern California in 1962 showed the red scale at its lowest levels in Orange County since 1900.[8] The scale is considered to be under control in most of San Diego County; infestations here and there are attributed to ants, road dust, and DDT. The cost of red scale treatments in Los Angeles County declined 50 per cent from 1958 to 1961. In many areas chemical treatments have been eliminated or reduced to applications once every one or two years. The story is the same throughout the coastal and "intermediate" areas, but the scale is still a serious pest in the interior Imperial Valley.

APHYCUS AND THE BLACK SCALE

Black scale (*Saissetia oleae*), like the purple and red species, ranks as a major pest of citrus, and for many years the search for its enemies was worldwide. More than seventy species of chalcids have been reared from this scale, and some thirty species of parasites and predators have been imported and colonized in this country. The lady beetles and egg predators imported for this purpose have already been discussed. Of the eight species of parasites established, the most important are *Aphycus helvolus* and *Aphycus lounsburyi*.

A. *helvolus* is a solitary internal parasite that attacks the early nymph stages of the black scale. In ovipositing the female thrusts the egg into the side of the scale, and the larva feeds on the body fluids. The parasite develops from egg to adult in thirteen days at summer temperatures. Eight or more generations develop in the so-called "even hatch" areas of the scale, and two for each of the host generations in the "uneven hatch" areas. A. *lounsburyi* is a solitary or gregarious internal parasite of the older black scale. The female thrusts the egg through the soft underside of the scale. The length of the cycle from egg to adult is sixteen days, and single generations are produced each year.

[8] P. H. DeBach, J. Landi, and E. B. White "Parasites are Controlling Red Scale in Southern California Citrus," *California Agriculture,* Dec. 1962.

A. *helvolus* was brought to California from South Africa in 1937, and an extensive program of colonization was carried on for several years. A. *lounsburyi* was imported from Australia and first liberated in 1919; highly effective in the beginning, it was later handicapped by attack from a hyperparasite. A. *helvolus* has been the most important factor in the control of the black scale in California and has eliminated the need for spraying in the coastal and other regions of milder climate.

COCCOPHAGUS AND THE CITROPHILUS MEALY-BUG

The citrophilus mealybug (*Pseudococcus gahani*) first attracted attention in California in 1913 and soon became a serious pest. The early infestations were kept under control by yearly mass releases of the lady beetle *Cryptolaemus montrouzieri,* which had been imported to control the citrus mealybug. A search in Australia for other natural enemies resulted in the importation of two parasites, *Coccophagus gurneyi* and *Tetracnemus pretiosus,* and a predaceous fly. The adults of *Coccophagus gurneyi* feed on honeydew excreted by the host, but unlike many other chalcids they have not been known to feed on the host from the ovipuncture wound. The female lays upwards of 125 eggs and attacks any stage of the host. Although she makes the usual careful examination of the host, she is not able to detect whether the mealybug is already parasitized or not. The ovipositor is inserted to its full length and partially withdrawn in a probing motion—for the very definite reason that if it finds a larva of the other parasite, *Tetracnemus pretiosus,* already in the host, the egg will be deposited in or on the latter and the larva will develop as a hyperparasite. The sex of *Coccophagus* in this case will be male, since the males are produced only as hyperparasites. The male *Coccophagus* may develop as either an internal or an external parasite of the first occupant of the mealybug. Where a male and female egg of *Coccophagus* are deposited in the same host, conditions are not favorable for the male to hatch until the female has consumed the contents of the host. When the male hatches, he must feed on the host contents at second hand—by consuming the female. As Flanders points out, this is not wasteful of the species, but rather the opposite; since females predominate at low host densities, the sacrifice of the female serves to perpetuate the species by sustaining the male.[9] Eggs containing females hatch in three or four days; the embryonic development of the male is completed in three days, but hatching does not take place until the primary parasite has consumed the body fluids of the host. The length of the cycle from egg to adult varies from twenty-four to forty-three days, depending on the temperature.

The female of *Tetracnemus pretiosus*, a solitary internal parasite, deposits her eggs in the early nymph stage of the mealybug, sometimes just after the larvae have hatched. During incubation the parasite egg increases in size, and nearly half the development of the first larval stage is completed within the egg shell. The cycle from egg to adult is completed in about four weeks at summer temperatures. *T. pretiosus* is a very effective parasite of the citrophilus mealybug, and is capable of controlling the pest without assistance; it is dominated by *C. gurneyi*, however, because of the latter's habit of producing hyperparasitic males.

Both parasites spread rapidly after the releases beginning in 1928, and in two years brought about complete control of the citrophilus mealybug in California. According to Clausen, this biological control project was "in completeness and consistency" equal to that of the cottony cushion scale by the vedalia lady beetle. A resurgence of the citrophilus mealybug has not thus far followed the advent of the chlorinated hydrocarbon insecticides, as it did in the case of the cottony cushion scale.

APHELINUS AND THE WOOLLY APPLE APHID

The woolly apple aphid (*Eriosoma lanigerum*) is a native of northeastern North America, as is its parasite *Aphelinus mali*. With

[9] Stanley E. Flanders, "The Parasitic Hymenoptera: Specialists in Population Regulation," *The Canadian Entomologist,* November, 1962.

the spread of apple culture to the Pacific northwest the pest went along, but not the parasite. A troublesome fungus disease, the perennial apple canker, is usually associated with the aphid, since it develops only on tissues attacked by it; thus large colonies of aphids developing around pruning cuts and bark wounds induce the infection. The woolly apple aphid has a complicated life cycle. The overwintering eggs are deposited on an elm or other secondary host plant; two generations usually develop here. The third generation is winged and migrates to the apple tree, where three or more generations develop; from there winged forms migrate in the fall to the overwintering host plant, where they deposit their eggs and the cycle is repeated.

Aphelinus mali is an internal parasite of immature and mature forms of the woolly apple aphid. The female deposits one or more eggs in the abdomen of the aphid, but only one of these will develop to maturity; she is capable of laying about 100 eggs. When an aphid dies a liquid oozes from the body and hardens, gluing it to the twig; the aphid shells then becomes black and mummified. After pupation has been completed, the adult parasite cuts an escape hole in the hardened shell and emerges. The life cycle of this wasp requires about thirty days to complete; it overwinters as a mature larva in one of the black, mummified aphid shells. Large masses of aphid shells with holes in the tops, clustered about a twig, show the effectiveness of these parasites.

A. mali was introduced with great success in to the Hood Valley in Oregon in 1929 and into the Wenatchee and Yakima areas of Washington in 1930. The woolly apple aphid was reduced to noneconomic levels in a short time, and the perennial apple canker disappeared. According to Clausen, this was the situation until the late 1940's, when the widespread use of DDT and other chlorinated hydrocarbons drastically reduced the parasite populations, and brought on a resurgence of both aphids and perennial canker. The parasite was first introduced into British Columbia from Ontario in 1921. Success in the northwest region of the United States and Canada led to the introduction of A.

Eggs of pentatomid bug on live oak. The eggs have been parasitized by a chalcid wasp. (*E. S. Ross*)

mali into the apple orchards of fifty different countries, and its establishment in forty of them.

SOME EGG PARASITES

Two families of chalcid wasps, Mymaridae and Trichogrammatidae, are strictly egg parasites and include some of the most diminutive of insects; one of the mymarids (*Alaptus magnanimus*), which is only .21 mm. long, is the smallest insect known. Short-lived as adults, mymarids oviposit immediately after emerging, laying one egg per host in the majority of species. Where the parasitized host egg is large, several may develop in a single egg. The eggs usually hatch very soon after being deposited in the host egg, and the tiny larvae move freely about through its contents. Several generations a season are usual, and overwintering takes place in the host egg. The wasps' diminutiveness has its advantages; for one, the adults are able to search out eggs hidden in narrow crevices. Some species even enter the water to

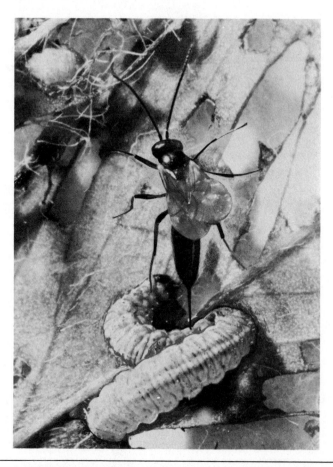

Adult *Bathyplectes curculionis*, a chalcid wasp, ovipositing in an alfalfa weevil larva. (*USDA*)

attack aquatic insects. *Polynema saga*, a parasite of leafhoppers, is found in continental United States as well as Hawaii. *Patasson nitens*, a native of Australia and a parasite of the eucalyptus weevil (*Gonipterus scutellatus*), was introduced into New Zealand, South Africa, and Madagascar with good results. A native of New Zealand, *Anagrus armatus*, was successfully introduced into Tasmania for control of the apple leafhopper (*Typhlocyba froggatti*). Between 1925 and 1928 *Mymar pratensis* was imported from Italy and became established in Utah as a parasite of the alfalfa weevil (*Hypera postica*). It is more commonly found as a parasite of the cloverleaf weevil, however, and the alfalfa weevil is believed to be an alternate host only. The wasp is a solitary parasite of alfalfa weevil eggs, but two individuals usually develop in those of the clover weevil.[10]

The Trichogrammatidae, the best known of all egg parasites, prey upon nearly every kind of insect egg, and are known to attack over two hundred species of insects. More than a hundred species of the parasite have been identified, those in the genus *Trichogramma* being the most familiar. It is a telltale sign of parasitization by Trichogrammitidae when the eggs turn black—though the same effect is produced by a few species of Scelionidae, another important family of egg parasites. *Trichogramma minutum* is the most noted of all egg parasites because of its extensive use in biological control. The numbers of the eggs deposited in the host egg and of the resulting progeny depend on the size of the egg parasitized, and may vary from one to fifty or more. The female in some instances may oviposit from twenty to twenty-five eggs at a time. As soon as the tiny larvae hatch they begin moving about in the host egg; development of the embryo in the host egg stops immediately. The cycle from egg to adult varies with temperature and moisture, and may require anywhere from seven to seventy-five days. The number of generations in a season varies considerably—from thirteen in some eastern states to fifty or more under optimum conditions. *T. minutum* overwinters as a larva in the host egg and mates very soon after emerging. It can reproduce by parthenogenesis, in which event the progeny are all males. Females normally outnumber males, the ratio depending on the amount of food available.

[10] A more successful importation from Italy against the alfalfa weevil has been the ichneumonid *Bathyplectes curculionis*, a solitary internal parasite of alfalfa weevil larvae. It has become an important factor in controlling this pest in Utah and the adjoining states, as well as parts of California, but early cuttings reduce its effectiveness. It is especially destructive to the weevil at the beginning of the season, when it often kills 80 or 90 per cent of the pest larvae.

Trichogramma minutum attacks the eggs of many insect pests and in many instances is an important factor in natural control, though it varies greatly in abundance. It is present in almost every cornfield, and "in some seasons in southeastern United States fully 90 per cent of the earworm (*Heliothis zea*) eggs fail to hatch because of the work of this insect."[11] It is not, however, so important in other regions. *T. minutum* is also a common parasite of the spruce budworm (*Choristoneura fumiferana*) and is usually found where there are outbreaks of this forest pest, with parasitism varying from 1 to 70 per cent. The heaviest budworm parasitism was reported in 1911, when egg collections in Quebec showed a rate of 43 per cent, those in Ontario showed 76 per cent, and those in British Columbia 77 per cent! It is believed that this wasp's effectiveness as a parasite of the spruce budworm is limited by the availability of alternate hosts and to some extent by multiple parasitism; adult wasps emerging from budworm eggs were estimated to be 2.1 per budworm egg in one area and 3.7 in another.[12]

Efficient mass production techniques for this parasite have been worked out, using the Angoumois grain moth as host insect. In several parts of the West Indies and South America, the use of *T. minutum* in biological control of the sugar cane borer (*Diatraea saccharalis*) has been highly successful. Early spring releases of from five to ten thousand parasites per acre have been effective in preventing severe damage by the pest. Attempts to control the sugar cane borer in Louisiana have been less successful, possibly owing to differences in cultural practices. In the United States the cane is cut at the end of each season, whereas in the tropics it is allowed to grow for from eighteen to twenty-four months before harvesting. Comment has already been made on the at-

[11] R. A. Blanchard and W. A. Douglas, *The Corn Earworm as an Enemy of Field Corn in the Eastern States* (Washington: USDA, Farmers' Bulletin No. 1651, Nov. 1953).

[12] C. A. Miller, "Parasites and the Spruce Budworm," in *The Dynamics of Epidemic Spruce Budworm Populations*, R. F. Morris, ed. (Memoirs of the Entomological Society of Canada, No. 31, 1963).

tempts to control the codling moth, oriental fruit moth, and European corn borer with *T. minutum.* From 1928 to 1933 large numbers of several species of *Trichogramma,* ranging from 250,000 to 10 million per year, were released against the oriental fruit moth in the Niagara peninsula of Ontario. These included large numbers of *T. evanescens,* the original stock of which was secured from the southern United States. The wasps were very effective following release—although they did not persist—and were used for a time as part of the control program. In spite of the rather unimpressive showing in these records, *Trichogramma* parasites are being produced today in great numbers for biological control in the United States as well as in Europe, South America, and the U.S.S.R. According to Theodore W. Fisher, large numbers of these parasites are purchased by cotton growers in the south-western United States for control of the cotton bollworm (*Heliothis* spp.).[13] It is believed that control of the pest in this region with the release of *Trichogramma* wasps may be due in part to the resurgence of native parasites and predators resulting from a curtailment of insecticides. The extensive use of this parasite in the U.S.S.R. was reported by a group sent there by the U.S. Department of Agriculture in 1959 to study the work being done in biological control of insect pests. They commented as follows:

In the Ukraine and elsewhere parasitic wasps of the genus *Trichogramma* are used against three important lepidopterous pests, as well as against some of less importance. *Trichogramma* is widely used against the cutworm *Agrotis segetum* and less extensively against *Mamestra (Barathra) brassicae* and *Pyrausta nubilalis* (corn borer). It is said that 68 per cent of *Agrotis* eggs and between 90 and 100 per cent of *Mamestra* (cabbage moth) eggs are parasitized.

The Biological Control Laboratory at Belaya Tserkov, Ukrainian S.S.R., coordinates the work of *Trichogramma* production, which is accomplished in the laboratory with eggs of grain moths (*Sitotroga*) as hosts, and distributes both *Trichogramma* and *Sitotroga* to subordinate laboratories and collective farms, where parasites are produced in the desired numbers each season. This laboratory also trains tech-

[13] Theodore W. Fisher, "What is Biological Control?" in *Handbook of Biological Control of Plant Pests* (Brooklyn Botanic Garden, 1960).

nicians from the collective farms. Production of parasites on the farms is carried out only during the growing season. Release rates of parasites against different pests were given as follows:

PEST	PARASITES (THOUSANDS) PER HECTARE [14]
AGROTIS	15-20
MAMESTRA	30-50
PYRAUSTA	30-50

Cost of parasite production was given as from 2 to 8 rubles[15] per hectare. Releases are made at from 10 to 15 sites per hectare. One release is made when the host begins egg laying. Two releases were found to be no better than one. The extent of biological control practice in the Ukraine can be estimated by the Soviet statement that 300,000 hectares were treated with *Trichogramma* in 1957 to control the three pests listed above.

Three species of *Trichogramma* are used in the Soviet Union, and each is said to be represented by biological strains or races. It was emphasized that for successful control the strain used must be adapted to the environmental conditions in which the pest species occurs.[16]

Some valuable egg parasites are included in other chalcid families. *Ooencyrtus kuwanai* (Encyrtidae), a solitary parasite of gypsy moth eggs (and those of some other moths), overwinters as a fertilized female in the forest litter. It prefers an egg in which the embryo is well advanced; in most cases the egg is actually deposited within the larva (inside the egg). In New England four complete generations develop during the season. The female will deposit an average of 200 eggs. Females normally outnumber males three to one; unmated, they produce only males. The parasite was imported from Japan and was first released in Massachusetts in 1909; by 1927 over 25 million had been reared and released. Field parasitization of 48 per cent has been found in some localities.

Anastatus disparis (Eupelmidae) is another valuable egg parasite of the gypsy moth. Unlike *O. kuwanai*, it prefers its eggs

[14] One hectare equals 2.471 acres.
[15] One ruble is equal to ten cents.
[16] *Entomology in the Soviet Union: Report of a Technical Study Group* (Washington: USDA Agricultural Research Service, June 1961). The group consisted of six entomologists and one chemist.

fresh—before embryonic development has begun. A solitary parasite, the larva is fully grown in two weeks but remains inactive in the host egg until the following spring. It emerges when the new host eggs have been laid. A. *disparis* was first imported from Russia and Japan in 1908. More than 65 million of the species were reared and released in New England up to about 1925, and at one time field parasitization there averaged about 30 per cent. Multiple parasitism of gypsy moth eggs by *O. kuwanai* and *A. disparis* occurs to some extent. When *Anastatus* oviposits in an egg already containing an *Ooencyrtus* egg, its larva develops and the other does not.

The importance of a chalcid egg parasite, *Closterocerus cinctipennis* (Eulophidae), was demonstrated in a study made of the red-headed pine sawfly (*Neodiprion lecontei*) in Illinois and Michigan from 1947 to 1949. It was found to be

one of the most significant biotic factors limiting sawfly populations on the Shawnee National Forest (in southern Illinois) . . . Its importance was initially revealed during prespray surveys conducted in shortleaf pine plantations in 1947 when, as a result of reduced larval hatch in the first generation, 1,900 acres of heavily infested plantations were omitted from a 6,000 acre spray program. Eggs collected on four of the thirteen plantations where this reduced hatch occurred were heavily parasitized by *C. cinctipennis;* parasitization averages 88.7 per cent with a range of 70.3 to 93.1; four of the twenty egg batches were 100 per cent parasitized. . . . During the two and three quarter years the sawfly population was under observation on the roadside pitch pine plantation, 152 egg batches containing 16,161 eggs were laid on five pines. Parasitization averaged 95.2 per cent and reduced the sawfly population to 771 eggs. . . . That severe defoliation did not result is evidence of the critical role of *Closterocerus* in controlling the sawfly population.[17]

Two imported egg parasites—*Holcothorax* sp. (Encyrtidae) and *Phanerotoma flavitestacea* (a braconid)—show considerable promise for biological control of the navel orangeworm (*Para-*

[17] Daniel M. Benjamin, *The Biology and Ecology of the Red-Headed Pine Sawfly* (Washington: USDA Technical Bulletin No. 1118, August 1955).

myelois transitella) on almonds and walnuts in California. Since most of the time the larvae of orangeworms are protected from their enmies by boring into the shells, and their eggs are exposed, the egg parasites have an advantage. *Holcothorax* was imported from Mexico. Each female lays about 60 eggs, but the number is greatly multiplied by polyembryony; for this parasite the number produced by the division of the egg averages about 500, but it may be as many as 1,200! Usually only one egg is oviposited in each host egg; the parasite larvae feed on the larva of the host, which is not killed until it spins a cocoon.

P. flavitestacea, a tiny wasp that is about .18 inch long and orange-yellow in color, was imported from Israel in 1962. It parasitizes the carob pod moth (*Ectomyelois ceratoniae*) in Israel but will attack navel orangeworms as well. The female wasp oviposits an average of about 350 eggs—one to each egg of the orangeworm—and the development of the wasp larva is completed in the larva of its host after the latter spins a cocoon. Techniques for mass production of these parasites are being worked out by the University of California's Division of Biological Control at Berkeley.[18] It is hoped that strategic releases of the egg parasites, supplemented by native enemies of the orangeworm, will provide satisfactory control of the pest.

SOME TACHINID PARASITES

The Tachinidae are by far the most important family of Diptera in their effect on insect pest populations; their contribution to biological control has been very substantial. Though a few are small, these robust, bristly flies are for the most part medium to large in size, and many resemble the common housefly. Strong, swift fliers, they are frequently seen around flowers where the adults feed on nectar and other plant exudates. Some species feed on the honeydew of other insects, and others occasionally feed on body fluids oozing from a wound they have inflicted on the host.

[18] L. E. Caltagirone, K. P. Shea, and G. L. Finney "Parasites to Aid Control of Navel Orangeworm," *California Agriculture*, Jan. 1964.

Yeasts and microorganisms in the various foods they imbibe are believed to have a nutritional role.

Only a few tachinid species have the piercing ovipositor, the egg-laying mechanism characteristic of the Hymenoptera. *Compsilura concinnata*, a parasite of the gypsy moth and other Lepidoptera, has the piercing type of ovipositor, which it uses to thrust living maggots into the caterpillars. The females of many species are provided with the means of incubating their eggs or hatching the larvae before disposition. Like all maggots, the larvae do not have legs, and move about with the aid of spines. Generally the tachinids get their oxygen directly from the atmosphere by means of a respiratory "funnel" connected to an opening in the host's skin or to the trachea, the breathing apparatus of the host. The larva breathes through a pair of openings, the spiracles, at the posterior end of the body. In some species which bore into the host from outside, the "tail" is fixed at the opening, where it becomes covered by a growth of the host's skin; the funnel-like sheath thus formed serves to hold the maggot in place. A similar funnel is formed when contact with the air is made through a tracheal trunk of the host. Such a funnel is a pathological growth of the host tissue in response to the irritation caused by the piercing of the skin or trachea by the parasite.

The majority of tachinids attack the larval stage of the host. However, an unusual adaptation occurs in the case of *Erynnia nitida*, a parasite of the elm leaf beetle, which attacks the larva but completes its development in the adult beetle. A few species attack the adults directly—in some instances while in flight. Some species deposit their eggs on the surface of leaves; the gypsy moth parasite, *Blepharipoda* (*Sturmia*) *scutellata*, is one of these.

One group of large tachinid flies produce larvae armored with protective scales and plates, which they deposit on the leaves of the appropriate plants. The posterior end of the maggot is equipped with a tiny membranous cup which the female fastens securely to the surface of the leaf as she deposits her progeny. At a disturbance of the surface signaling the approach of a potential host, the maggots rear up and wave their heads with a circular motion in expectation of making a contact. At the mere touch of the caterpillar they seize hold of it, releasing their grip on the leaf; once on, they quickly bore into the victim. *Archytas analis,* a widely distributed native parasite of the variegated cutworm (*Peridroma saucia*), belongs to this group.

Some spectacular results have been achieved with tachinids in biological control. The rescue of the sugar cane industry in Hawaii from the sugar cane borer (*Rhabdoscelus obscura*) by importation of the tachinid *Microceromasia sphenophori,* and of the copra industry in Fiji from the moth *Levuana iridescens* by importation of the tachinid *Ptychomyia remota,* are comparable with the control of the cottony cushion scale by the vedalia beetle in California. In a little more than a year the *Levuana* moth was completely suppressed by *P. remota,* a parasite of a closely related moth (*Artona catoxantha*) that had been brought from Malaya to Fiji in 1925.

One of the most valuable native parasites is the tachinid *Winthemia quadripustulata,* which attacks several crop pests, including armyworms and cutworms. It is widely distributed throughout North America and Europe. Rapid multiplication is made possible by several overlapping generations in a season.

LYDELLA AND THE CORN BORER

The tachinid fly *Lydella stabulans grisescens* is common in Europe and the Far East as an enemy of the corn borer. It is a solitary internal parasite of the host larva, favoring the later stages. The females are ready to mate as soon as they emerge; the males require one or two days to mature. The reproductive capacity is high; the average number of eggs produced by a female is about 350, as many as 1,000 eggs having been found in the uterus of dissected specimens. Larvae, not eggs, are deposited in the frass and excrement thrown out by the borer at the entrance to the tunnel. Hatching takes place not in the uterus but during the act of larviposition, which is described by Baker *et al.* as follows:

A female, when larvipositing, stands over the opening to the host's burrow and bends her abdomen under until the ovipositor is pointing downward and slightly forward. The tiny larvae are forced out of the vent onto the surface or are brushed off with a quick downward and backward movement of the tip of the abdomen as the female regains her normal position.

The females apparently are attracted to a corn borer burrow by the odor given off from the excrement and possibly from the host itself. The female runs hurriedly along a stalk and appears to be searching from side to side. Often when she comes upon frass she feeds a moment before larvipositing.[19]

One to four larvae or an average of two are deposited at one time. Not all the eggs hatch in time to survive; and larvae or eggs are deposited indiscriminately in the order in which they occur in the larval sac. An average of two eggs are ejected at each deposition, but these rarely hatch after leaving the ovipositor. If the female does not have the opportunity to larvaposit—for example, if she can't find enough sites—she retains the eggs in her uterus. In this event hatching may take place in the uterus and the larvae must find a way out, either through the genital opening or by puncturing the parent's body wall; when the latter happens the mother dies. Larvae have been observed working their way out through the eyes of a dead female that had been normal and active a few hours before.

As soon as the larva is deposited at the burrow opening it seeks out the host and enters it through a body opening or by puncturing the skin with its mandibles. Inside the host, it immediately seeks the main tracheal trunks of the breathing apparatus, cuts one of these, and forms a connecting funnel to supply itself with oxygen during development. When feeding is completed, the fly maggot leaves the host by puncturing its skin, and spins a cocoon alongside the host skin, or near by. The parasite produces two generations annually; adults of the second generation emerge the

[19] W. A. Baker, W. G. Bradley, and C. A. Clark, *Biological Control of the European Corn Borer in the U. S.* (Washington: USDA Technical Bulletin No. 983, Dec. 1949).

following spring after overwintering as young larvae in the body of the host.

Lydella is well established in Massachusetts, Connecticut, and Rhode Island, and in the Middle Atlantic states, as a parasite of the European corn borer; parasitization there ranges from 16 to 45 per cent. The parasite has been extensively colonized in the north central states since 1944 with the result that it is widely established in that area also. Field parasitization in Illinois, Indiana, Iowa, Kentucky, and southwestern Ohio has ranged from 45 to 75 per cent. *Lydella* and *Macrocentrus gifuensis* are the two most valuable of the species introduced for control of the European corn borer; but the former is outstanding.

ENEMIES OF THE BROWNTAIL AND GYPSY MOTHS

Townsendiellomyia nidicola, a tachinid fly, came with brown-tail moth shipments from Europe between 1905 and 1911. A solitary internal parasite of the browntail moth larvae, it produces one generation each year. The reproductive capacity of the female is high; she may lay as many as 600 eggs. The adult fly emerges in July, and the female deposits her eggs—already incubated in her oviducts—on the host. The maggot quickly hatches and bores into the host's body cavity. From there it migrates to the esophagus, where it remains during hibernation and until May or June of the following spring. It then penetrates the body cavity again, but this time constructs a breathing funnel to an opening in the host's skin. Two to three weeks after entering the body cavity, its feeding is complete and it emerges from the now dead moth larva. The life cycles of host and parasite are perfectly synchronized, and no other host of the parasite is known. With colonizations in 1907 and 1911, the parasite was widely established over the area of the browntail moth by 1916.

Importations of the tachinid *Blepharipoda scutellata* for control of the gypsy moth began in 1905 and continued through until 1927. The parasite became well established throughout the range

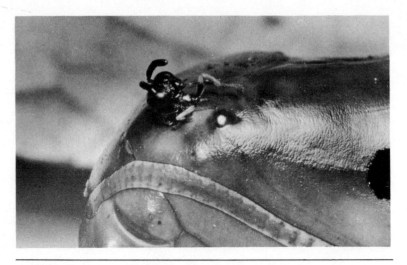

A chalcid wasp emerging from the chrysalid (pupa) of a noctuid moth. (*E. S. Ross*)

of the gypsy moth; at one time samplings indicated an average field parasitization of 49 per cent. It is a solitary internal parasite of the moth larvae, one generation being produced annually. It overwinters as a pupa in the soil and emerges in the spring shortly before the gypsy moth eggs hatch. The minute black eggs are deposited on leaves and ingested by the gypsy moth larvae as they feed. The egg production of a single female sometimes reaches 5,000. The eggs have already been incubated in the oviduct of the female parasite, and hatch in the host's digestive tract. The maggot migrates to the body cavity and feeds until the host larva is fully grown or transformed into the pupa stage. As a rule the fully grown maggot emerges from the pupa, although it sometimes does so while the host is still a larva; it then drops to the ground, where it pupates.

The tachinid *Compsilura concinnata* is the most valuable of all the parasites imported to combat the gypsy moth. Importations from Europe began in 1906; from 1911 to 1927 a total of 69,000 releases of the parasite were made in New England. One colony near Boston dispersed twenty-five miles the first year. The parasite became widespread in New England, where samplings have shown parasitization to be as high as 40 or 50 per cent, though at times it is less than 10 per cent. Colonies have been liberated in New York, New Jersey, Pennsylvania, Florida, and several western states. The parasite has been recovered from over two hundred species of Lepidoptera—a profusion of alternate hosts that enables it to maintain continuously high population levels. It is a valuable parasite of the satin moth as well as of the gypsy and browntail moths.

C. concinnata may be either a solitary or a gregarious internal parasite; the number attacking a single host ranges from one to four. It produces three or four generations each year, overwintering as a maggot in the host. It will attack any stage of the host larva, which the female pierces with her ovipositor before depositing a maggot in the body cavity. The maggots complete their development in about two weeks, whereupon they emerge from the host larvae and pupate in the soil. The female's reproductive capacity does not exceed 100 eggs. Since the gypsy moth overwinters in the egg stage and the browntail moth in colonies of tiny caterpillars webbed together in a cluster of leaves attached to twigs of the tree, the parasite is unable to overwinter in either.

ENEMIES OF THE JAPANESE BEETLE

A pest of some 275 kinds of trees, shrubs, and plants, the Japanese beetle (*Popillia japonica*) was first noted in a nursery near Riverton, New Jersey in 1916.[20] Search for the natural enemies of the beetle began in 1920 and continued through 1933. Although common in Japan, it was not a pest of any importance for the reason that it was subject to attack from a large number of predators and parasites at various stages of its growth. About forty-nine species of parasites and predators were shipped from Japan, Korea, Formosa, China, India, Australia, and Hawaii to the

[20] Walter E. Fleming, *The Japanese Beetle: How to Control It* (Washington: USDA Farmers' Bulletin No. 2151, April 1962); also *Controlling the Japanese Beetle* (Washington: USDA Farmers' Bulletin No. 2004, January 1949).

USDA's laboratory at Moorestown, New Jersey for rearing and release against the pest. These included several species of flies parasitic on the adult beetles and grubs, as well as hymenopterous parasites of the grubs. Five of these became established in the northeastern United States—three tachinid flies and two tiphia wasps. *Hyperecteina aldrichi (Centeter cinerea)* was among the first of the natural enemies of the beetle to be discovered in Japan. It is unique in that it attacks the adult stage rather than the larval or other stages of the pest as parasites commonly do. The fact that it parasitized 90 per cent of the beetle population at low densities, which was the main reason why the beetle was held in check in the northern Japanese island of Hokkaido, appeared to offer great promise. In all about 637,000 dead parasitized beetles containing pupae of the fly were imported. It became established over a wide area of New Jersey and Pennsylvania and at other points, but a lack of good synchronization with the host was a drawback.

The flies emerge several weeks before the beetles; the early beetle population is attacked but the fly does not persist during the peak period of the beetle's emergence. The fly produces one generation each year, and overwinters, as a pupa within the dead body of the adult beetle, in soil or litter. The adults emerge for the most part in June, and the female deposits the great majority of her eggs on the thorax of the female beetle. The white, hard-shelled eggs are easily visible against the shiny, metallic dark green of the beetle; more than one egg may be placed there, but only one parasite develops to maturity in a single host. The maggots, which hatch in about two days, bore through the hard wall of the thorax and into the body cavity, where they move about freely. No permanent attachment for respiration is made with the body wall or trachea as is common with the tachinids. The host dies in less than a week, and the parasite's larval development is completed in little more than a week; the pupa is always found with the head pointed toward the tip of the abdomen, making it easier for the adult fly to emerge.

Dexilla ventralis and *Prosena sibirita*—the other two tachinids established as a result of these early importations—are solitary internal parasites of the Japanese beetle and other scarabaeid grubs. Eggs in various stages of incubation, or larvae, are deposited on the soil—apparently near the host grubs. The maggots must burrow through the soil in search of the host, which they enter by boring through the larval skin. At the point of entry *D. ventralis* constructs a respiratory funnel which, being plainly visible, is a positive indication of parasitization. Signs of *P. sibirita* are not generally visible since the funnel is attached to the trachea of the host. The parasites overwinter in the host grubs as larvae; pupation takes place in the soil near the dead grubs. Adults of *P. sibirita* emerge in July and August, and the females produce up to eight hundred eggs or larvae. Active in twilight, they feed on blossoms and the nectar of flowers. The lack of suitable alternate hosts to bridge the summer period is believed to be the reason why these parasitic flies are not more effective in this country.

The most important of the imported parasites of the Japanese beetle are the two wasps *Tiphia vernalis* and *Tiphia popilliavora* of the family Tiphiidae, which contains many species that parasitize soil-inhabiting scarabaeid grubs. *Tiphia vernalis*—commonly called the "spring tiphia," and the more valuable of the two—overwinters as an adult within the host cocoon in the soil. It emerges in May when the Japanese beetle grubs are almost fully grown. The females feed almost entirely on the honeydew secreted by aphids. *Tiphia popilliavora*—commonly called the "fall tiphia"—overwinters in the host cocoon as a larva and emerges in August when the Japanese beetle grubs are small; this has detrimental consequences because of the female's tendency to lay unfertilized eggs on small grubs, with a resulting preponderance of male progeny. The female *popilliavora* feeds mostly from blossoms of the wild carrot. (Occasionally, however, it bites off one of the grub's forelegs and feeds on the oozing body fluids.) Eggs are deposited on the grub after temporarily but completely paralyzing it. The parasite consumes all but the legs and head of the host grub; larval development is completed in a month or less.

Left, adult *Tiphia vernalis* (the "spring tiphia"), an important parasite of the Japanese beetle; *right,* larva of the spring tiphia wasp feeding on Japanese beetle grub in the soil. (*USDA*)

Surveys showed that by 1951 the spring tiphia "was generally distributed over an area of some 5,300 square miles of eastern Pennsylvania, Delaware, and southern New Jersey" and "at many scattered points in the beetle infested territory outside this area. . . . The surveys disclosed a range of parasitizations from 19 to 61 per cent, with a general average of about 43 per cent. The spring Tiphia is the most effective of the introduced insect parasites of the beetle, but the other established parasites are also contributing to the reduction of the beetle population."[21]

The Japanese beetle is also subject to attack from a parasitic nematode, *Neoaplectana glaseri.* An economical method of rearing this nematode in the laboratory was worked out by state and federal agencies in cooperation with the Rockefeller Institute of Medical Research. A large-scale colonization program was under-

[21] Charles H. Hadley and Walter E. Fleming, "The Japanese Beetle" in *Insects: Yearbook of Agriculture* (Washington: Government Printing Office, 1952).

Female tachinid fly, *Sturmia harrisinae*, preparing to oviposit in larvae of the western grape leaf skeletonizer, *Harrisinia brillians*. (*O. J. Smith, courtesy C. P. Clausen*)

taken in New Jersey prior to 1940 and was believed to be an important factor in reducing the Japanese beetle population in parts of New Jersey at the time. Several species of fungus attack the Japanese beetle, the most important of which is the green muscardine fungus, *Metarrhizium anisopliae*. It is widespread and under favorable conditions is an important factor in control. The most promising agent for biological control of this pest is the "milky disease," a bacterial infection caused by *Bacillus popilliae*, which was first discovered in New Jersey in 1933.[22] Bacterial spore-dust mixtures causing the milky disease have been available commercially for many years under license from the USDA. The long larval stage of the Japanese beetle is favorable to the development of the disease as a control measure. Eggs of the Japanese beetle are laid in the soil by the female in the summer, and the larva does not change to the pupal stage until the following

[22] Walter E. Fleming, *Milky Disease for Control of the Japanese Beetle Grubs* (Washington: USDA Leaflet No. 500, December 1961).

spring. Thus nearly a full year is required for its development from egg to adult. Under the most favorable conditions, good control will not be established until the second season; but it has the advantage of being permanent once established. Community projects employing this method of control could be very effective and would preclude the use of chemical pesticides.

Small animal predators help reduce grub populations. Among the birds, starlings and English sparrows are the most important predators. Sea gulls and domestic poultry consume large numbers of the beetles when they have been exposed by plowing, and moles and skunks feed on the grubs.

ENEMIES OF THE MEXICAN BEAN BEETLE

The search for enemies of the Mexican bean beetle (*Epilachna varivestis*) began in 1922 in Mexico, where the tachinid fly *Paradexodes epilachnae* was found to parasitize up to 80 per cent of field populations of the pest. Over 60,000 parasites were imported into the United States from Mexico during the 1920's, and in 1930 a large-scale rearing program was begun, with releases in nineteen states. The spread of the parasite was rapid in many localities, and parasitization reached 90 per cent in many fields; but the fly did not become established. The reason was the lack of alternate hosts during the long inactive season in the northern climates. Another tachinid, *Lydinolydella metallica,* was found parasitizing the bean beetle in Brazil, and was imported in 1940, but also failed to become established. Two native flies, the tachinid *Phorocera claripennis* and the sarcophagid *Helicobia rapax*—were found to parasitize the beetle in Alabama, but are not abundant enough to be of any great value.

In the southeastern states the spotted lady beetle feeds on the eggs and young larvae of the bean beetle, and the anchor bug *Stiretrus anchorago* attacks the larvae, pupae, and adults of the pest; the spined soldier bug attacks all stages. Populations of the pest vary from year to year with weather and other factors. Rotenone, derived from cube and derris root, is recommended as the "most satisfactory" and "consistently effective" control measure where this is necessary.[23] (This material does not leave residues harmful to man and other warm-blooded animals and is less damaging to beneficial. insects than are other insecticides.) The Mexican bean beetle is highly susceptible to the fungus *Beauveria bassiana*—as is the European corn borer—but no effort has been made to produce the organism commercially as a microbial insecticide.

ENEMIES OF THE SAWFLIES

Some tachinid flies have become an important part of the parasite control complex operating effectively against several sawflies. As has been mentioned, *Drino bohemica*, a tachinid parasite of the European spruce sawfly, has become an important factor in control of this pest at low densities. The parasite was imported from Europe and became part of the release program beginning in 1934. Eggs of the fly are laid on late-stage sawfly larvae in July and feed internally. When feeding is completed the maggot emerges from the empty host skin; in the majority of cases this occurs after the host has formed a cocoon. Most of the fly larvae pupate outside the host cocoon, in the litter of the forest floor, but some pupate within the sawfly cocoon. One generation and part of another occur each year in New Brunswick. Some of the parasites overwinter as larvae within the host cocoons, but most of them do so as puparia in the forest litter; for this reason the degree of parasitization cannot be determined accurately from host cocoon samplings. Although slower to become established than most of the other introduced species, this parasite is superior to all others in its ability to survive at low densities of the spruce sawfly. Releases have been made against other sawfly pests, but few recoveries have been made from other than the spruce sawfly, *Diprion hercyniae*.

Prior to the establishment of the ichneumonid parasite *Meso-*

[23] *The Mexican Bean Beetle in the East and Its Control* (Washington: USDA Farmers' Bulletin No. 1624, October 1953).

leius tenthredinis, the native tachinid *Bessa harveyi* was the most effective parasite of the larch sawfly in the maritime provinces of Canada. It attacks the late-stage larvae, with one and a partial generation each year in New Brunswick. Superparasitism is common, but more than one parasite rarely reaches the adult stage in that event. Some multiple parasitism occurs with *M. tenthredinis,* and in that event *B. harveyi* is successful over the ichneumon. *B. harveyi* is able to parasitize spruce sawflies when larch sawflies are scarce. Its effectiveness is thought to be reduced by the sloughing of eggs and maggots by the spruce sawfly, and also by the habit of superparasitism. Like *Drino bohemica,* it can also pupate outside the host cocoon.

AQUATIC INSECTS, SCAVENGERS, AND WEED-FEEDERS

9

The Ephemeroptera (mayflies), Plecoptera (stoneflies) and the Trichoptera (caddisflies) benefit us indirectly as important sources of food for fish and other animals. Together they constitute the main source of food for trout. Everyone is familiar with the delicate mayflies, with their transparent wings and soft, pointed bodies terminating in two or three long "tails." They become a nuisance as they pile up in windrows on beaches, or swarm by the thousands around street lights. This swarming is probably the culmination of their nuptial flight, during which they mate and deposit their eggs.

The name Ephemeroptera is derived from its members' ephemeral nature. They live only a few hours of adult life, during which they eat no food—in fact, in this stage they do not have the necessary mouth parts for eating. Their metamorphosis is incomplete, and includes a unique nymphal stage, of very brief duration, in which they develop wings and can fly, whereas other insects have this locomotive power only as adults. The entire life of the nymphs is by no means ephemeral; in some species it may be as long as two or three years. During this time they live

Mayflies. (*Enid Furlonger*)

chiefly on aquatic vegetation and serve as a source of food for fish; they are also eaten by a host of other animals—stoneflies, dragonflies, turtles, birds, and so on. Fly-fishermen refer to the adult mayflies as "drakes" and imitate them in the construction of dry flies; wet flies simulate the nymphs.

Mayfly nymphs are found only in fresh water—most of them in streams, rivers, or lakes whose rocky shores are subject to wave motion. Oxygen becomes dissolved in water through diffusion and as a result of photosynthesis by algae and other plants. The amount of oxygen available to the nymphs depends on the motion of the water; normally, its constant movement will assure them an adequate supply of oxygen. The species that live in still water provide this motion by the movement of their tracheal gill.[1]

[1] J. R. Harris, An Angler's Entomology (Woodstock, Vermont: the Countryman Press).

Organic pollutants that remove oxygen from streams by encouraging the growth of bacteria may be fatal to the nymphs; for the fish the effect is double-barreled, since they are deprived of the oxygen *they* need and of their food supply as well. Insecticides have also become an increasing hazard to fish and to the animals they depend on for food. The great spring swarms of mayflies that were once to been seen in the communities around the lower Great Lakes are now largely a thing of the past.

STONEFLIES

The stoneflies are more numerous in total species than the mayflies, but they are far less conspicuous. The adults may be seen resting on stones or bushes along streams or flying over the water, but are not often attracted by lights. Like the mayflies, they are found only in fresh water; their preference is for streams with stony or gravelly bottoms. They have two pairs of wings which fold back straight over the body, giving them a boxed effect, and two long antennae. As adults they are yellow, green, or brown and are up to an inch and three-quarters long. The nymphs —which in some species may be over three inches long—may be found under stones or debris at the bottom of streams, where they live mostly on aquatic vegetation and to some extent on small aquatic animals. As nymphs and adults stoneflies are an important source of food for game fish. The nymphs are also eaten by such aquatic animals as dragonfly nymphs, frogs, and turtles, and the adults are eaten by a wide variety of birds. The adults are used as bait by fishermen, who refer to them as "browns," and are imitated in wet and dry flies.

CADDISFLIES

Like the stoneflies, the insects of this order (Trichoptera) are important chiefly as a source of food for fish. In the aquatic stage, however, they have some useful predatory habits. Numerically the caddisflies are the largest group of water flies. Like the others, they are found only in fresh water; but in general they tolerate a

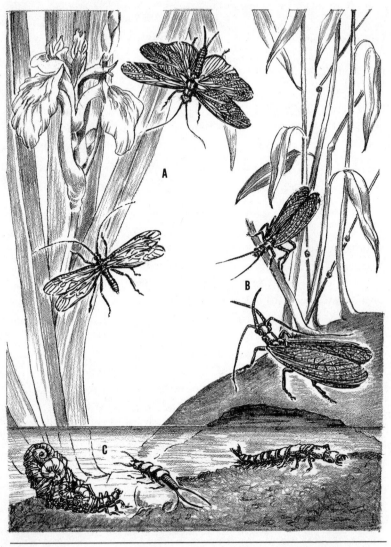

Aquatic insects: (a) stonefly; (b) caddisfly; (c) dobsonfly. (*Enid Furlonger*)

wider range of habitat than either the mayflies or stoneflies, and are commonly found in unpolluted streams, lakes, ponds, ditches, and reservoirs. The caddisflies have a complete metamorphosis and are aquatic as larvae and pupae. The adults, which resemble moths, have two pairs of large brown wings covered with hairs, which at rest are folded over the body in the form of an inverted V. Caddisflies are fleet of foot but weak in flight, and stay close to the water. Active by night, they are lured by the lights as most of the nocturnal fliers are. After mating over the water, the female deposits her eggs in gelatinous masses around rocks and plants, in shallow water. One generation is usually produced in a year. In some species the larva forms a protective case around its body, maintaining mobility by leaving head and legs protruding; it also pupates in this case. Others spin silken tubes or have no special protection; some spin silken nets to catch small food particles moving downstream with the current. The larvae of caddisflies feed on aquatic vegetation and animal matter, including insect larvae, crustaceans, and insect eggs. They can play havoc in trout hatcheries, since if no other food supply is available they will eat the fish eggs. They constitute a large percentage of the food of eastern brook trout, and are referred to as "duns" by anglers. The adult forms are imitated in dry flies, the larvae in wet flies. In Europe some species are parasitized by flies and wasps. Of the seventeen North American families, the Phryganeidae include the largest species, typified by *Ptilostomis semifasciata*.

Observations made in Utah over a period of several years indicate that caddisflies (*Hydropsyche* and *Rhyacophila*) are the most important insect predators of black flies (Simuliidae).[2] They are common in the riffles, and in the shelter of cracks in the swift-flowing streams where black fly larvae are found. They have also been observed to prey on black fly larvae in the Algonquin Park region of Ontario.

[2] B. V. Peterson, "Notes on Some Natural Enemies of Utah Black Flies," *The Canadian Entomologist*, April 1960.

WATER BUGS

Water bugs belong to the order Hemiptera, the true bugs. Most of them are predaceous. They are generally nocturnal fliers and are attracted to lights. The eggs are attached to plants or other objects, or are inserted in the stems of aquatic plants. The giant water bugs (Belostomatidae) include some of our largest insects; some species in the American tropics reach a length of four inches. A common freshwater species, the "electric light bug" *(Lethocerus americanus),* is two inches long and a fierce predator, attacking a wide variety of insects, snails, and even frogs and other small amphibians as well as fish. A strong flier too, it is sometimes attracted to lights and if given the opportunity can inflict a very painful bite, thanks to a powerful digestive enzyme that is injected with it and that destroys the tissues around the puncture. In some species the female cements the eggs on the back of the male until he is covered with what look like racked billiard balls. He carries them until the nymphs hatch—fierce little youngsters that are sometimes cannibalistic, the older devouring the younger.

The waterscorpions (Nepidae) have two short front legs modified for catching prey; the resemblance of these claws and the long "tail"—actually a breathing tube—to those of the scorpion accounts for the name. Waterscorpions are long, slim bugs, measuring from one to two inches, with long legs; they spend most of the time crawling on the bottom but must occasionally come to the surface for air. Their predatory habits resemble those of the giant water bugs. They can fly and are sometimes attracted by lights. The backswimmers (Notonectidae) are interesting little creatures about half an inch long, with specialized legs: the longer hind pair are widened at the tips like oars, and serve the same purpose; the middle pair are intermediate in length, and are used for holding; the shorter front pair are used for grasping. Waterscorpions carry a supply of air for underwater swimming in bubbles that form around the hairs attached to a groove in the abdomen. They can fly, and take off by flipping backward out of the water and then over onto their bellies. They prey on small fish and are themselves an important source of food for larger fish. Like the giant water bugs, they can inflict a painful bite if given the chance.

WATER BEETLES

The aquatic beetles have adaptations and habits similar to those of the aquatic Hemiptera, and some are among our largest insects. The predaceous diving beetles (Dytiscidae) are more than an inch long, and are ferocious predators in both adult and larval stages. These dark, shiny underwater swimmers are often seen with head down and rear end projecting just above the surface of the water. This is a breathing posture; their spiracles or breathing pores— which in most other insects are arranged along the sides of the body—are all at the back. Before diving a water beetle stores a bubble of air underneath its wing covers. The larval forms are without the gills possessed by most other aquatic larvae, and come to the surface in the same way as the adults. Tufts of hair at the posterior end contain air and keep the end above water while the larva is taking on a fresh supply. Water beetles pupate in mud along the banks; there is one generation a year. The adults are good fliers and are sometimes attracted by lights. The male is distinguished by a modification in the two front pair of legs, three joints of which are broadened, resembling discs; these are used for grasping its mate. After fertilization the female deposits her eggs singly in the stems of aquatic plants.

The dytiscids are said to live about a year, but have been known to thrive on raw meat in an aquarium for as long as five years. No other small forms of life will survive in an aquarium with these voracious creatures. Both adults and larvae devour other aquatic insects and various small animals such as snails, mussels, fish, tadpoles, and salamanders; they can be very destructive in fish hatcheries. The larvae, unlike the adults—but like those of many of the ground beetles—inject a digestive fluid into their victims and suck out the liquefied body contents through its grooved, curved mandibles. But the hunter is also hunted. Even though these beetles can give off a disagreeable fluid from glands at both ends of the body, they are eaten by ducks, fish, frogs, and turtles. They are also attacked by mites and parasitized by several species of tiny wasps, which even go down into the water to reach the larvae and deposit their eggs. The great diving beetle, *Dytiscus marginalis,* is a common and widespread species in North America as well as England.

The little, black, oval whirligig beetles (Gyrinidae), whose aggregations are a familiar sight on fresh waters, are the figure-skaters of the insect world. Their rapid turning and whirling motion is their way of searching for food. When alarmed they dive, each carrying down a big bubble of air attached to its rear. The larvae have tracheal gills for breathing under water. In the adults, what appear to be four compound eyes are in reality two divided horizontally, so that the lower portion can be submerged while the beetle is swimming on the surface. Apparently the whirligig is able to look in two directions at once—no doubt a useful attribute, at the rate gyrinids whirl about. Stink glands, long front legs modified for grasping, and short hairy hind legs designed for swimming are other distinctive features of these lively little creatures. The eggs are laid end to end in rows on submerged plants, and the larvae leave the water to pupate. The adults are mainly scavengers, living on dead insects; the larval stages feed on fly larvae and the immature forms of other aquatic insects. Both, in turn, serve as food for water birds and fish. A species common and widespread in North America is *Dineutes americanus.*

The water scavenger beetles (Hydrophilidae) have the same general features as the water beetles just described, but are larger. Our common species, *Hydrophilus triangularis,* is nearly an inch and a half long; in Britain *Hydrophilus piceus,* said to be nearly two inches long, is the second largest beetle. In adults of this genus the spiracles for breathing are on the underside of the thorax rather than at the end of the abdomen. The hairs covering the spiracles collect air for underwater breathing as the insect, after coming to the surface, turns to one side and brushes them with its antennae to break the water film. These beetles are good fliers and are sometimes attracted to lights. The female lays her eggs in a sort of cocoon which is attached to a plant or allowed to float on the water.

The beetles in this family may be terrestrial as well as aquatic; the adults are largely scavengers, feeding on decaying animal and vegetable matter. The terrestrial scavengers also feed on fly larvae associated with dung or animal carcasses. The larvae are all largely predaceous on other insects, but also include snails in their diet. Hydrophilids have been used for biological control of sugar cane borers in Hawaii and the West Indies. *Sphaeridium scarabaeoides,* a small beetle introduced from Europe, and a feeder on dung and fly larvae, is now quite common in the eastern United States.

THE SCAVENGERS

The scavengers (or saprophagous insects) feed upon waste materials—decaying plant or animal matter, or animal excrement. They are therefore beneficial to man. Most of these are found in the orders Thysanura (silverfish), Collembola (springtails and snowfleas), Orthoptera (especially the family Blattidae, or roaches), and in the lower ranks of the Coleoptera (beetles) and Diptera (flies). The scavenger trait is uncommon among Lepidoptera (moths and butterflies) and the Hymenoptera (bees and wasps)—although the ants are a notable exception among the latter, and there are two species of Lepidoptera—*Aglossa suprealis* and *Aphomia sociella*—that may be exceptions also. Scavengers occupy a wide range of environments, those that feed on excrement are found closer to the poles than any other insects. Darwin noted a beetle (*genus Quedius*) on barren rocks 540 miles off the coast of South America, where no plant, not even a lichen, grew; and Byrd found Collembola and a wingless fly of the family Chironomidae in Antarctica.

Sisyphus beetles rolling dung. (*Enid Furlonger*)

THE DUNG BEETLES

Some families of beetles include scavengers along with some of the most destructive species. Among the Scarabaeidae (scarab beetles), for example, are on one hand the interesting and beneficial dung beetles, which feed on animal excrement, and the well-known and destructive May beetles (*Phyllophaga fusca*) and rose chafers (*Macrodactylus subspinosus*) as well as the Japanese beetle (*Popillia japonica*). *Scarabaeus sacer*, a species of dung beetle found in the Nile Valley, was worshiped by the Egyptians five thousand years ago as a symbol for Ra, creator of all things. This association with the concept of immortality was apparently due to the beetle's metamorphosis—its disappearance into the ground and its later appearance after what was thought to be a resurrection.

Those who are not too squeamish find the dung beetles fascinating creatures. A fresh mound of cattle or sheep manure will bring them from a considerable distance. The dung rollers, or "tumblebugs" as they are sometimes called, have the habit of shaping their part of the feast into a ball, which they roll some distance away and then bury to be consumed in underground seclusion. A single beetle may eat and digest its own weight in dung within twelve hours. A mated female lays a single egg in a dung ball that has been buried and reworked into a pear shape underground. Fabre had great admiration for the hard-working dung rollers, and described their habits in *Social Life in the Insect World* with affectionate charm. He pictures one of the smaller species, the sisyphus beetle, in what would appear to be a touching connubial scene, with the male helping the female to form the ball and then to transport it overland to the place of burial. He stands guard and fondles the ball while she digs the hole, assists her in placing the ball in it, and waits patiently until she has deposited the egg; whereupon they depart to repeat the process.

One of the common dung rollers of North America, *Canthon pilularius,* is similar in habits to Fabre's *Sisyphus.* The most spectacular of our dung rollers is *Phanaeus vindex,* found east of the Rockies. The male of this species has a long horn protruding from his head and pointed back over the thorax. A small European species (*Aphodius fimetarius*) is now quite common in North America, as is *Geotrupes splendidus,* which buries the dung before feeding but does not roll it into a ball.

DEAD WOOD FEEDERS

Another member of the scarab family is the rhinoceros beetle (*Dynastes tityus*), the largest of its kind in North America. A scavenger for the most part, it lives on dead wood, but sometimes invades healthy tissue. Likewise, the carpenter ants (*Camponotus herculeanus*), the largest North American ants, normally build their nest in decaying stumps or dead timber, but sometimes establish new colonies in living trees or the timbers of buildings. Their damage to trees seems to consist mostly in weakening their structure. The ferocious-looking stag beetles (Lucanidae)—so called because the male has mandibles that resemble antlers—also live on rotted wood. They are sometimes drawn toward houses by the lights, and males may be seen locked in desperate combat for possession of the females. A species commonly called the pinch—or pinching—bug (*Pseudolucanus capreolus*), is prevalent in the eastern half of the United States. The Bessybugs or horned beetles (Passalidae) are another interesting family of scavengers that subsist on rotted wood. These large, shiny insects are notable for the care given to the larvae by the adults, which are in constant attendance and feed them on wood they have first prepared by chewing it themselves.

CARRION FEEDERS

The carrion beetles form another interesting family of scavengers, which are useful in disposing of dead animals. Some species consume the maggots of scavenger flies, and probably those of harmful flies as well. Among the carrion feeders may be classified those that feed on the freshly killed animal, those that feed on the decaying flesh, and those that feed on the dried parts—the skin, hair, and feathers. Among those of the first class are the blowflies (Calliphoridae) and flesh flies (Sarcophagidae), which deposit their eggs or larvae on freshly killed meat. The blowflies are small insects, colored a metallic blue or green, that resemble houseflies. One of the most familiar of those is the bluebottle fly (*Calliphora vomitoria*). Although flies are generally valuable as scavengers, one species known as the screwworm (*Cochliomyia hominivorax*), infests cuts and sores in the bodies of animals, sometimes killing the victim; another is an internal parasite of earthworms. Some species, on the other hand, promote the healing of wounds by consuming dead tissue and apparently giving off some beneficial substance. Some species, including *Phoenicia sericata*, were at one time used in the treatment of osteomyelitis.

The flesh flies are dull-colored and thus resemble the housefly and other Muscidae even more closely than the blowflies. Their distinguishing marks are the bare-tipped antennae (unlike those of the muscids, which are feathered) and in invariably having three black stripes on the thorax, whereas the muscids have either two or four. The larva of the flesh fly hatches within the body of the female, and is deposited directly on animal flesh. This type of reproduction is said to be "ovoviviparous" as distinguished from the "viviparous" reproduction of mammals, in which the embryo is joined to the mother by the placenta.

THE LATE-COMERS

As fermentation sets in, certain other flies are attracted to decaying matter—for example the anthomyiid flies and the humpbacked flies (Phoridae). The latter are tiny insects with a pronounced hump of the thorax, and are commonly seen resting on vegetation or elsewhere. The larvae of some species are found in carrion, those of others in dung, and those of still others as "guests" of ant, bee, or termite colonies. The scavenging species *Diploneura nitidula* is common throughout the United States.

As the carcass approaches a liquid state, a new set of insects arrive—the carrion beetles (Silphidae) and certain members of the rove and hister beetle families (Staphylinidae, Histeridae). Perhaps the most interesting of these are the burying or sexton beetles. A common species in the United States is the orange and black *Nicrophorus marginatus*. A pair of these beetles will excavate beneath the carcass of a bird or mouse (or even a larger animal) until it is completely undermined, thus lowering it into the ground. They work rapidly and may do the job in a matter of a few hours. The female lays her eggs alongside the carcass; both adults remain with the larvae and help them to feed. These beetles show considerable ingenuity in circumventing or removing obstructions such as roots. One observer cites a case where a wire was attached to the animal's foot; after vainly trying to sever the wire, the beetle finally cut through the leg to release its prize. Before digging, the beetles may move the carcass for some distance to a spot more favorable for excavating—all of which obviously entails a prodigious effort. Male beetles have been observed lying on their backs and pushing mightily against the carcass with all six of their legs while the female cleared the way ahead.

The carrion beetle (*Silpha noveboracensis*) feeds on both carrion and on the fly larvae found in it, as well as on those in dung and decaying fungi. The hairy rove beetle (*Creophilus maxillosus*) and the hister beetle (*Hister abbreviatus*) are both species that live in carrion and on the fly larvae within it. The larvae of the house and stable flies (Muscidae) and the roaches (Blattidae) are also scavengers on excrement and carrion, and on decaying plant material as well. But their damage far outweighs the good they do as scavengers.

Insects of the third and last group arrive to finish a carcass after the flesh has been devoured. They may belong to the family Scarabaeidae (the scarab beetles), as does the skin beetle, *Trox unistriatus;* or to the family Dermestidae, which include the carpet beetles; or to the family Nitidulidae, which includes the dried-fruit beetles. Some of these beetles are of course very destructive to stored hides, and some find carpets to their particular liking. The larvae of one species (*Dermestes maculatus*) in the family of the carpet beetle are used by museums to clear dried flesh from delicate skeletons that are to be preserved and displayed.

ANTS AND TERMITES

Ants are generally important as scavengers. They carry almost any kind of waste organic matter to their nests—the exudations of sap from trees, dead insects (and live ones as well), fragments of dead plant and animal matter, and so on.

Termites or "white ants" (which are not ants at all, but belong to the more primitive order Isoptera) are important scavengers in the tropical countries. Their partiality for dried timber is so notorious that their virtues have gone unnoticed. Thus William Morton Wheeler wrote:

Closer observation reveals the fact that the activities of the termites are both extremely helpful and extremely injurious to man. In

South Africa, Drummond long ago found that they perform an important function like that of the earthworms in moist temperate regions, but on a vaster scale. Since they are so very numerous and feed almost exclusively on dead vegetable substances they conspire with the bacteria, high temperature, and humidity to accelerate the disentegration of all the lifeless plant matter and to convert it into humus which can be at once utilized by the growing vegetation. The termites are therefore important agents in assisting the growth and renewal of the great rain-forests of the Amazon, Congo, and East Indies. But even in the dry savannas of South America and Africa and the open forests of Australia they hasten the dissolution of the dead grasses and other herbaceous plants as well as the sparse bushes and trees. On the other hand their insatiable appetite for cellulose and anything containing it makes these insects a terrible menace to all wooden constructions. . . . It has even been claimed that their fondness for literature is in part responsible for the slow cultural growth of many tropical countries. Alexander von Humboldt states that he rarely saw books more than fifty years old in northern South America. The termites have undoubtedly obliterated so many of the records of human achievement that they must be regarded as the subtlest enemies of the historian and archeologist.[3]

INSECTS TO CONTROL PLANT PESTS

Some plant-feeding insects are beneficial because they live on weeds—a weed being defined as "a plant in the wrong place"[4]— hence performing a useful purpose just as the scavengers do. These insects can be manipulated like predators and parasites. Biological control of weeds—the introduction of insects that feed on the plants—is of course the exact reverse of biological control of insect pests. Both are nevertheless based on the same ecological principle—namely that insects can play a vital role in controlling certain pests, whether those be plants or insects.

Like most insect pests, the really serious plant pests are nearly always of foreign origin. Exotic plant varieties, like those of insects, usually arrive without their enemies (the plant-feeding insects), and often become rampant where the environment is

[3] William Morton Wheeler, *Social Life Among the Insects* (New York: Harcourt, Brace & Co., 1923).
[4] C. B. Huffaker, "Fundamentals of Biological Control of Weeds," *Hilgardia*, Sept. 1957.

favorable and there is little or no competition. A thorny plant, *Lantana camara*, which in 1860 a famous botanist brought into Hawaii for ornamental purposes, spread rapidly and became a pest in pastures and fields. In 1902, after it had been noted that on one of the islands a scale (accidentally introduced) was killing *Lantana* plants, growers introduced the insect to the other islands. This is believed to have been the first attempt to apply biological control to a weed.[5]

When a weed-feeding insect is considered for introduction, starvation tests are conducted both in its native country and in the new environment, to determine whether under conditions depriving it of its normal plant food, the insect will feed on other plants of economic importance and continue to reproduce. Some insects are quite specific not only as to the food they eat but also as to the food needed to maintain the female's ability to produce eggs. Even if she occasionally resorts to another plant, introduction of the species need not be precluded so long as she still depends on the weed plant in order to reproduce. The plants tested are usually related to the weed plant. Huffaker points out that for an introduced species to be a valuable control agent, it must be able to destroy the pest plant decisively, thereby controlling the abundance both of the plant and, in turn, of its own species, whose numbers are then adjusted to the food supply. In biological control of weeds the object is not to eradicate the pest species but to control it.[6] Biological control agents must be capable of large-scale production to the exclusion of their parasites.

MOTH VS. PRICKLY PEAR

The introduction of the prickly pear cactus into Australia, and its rapid spread there, is the outstanding example of invasion by a plant species, and provides a classic example of biological

[5] Harvey L. Sweetman, *The Principles of Biological Control* (Dubuque, Iowa: Wm. C. Brown Co., 1958).

[6] C. B. Huffaker, "Fundamentals of Biological Control of Weeds," *Hilgardia*, Sept. 1957; "Some Concepts of the Ecological Basis of Biological Control of Weeds," *The Canadian Entomologist*, May 1962.

control of a weed. The prickly pear belongs to the plant family Cactaceae, and is native to southern North America and parts of South America, where about 350 species of the genus *Opuntia* are found. Along with them in the same regions are somewhere around 150 species of insects that feed on the plants—which explains why they are not generally a nuisance here. But in various other parts of the world—India, South Africa, Australia, and Hawaii—where they have been introduced as ornamental curiosities, they have become a pest. In Australia the most troublesome species is *Opuntia* (*inermis*) *bentonii,* a native of the southern United States that is believed to have been introduced around 1839; by 1920 over 50 million acres were heavily infested by this plant, and several million more were covered with *Opuntia stricta,* a native of Florida and the West Indies.

After fire, chemicals, and plowing had all been tried in a losing battle against the advance of the cacti, an investigation was begun of the insects that held the plants in check in their native countries. After about fifty species of insects had been tested, twelve were selected for introduction. Among several useful species (a caterpillar, five species of mealybugs, a true bug, and a beetle), the most effective was found to be the caterpillar of a moth, *Cactoblastis cactorum,* found in Argentina—where, curiously enough, these species of *Opuntia* do not occur! A small moth with a wingspread of only an inch, *Cactoblastis* lays its eggs in a chain at the end of a cactus spine, which thus acquires the appearance of a little stick. A female moth will deposit up to 150 eggs (an average of 75) per spine, and will "plant" three or four in one laying; she lives in all only a few days, just long enough to perform this essential function.

The caterpillars, which hatch in three to six weeks, live inside the segments of the cactus stem in colonies of between twenty and a hundred, eating their way from one segment to the other until nothing remains but the thin outer cuticle, and then cutting their way into the bulb and roots of the plant, leaving behind only a shell. The spread of these insects and the destruction they wreak upon the cacti is nothing short of phenomenal. Sweetman

Biological control of weeds: result of introducing *Chrysolina* beetles on range land infested with the noxious Klamath weed (St. Johnswort) in northern California. The beetles have cleared the grassy area beyond the flowering weeds in the foreground. (*J. K. Holloway,* courtesy *T. W. Fisher*)

has estimated the number of *Cactoblastis* in Australia to be "many thousands of millions"—all originating from an introduction of 2,750 eggs in 1925. During the intensive control program from 1925 to 1931, close to three billion *Cactoblastis* eggs were distributed throughout Australia, and vast areas have been restored to range land and other useful purposes.

BEETLES VS. ST. JOHNSWORT

Another outstanding instance of biological control of a weed by insects has been the clearing of the noxious plant *Hypericum perforatum* from thousands of acres of western range land by two species of small leaf-eating beetles of the genus *Chrysolina*. In California the pest is called the Klamath weed, after the river from whose vicinity it was first reported in 1900; in other western states it is more often called the goatweed, and in its native Europe it is called St. Johnswort, the legend being that it always blooms on June 24, the feast day of St. John the Baptist. The species has invaded extensive areas of range land in the western states, Canada, Australia, and New Zealand. At one time the infested areas in California were estimated to be 400,000 acres. The noxious plant crowds out the valuable grasses, causing sore mouths and blistering of the skin in the cattle that eat it.

The search for insects that feed on St. Johnswort was begun in Australia in 1920. After eight years of search and testing in Europe, two leaf-eating beetles, *Chrysolina hyperici* and *C. gamellata*, were introduced with good results. These and a root borer, *Agrilus hyperici*, were imported into California in 1944; in 1946, after feeding tests, 13,650 adults of *C. gamellata* were released, and 330,000 adults of *C. hyperici* imported from Australia were released in 1947. By 1948 both species were well established and no further importations were necessary. *C. gamellata*, the more valuable of the two beetles, became "so numerous and widespread in California by 1950 that redistribution became a local problem."[7] The beetle does not kill the plant directly but reduces the foliage to such an extent that it can no longer support a root system sufficient to enable it to compete with other plants. It is believed that with the destruction of the Klamath weed by these beetles, the characteristic annual plant cover of northern California has a good chance of being restored.

WEEVILS AND THE "BED OF SPIKES"

Recently another troublesome plant in California has been the aptly named *Tribulus terrestris*, which literally means "earthly

[7] James K. Holloway and C. B. Huffaker, "Insects to Control a Weed," in *Insects: Yearbook of Agriculture* (Washington: Government Printing Office, 1952).

bed of spikes." Its seeds are covered with burrs so sharp and tough that they rip the hides of cattle, and can puncture a bicycle tire—whence the common name of "puncture vine." The recorded presence of the weed in this country cannot be traced back any further than 1903, and there is a strong supposition that it came here from Italy or Spain.[8] In 1956, after many years and substantial sums of money had been spent on control projects without much success, county agricultural commissioners in California decided to make a thorough investigation of the biological control of this weed. Long before this, the idea of controlling it by biological means had been suggested by G. W. Angalet of the United States Department of Agriculture, after noticing that the vine was rare in India, and learning upon investigation that two species of weevils were attacking it. Intensive testing in France and Italy by Angalet and others, and in California by Huffaker, showed the food preference of two weevils—*Microlarinus lypriformis,* a stem-boring insect, and *Microlarinus lareyniei,* a seed-eating insect—to be limited almost entirely to the puncture vine.[9] Importation and release of the weevils—in small quantities (not over 1,000 at a time) to insure positive identification—began in 1961. At some points of release the multiplication of the weevils has been remarkable. Following a release at one point in mid-July, the September population within fifty or sixty yards was an estimated 25,000 to 100,000 weevils—almost all of them the progeny of the fifty females originally released just two months before!

A seed-eating weevil, *Gymnaetron antirrhini,* and a flower-eating beetle, *Brachypterolus pulicarius,* have been found to be the principal insects attacking the toadflax (*Linaria vulgaris*) in Canada.[10] This weed is of Eurasian origin and has been present

[8] "Pest Against Pest," *Time,* Aug. 31, 1962.

[9] C. B. Huffaker, D. W. Ricker, and C. E. Kennett, "Biological Control of Puncture Vine with Imported Weevils," *California Agriculture,* Dec. 1961.

[10] P. Harris, "Control of Toadflax by *Brachypterolus pulicarius* (L) (Coleoptera: Nitidulidae) and *Gymnaetron antirrhini* (Payk.) (Coleoptera: Curculionidae) in Canada," *The Canadian Entomologist,* Nov. 1961.

in Canada for many years, but its rapid spread in the prairie provinces since 1940 has recently caused some concern. The flower-eating beetle occurs in all provinces, but the weevil is not found in the West—apparently because the beetle eats the weevil eggs as it feeds on the flowers. For this reason, attempts to colonize the weevil in the west have been abandoned. In the East, the life cycles of the two insects are more favorably synchronized; the beetle does eat some of the eggs in the early summer, but the weevil comes into its own in the fall and devours the seeds when the beetle is no longer present.

WHEN AN ORNAMENTAL IS NOT AN ORNAMENT

The introduction of the ornamental *Lantana camara,* a native of America, into Hawaii in 1860 has already been mentioned. It is interesting to note that no particular problem existed up until the importation of two birds—the Chinese dove (*Turtur chinensis*) and the Indian mynah (*Acridotheres tristis*)—which spread the seeds over the islands. The plant has become a pest wherever it has been introduced in the South Pacific and in India. In 1902 twenty-three species of insects that attack the plant were collected in Mexico by Albert Koebele, and sent to Hawaii; eight of them became established and some turned out to be feeders on crop plants as well. The most effective of these species in controlling *Lantana* is the larva of a tortricid moth, *Epinotia lantana,* which consumes the flowers and fruit. The larva of a plume moth, *Platyptillia pusillidactyla,* also destroys many of the flowers, and the larva of a seed fly, *Agromyza lantanae,* attacks the ripening berries.

A similar case is that of *Clidemia hirta,* a plant native to the West Indies and to central and northern South America, which is believed to have been introduced into the Fiji Islands in 1890. Native doves and pigeons and the introduced Indian mynah broadcast the seeds until in thousands of acres of grazing lands the plant pest had choked out all other vegetation. A search in Trinidad revealed that the thrips *Liothrips urichi* was the chief factor in controlling the plant there, and that its tastes were strictly limited to *Clidemia*. In 1930, when the first colonies were brought to Fiji, 20,000 adults were liberated. Unchecked by their natural enemies, the thrips quickly spread throughout the islands, across seas, and into the thick jungles despite their aversion to shade. The thrips are effective not because they destroy the plants directly but because by eating the terminal shoots they retard its growth, allowing other plants to overtake and choke it off—an instance of what Huffaker calls "control of a plant species through a curbing of its competitive superiority."

There is little doubt that biological control of weeds will find wider application. Over vast and remote areas such as the cattle ranges, chemical forms of control are likely to be uneconomical, or undesirable in other respects; and there are some weeds that do not respond to chemical treatment. An instance of the latter is that of the leafy and cypress spurges (*Euphorbia esula* and *E. cyparissias*). Tests are being carried out at the Institute for Biological Control in Belleville, Ontario with the spurge hawk moth (*Celerio euphorbiae*) as a possible means of controlling these weeds. A few years ago the USDA's Research Service began a hunt in North Africa and the Near East for an insect to control halogeton, a poisonous weed found on the western range. Since this is an Asian plant, there is good reason to believe that insects which feed on the plant can be found in that region.[11]

[11] "Search for Insect to Kill Halogeton," *Science News Letter*, April 21, 1956.

*Incalculable numbers of niches . . . are occupied by
microorganisms with their omnivorous habits and almost
ubiquitous occurrence.*

—EDWARD A. STEINHAUS

DISEASES DUE TO BACTERIA AND FUNGI

10

Commenting on the adaptive capacity of microorganisms, particulary bacteria, Steinhaus points out, "The organic compound that cannot be used as nutrient by one or more microorganisms probably does not exist in nature."[1] Some bacteria can eventually become resistant to certain poisons and therapeutic agents, and may acutally use them as food. This involves a genetic adaptation, and is possible only because of their short lives and the incalculable number of generations through which they pass over a brief period of time. The best-known examples are the strains of bacteria which in less than ten years have become resistant to certain sulfonamides and to antibiotics such as penicillin.

This adaptibility and the omnivorous habits of microorganisms can be put to use in some unlikely but practical ways. Some years ago, when the dumping of phenol (carbolic acid) wastes into the St. Clair River by refineries at Sarnia, Ontario drew protest from downriver communities, the means of treating these wastes was found in lowly bacteria that thrive on the chemical, and that now

[1] Edward A. Steinhaus, "The Effects of Disease on Insect Populations," *Hilgardia*, Dec. 1954).

reduce thousands of gallons each day in huge open tanks; they do so good a job that the offensive odor of phenol is replaced by the pleasant aroma of new-mown hay. The use of bacteria that live on natural (heating) gas and on oil deposits as a means of detecting under ground deposits of these hydrocarbons without costly drilling, has been suggested.[2] A patent was obtained for a method of detecting oil by measuring how long it takes the oil-eating bacteria to break down a known amount of hydrocarbon mixed with a soil sample.[3] Going even further, a French petroleum chemist has suggested the use of bacteria to convert cheap grades of oil to food for animals and possibly for man; and a pilot plant is being constructed by a British oil company for this purpose. In consuming the oil, the bacteria are said to produce an excellent protein concentrate rich in B vitamins and the amino acid lysine.[4]

The various microorganisms that attack insects are of five kinds: bacteria, fungi, viruses, protozoa, and rickettsiae. Of the animal species an estimated 97 per cent are invertebrates (a majority being insects), which as a group "are subject to as wide a spectrum and variety of diseases as are the vertebrates." Thus the study of insect diseases is of prime importance not only for its contribution to the biological control of insect pests, but as Steinhaus has suggested, for its possible contribution to the pathology of higher animals, including man.[5]

Disease organisms, with the exception of fungi, infect insects via the digestive tract; in other words, the organism gains entry through the mouth when the insect eats plant food contaminated with the pathogen. This is why insects with sucking mouth parts, such as aphids and scale insects, are relatively free from insect diseases, aside from those caused by fungi, which, with few

[2] Ernest Beerstecher, Jr., *Petroleum Microbiology* (New York: Elsevier Publishing Co., 1954).

[3] "Invention: Petroleum Prospectors Ask Bacteria, Then Drill," *Science News Letter*, March 7, 1959.

[4] "Microbiology: The Oil Eaters," *Time*, Dec. 21, 1962.

[5] Edward A. Steinhaus, "Insect Pathology and Biomedical Research," Editorial, *Journal of Insect Pathology*, March 1963.

exceptions, gain entry through the insect's "integument," or skin. Thus, the microbial diseases most apt to control sucking insects are those caused by fungi. The common structural characteristic of these pathogenic microorganisms is either the single cell or an aggregate of independent cells. On the other hand, insects are also subject to nematode infections caused by multicellular or "metazoan" animals.

Most insect diseases are not infectious to vertebrates. Indeed there had been no recorded instance of an insect pathogen that was also found in a vertebrate animal until quite recently, when a fungus of the genus *Entomophthora,* known to attack insects, was discovered in the lesions of a diseased horse. The control of many insect pests is maintained continuously in nature by certain disease organisms, much as other pests are controlled by certain predators and parasites. Many of these pathogens can be grown in sufficient quantities to be disseminated artifically in the field, forest, or orchard so as to bring about biological control of certain insect pests, no less effectively than with some of the predators and parasites.

MICROORGANISMS AS BIOLOGICAL CONTROL AGENTS

As is true of predators and parasites, disease organisms are more effective at higher densities of the host and are therefore said to be "density-dependent" factors in the natural control of pest populations. This is evident in epizootics, where the disease spreads rapidly and all but wipes out the host in a short time. Epizootics can, however, be initiated in populations of low density by artificially introducing insect pathogens—which is why they are so valuable in biological control.

Often an insect pathogen is continuously present in an area under natural conditions, suddenly reaching epizootic proportions only when the insect population increases to a certain level, and when such conditions as temperature and moisture are exactly right. These natural epizootics do not inevitably occur before serious economic damage is done—a situation that in certain circumstances can be remedied by the artificial dissemination of the same or another pathogen. Epizootics can also be initiated, if the right pathogen is used, when no disease is apparent. In most instances where disease organisms have been introduced artificially, the pathogen does not remain as a permanent biotic factor, so that the effect is similar to that of a chemical insecticide. In some instances, however, the pathogen does become permanently established—as with some virus and fungus diseases, and notably the milky disease of the Japanese beetle.

It is generally believed that predators and parasites are more important as natural and biological control agents than insect pathogens, but there are exceptions.[6] As with predators, disease organisms tend to be more effective where there is a colonial type of insect organization than where the host population is scattered. Parasites, as has been indicated, because of their greater searching ability tend to be more effective where the host is scattered. Microorganisms, on the other hand, have certain characteristics that are advantageous in distribution: they are produced in great numbers and widely scattered by the wind and other agents, and they do not necessarily need a host to survive or in some cases even to reproduce. The spore-forming microorganisms can survive for long periods, often under extremely adverse conditions.

The introduction or appearance of a microbial disease can in some instances have an adverse effect on the normal relations between pest and beneficial species, so as to tip the balance in favor of the pest species, just as chemical insecticides often do. Population studies of the diamondback moth, *Plutella maculipennis* (a cabbageworm), in South Africa have shown that an epizootic of a disease caused by the fungus *Entomophthora sphaerosperma* is so effective that it reduces the host to the point where the insect predators and parasites disappear, thus per-

[6] Edward A. Steinhaus, "The Effects of Disease on Insect Populations," *Hilgardia*, Dec. 1954.

mitting the pest population to build up to a new high level before these factors come into operation again. There are instances, on the other hand, where a disease organism can tip the balance in favor of the beneficial species. This has been demonstrated in studies of the redbacked cutworm (*Euxoa ochrogaster*) in Saskatchewan. A destructive epizootic reduced the cutworm larvae to a very low level but altered the relation between the emerging moths and the parasites in favor of the latter.

There are many cases where parasite-predator populations seem to have no difficulty in building up to former levels and in re-establishing the balance following severe reduction of the host by an epizootic. There are also instances where the disease organism and the beneficial insects complement one another. In California alfalfa fields the "wilt" disease (a virus) normally kills the older larvae of the alfalfa caterpillar, while the *Apanteles* parasites destroy the smaller caterpillars. After an epizootic has occurred, the parasites are not long in coming from other fields when the virus has subsided and the pest population has begun to increase again.

The organisms that cause disease in insects will be discussed here in the order of their importance or effectiveness as control agents. Their effectiveness is dependent in varying degrees on temperature and moisture; the usefulness of fungi is especially restricted by their moisture requirements. It is possible that strains of fungi requiring less moisure might be developed, and that some practical means might be found for applying the amount of moisture required. Since fungi attack through the insect integument and are thus the most effective pathogen against plant-sucking insects, the development suggested would be of great importance. Most bacteria and fungi—but not the viruses and protozoa—can be raised quite easily by artificial means.

Among the advantages of microorganisms as control agents are: (1) they leave no toxic residues on plants consumed by man and other animals; (2) they are relatively cheap to produce as compared to chemical pesticides; (3) being specific, as a rule, they are not harmful to beneficial insects or to plants; (4) they can be applied as sprays or dusts, in combination with other materials or along with benefical insects; and (5) in some cases they may become a permanent addition to the environment, as do predators and parasites when successfully established, thus saving the expense of repeated applications. Steinhaus says concerning their value that "whether the economic entomologist wishes to recognize it or not, microbial control of insects is effective, does take place *in nature,* and is of great over-all economic importance."[7]

BACTERIAL DISEASES

Bacteria are the most numerous of the microorganisms associated with insects. They are one-celled, plantlike animals which multiply by simple division of the cells—the process known as fission. In a sense they are the simplest of the pathogens causing disease in insects. Bacteria gain entry through the mouth of the insect, and generally invade the body cavity; from there they are taken up by the blood, where they multiply rapidly, producing the condition known as septicemia. As a rule the infected insects become less active, cease feeding, and suffer from diarrhea; mouth discharges are also common. The tissues do not liquefy, or "melt," as in some of the virus diseases; generally the insect dries up and its color changes to dark brown or black. Most of the bacteria can be grown on synthetic media outside the normal hosts.[8]

The genus *Bacillus* comprises a large number of species that infect insects. The term "foulbrood" is frequently applied to any one of several species of *Bacillus* that infect the honeybee, *Apis mellifera*. Since the latter is a beneficial insect these organisms will not be discussed here; our concern is with the pathogens that

[7] Edward A. Steinhaus, *Principles of Insect Pathology* (New York: McGraw-Hill Book Co., 1949). The "economic entomologist" is one who specializes in insect control; most of this effort is directed toward the development of chemical pesticides.

[8] Steinhaus, *Principles of Insect Pathology.*

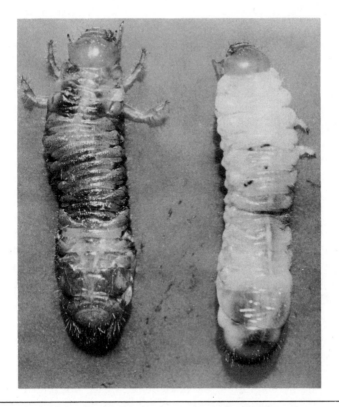

Effect of "milky disease" on Japanese beetle grubs: *left,* normal; *right,* diseased. Spore dust preparations of the bacteria (*Bacillus popilliae*) causing the disease are an effective control agent. (*USDA*)

harm insect pests and are thereby beneficial from the human point of view.

MILKY DISEASE

Several "milky diseases" resulting from Bacillus infections are known to affect white (scarabaeid) grubs in the soil; the best known of the pathogens is the spore-forming *Bacillus popilliae* which attacks the Japanese beetle, *Popillia japonica.* The infection resulting from this Bacillus is referred to as "Type A milky disease" to distinguish it from that caused by the spore-forming

B. lentimorbus, which also attacks the Japanese beetle grubs, and has been designated as "Type B milky disease." More than forty species of white grubs are subject to infections of this kind, but the Japanese beetle is probably more affected than any other, and the milky diseases of both types the most important of the infections.[9]

Bacterial spores ingested by the grubs germinate in the digestive tract and enter the blood in the "vegetative" form (a slender rod occurring singly or in pairs), and in this state multiply rapidly. When they are very numerous and when conditions are favorable, the formation of spores—or "sporulation," as it is called—takes place. (The spore stage enables the microorganism to withstand conditions that could not be withstood by the vegetative stage, and that may be encountered before it reaches the next host.) At the completion of this part of its life cycle the *Bacillus popilliae* spore with attached parasporal body has a distinctive shape that suggests a footprint. The number of spores that develop in a single grub averages from two to five billion. At the completion of sporulation the blood becomes milky, giving the grub the characteristic milky-white appearance. Diseased grubs are active until a few days before death but their life span is greatly shortened. A positive symptom of the disease is the appearance of the blood: when a leg is severed the liquid that oozes out is an opaque white if the insect is diseased rather than clear or only slightly cloudy as in a healthy insect. The contagion is usually transmitted from dead, diseased insects which disintegrate and scatter the spores in the soil where susceptible grubs ingest them in chewing at plant roots. The more dense the population is, the faster the disease will spread.

MICROBIAL CONTROL OF THE JAPANESE BEETLE

The study of milky diseases undertaken in 1926 and 1927 by the Japanese Beetle Laboratory of the USDA's Bureau of Entomology, led to the development of one of the most effective biological

---

[9] Walter E. Fleming, *Milky Disease for Control of Japanese Beetle Grubs* (Washington: USDA Leaflet No. 500, December 1961.

agents ever devised to control a major pest. This consists of a spore dust that can be spread over the ground infested with Japanese beetle grubs, thereby introducing the disease to a healthy population—a kind of "germ warfare." The spore dust comes very close to being "the ideal microorganism for use as a biological control agent" as defined by Irvin M. Hall, in that it (1) displays marked pathogenicity toward the insect pest; (2) is easily, rapidly and inexpensively produced; (3) is easily stored without loss of virulence; (4) is unharmful to man, beneficial insects, and plants; and (5) is easy to handle and apply.[10]

By 1939 the Japanese Beetle Laboratory had devised and patented a successful method for preparing the spores on a large scale. Cultures are stocked in the form of bacillus-infested blood, smeared, and dried on glass slides. The inoculant is prepared by suspending the glass slides in water, which is then injected into healthy grubs with a special micro-injector, about a million spores to each grub. The latter are then placed in soil-filled boxes divided to allow 500 grubs to a compartment. In this "incubator" the grubs are kept for from ten to twelve days at 86° F. The compartments are then broken down and the grubs are screened from the soil, dropped into jars of ice water, by which they are inactivated, and then stored in a refrigerator until enough have accumulated for the next step, which consists of passing them them through a meat grinder and then mixing the resulting mince with water. This is followed after the suspension has been standardized by the addition of calcium carbonate, which acts as a carrier, in such proportions as to provide a standard mixture of one billion spores per gram of dry material. When talcum powder has been added, the final preparation comes out about 100 billion spores per gram. The recommended method of application is with a hand corn planter adjusted to give two grams of material with each jab; spot treatment at ten-foot intervals in this way is sufficient to spread the spores in three seasons. It may also be spread along with a fertilizer.

[10] Irvin M. Hall, "Studies of Microorganisms Pathogenic to the Sod Webworm," *Hilgardia*, February, 1954.

Licenses were offered for commercial preparation of the spore dust; by 1944 it was available for general use, and despite the emphasis on chemical control, is on the market today.[11] Between 1939 and 1948 more than 90,000 sites covering almost 74,000 acres were treated, in thirteen states and the District of Columbia. In one park in the District of Columbia the Japanese beetle grub population before treatments were begun in 1940 was as high as 44 per square foot; by 1943 the number had dropped to 5 per square foot. Fruit growers, farmers, and home owners were included in the program. Besides keeping the Japanese beetle populations in check the infestations were promptly reduced to negligible proportions.[12]

Attempts to find a suitable medium for growing the milky disease bacillus on a much larger scale are being conducted in the Fermentation Laboratory of the Agricultural Research Service at Peoria, Illinois. If huge industrial vats holding several thousand gallons could be put to use for growing the bacteria and producing large quantities of spores, the cost would be reduced.

Type B milky disease in the Japanese beetle, caused by the spore-forming *Bacillus lentimorbus*, produces about the same effect on the late summer stage of the grub as Type A. The overwintering grubs retain the milky-white appearance until early spring, when they turn a muddy brown color.

THE GLAMOUR BACILLUS

Bacillus thuringiensis has probably become the most studied, the most frequently investigated and reported microorganism associated with insects, partly because of its extreme interest as an organism but more because of its tremendous potentialities as a biological control agent. Although primarily it attacks Lepidoptera, the list of insects known to be susceptible has expanded

[11] For example, "Japidemic," produced by the Fairfax Biological Laboratory, Clinton Corners, N. Y. in accordance with the method covered by U. S. Letters Patent No. 2258319.

[12] Steinhaus, *Principles of Insect Pathology*.

rapidly with the research that has attended the growing interest in the pathogen. Recognizing its possibilities as a "microbial insecticide," several drug and chemical companies have entered what appeared a promising field for product development. Insect pathologists—who had scarcely been heard of outside academic circles and government service before this sudden interest in *B. thuringiensis*—found their horizons suddenly extended into the world of business; in short, their services were in demand! Today several commercial preparations, under such brand names as Biotrol and Thuricide,[13] are now available to the farmer, orchardist, and gardener. The pathogen was approved in 1960 as an "insecticide" with exemption from any requirement of tolerance. It has proved to be nontoxic to human beings in feeding tests, and for this reason can be used close to harvest; it is practically tasteless and will not change the flavor of vegetables or fruits.

Bacillus thuringiensis was first reported—by E. Berliner in Germany in 1911—to cause a disease of the Mediterranean flour moth (*Anagasta kuhniella*). Berliner noticed it in a shipment of the moth larvae sent to him for study from a flour mill in Thuringia. Metalnikov, in Yugoslavia, one of the first to explore its possibilities as a biological control agent, reported in 1930 that he had had extraordinary success with it in controlling the European corn borer (*Ostrinia nubilalis*); and similar reports came from Hungary about the same time. For some unexplained reason these reports ceased shortly after 1930, and not much was heard of the bacillus until 1950, when Steinhaus started making tests in California to determine its possibilities as a biological control agent for the alfalfa caterpillar (*Colias eurytheme*), a serious pest of a crop of the greatest importance to the beef and dairy industry in that state.[14]

[13] The manufacturers of these products are respectively, Pennsalt Chemical and Nutrilite Products, Inc., and Stauffer Chemical and Bioferm Corporation.

[14] Edward A. Steinhaus, "Possible Use of *Bacillus thuringiensis* Berliner as an Aid in the Biological Control of the Alfalfa Caterpillar," *Hilgardia*, Feb. 1951.

B. THURINGIENSIS AND THE ALFALFA CATERPILLAR

The first signs of the disease in the caterpillars are sluggishness and apparent loss of appetite, which occur a few hours after the bacillus is ingested. Some diarrhea is evident, and shortly before death the larvae become flabby and shrunken. The value of the bacillus as a biological control agent is enhanced by the fact that it grows well on an ordinary nutrient agar without losing its virulence. A method of producing fairly large quantities of the material in the laboratory for field use and testing was worked out at the University of California, and has been described by Steinhaus.[15] The bacillus spores are grown on nutrient agar placed in 6-litre Povitsky bottles, which are rectangular in shape and can be laid safely on the wide side and stacked in compact rows. Each bottle affords 75 square inches of surface for growing the bacteria; in this way the spores can be grown without using much laboratory space. The surface of each bottle is sprayed with a diluted culture of the bacillus, using a small hand atomizer. After an incubation period of a week at ordinary room temperature the spores are harvested by washing them off the agar with distilled water. The mixture is then centrifuged, filtered, and poured into flat enameled pans for drying. The resulting dry, brittle material is scraped from the pans and ground into a fine powder. The yield from each bottle is from about .2 to .3 grams of dry spore powder. (The results of spraying a water suspension of the spores in the field to control the alfalfa caterpillar will be described in the discussion of viruses, and the results obtained from the two agents will be compared.) *B. thuringiensis* spore material can be stored at ordinary room temperature and kept indefinitely. An interesting phenomenon in connection with sporulation (change of the bacterium from vegetative to spore stage) is the formation of mysterious crystal-like bodies, or "inclusions,"

[15] Edward A. Steinhaus, "Living Insecticides," *Scientific American*, August 1956.

which seem to account for the toxicity of this pathogen to so many insects.

SOME USES OF B. THURINGIENSIS

Experiments conducted by W. A. Smirnoff and C. F. MacLeod in Canada have shown that *B. thuringiensis* is not toxic to birds or small mammals (rodents), which are important predators of forest insect pests. Using white laboratory mice, the starling, white-crowned sparrow, and slate-colored junco, they found that the pathogen does not lose its virulence after passing through the digestive tracts and being excreted by the animals.[16] Taking a cue from this, the investigators have come up with the ingenious idea of using these predators to spread the disease organism about the forest, through scattered feeding stations (a use reminiscent of the way birds distribute undigested seeds of certain trees and spread the species along the route of their migrations). The value of these small predatory animals would be considerably enhanced if they can be given the double duty of disseminating a "living insecticide" while carrying on their predatory activities—a trick that should make any efficiency expert envious. The use of this method is suggested where control is needed but the expense of spraying is not warranted.

Irvin Hall and Ken Arakawa have demonstrated that adult houseflies (*Musca domestica*) are only slightly susceptible to *B. thuringiensis*, but that the maggots are easily killed by large doses. It appeared at the time that death was due to the toxic effects of the crystals rather than to septicemia (although John D. Briggs later indicated that the death of the flies was due to a soluble toxin rather than to the crystals). The tests showed that differences in toxicity between various commercial preparations is sometimes quite marked, and is not necessarily due to differences in spore count. The possibility of using the pathogen as a larvicide to

[16] W. A. Smirnoff and C. F. MacLeod, "Study of the Survival of *Bacillus thuringiensis* var. *thuringiensis* Berliner in the Digestive Tracts and in Feces of a Small Mammal and Birds," *Journal of Insect Pathology*, September 1961.

control the housefly is suggested by these investigators.[17] Others
have followed the suggestion with some interesting results. For
example, Paul H. Dunn found that *B. thuringiensis* given to steers
as a feed additive had no ill effects on the cattle but was very
effective in preventing houseflies from completing their development in the manure. Most of the mortality occurred in the pupal
rather than the larval stage of the flies.[18] Briggs found pretty
much the same thing in tests made with hens. *B. thuringiensis*
added to chicken feed affected neither the hens themselves nor
the quality or quantity of their eggs, and prevented houseflies
from breeding in the chicken manure.[19]

The yellow fever mosquito, *Aedes aegypti,* appears to be only
moderately susceptible to *B. thuringiensis,* so that very large concentrations of spores and high dosages would be required to give
control.[20] Surprisingly, the earthworm (*Lumbricus terrestris*) has
been found to be very susceptible to *B. thuringiensis,* but there
is no evidence that the pathogen would survive in the soil. The
fact that earthworms are not affected by *B. cereus,* a non-crystal-
forming organism which is usually present in the same soils, suggests that the toxic crystals of *B. thuringiensis* are the cause of
the damage. With increased use of the bacillus, it is possible that
the crystals might build up in the soil and have an adverse effect
on earthworm populations.[21] It has been shown that the pathogen
can be safely used on flowering plants visited by honey bees,

[17] Irvin M. Hall and Ken Y. Arakawa, "The Susceptibility of the House
Fly, *Musca domestica* Linnaeus to *Bacillus thuringiensis* var. *thuringiensis*
Berliner," *Journal of Insect Pathology,* December 1959.

[18] Paul H. Dunn, "Control of House Flies in Bovine Feces by a Freed
Additive Containing *Bacillus thuringiensis* var *thuringiensis* Berliner," *Journal of Insect Pathology,* March 1960.

[19] John D. Briggs, "Reduction of Adult House-Fly Emergence by the
Effects of *Bacillus* spp. on Development of Immature Forms," *Journal of
Insect Pathology,* Dec. 1960.

[20] J. N. Liles and P. H. Dunn, "Preliminary Laboratory Results on the
Susceptibility of *Aedes aegypti* (Linnaeus) to *Bacillus thuringiensis* Berliner," *Journal of Insect Pathology,* October 1959.

[21] W. A. Smirnoff and A. M. Heimpel, "Notes on the Pathogenicity of
Bacillus thuringiensis var. *thuringiensis* Berliner for the Earthworm, *Lumbricus terrestris* Linnaeus," *Journal of Insect Pathology,* December 1961.

since the immature and adult stages of the honey bee are not susceptible to large doses of the bacillus. Heavy dusting of a colony with spore dust had no ill effects on adults (except to irritate them and increase their tendency to sting) or on the pupae and larvae. The deposits of spore dust in the cells had been removed by the bees within three or four days, and the level of honey production was maintained.[22]

B. thuringiensis can be an effective means of control where it is necessary to maintain the pest at low densities, and when only a few or even one of the pest individuals makes a product unsalable—where, in the jargon of applied entomology, the insect is said to have a "low economic threshold," as in the case of the corn earworm. Tests made in California by Y. Tanada and C. Reiner indicate that *B. thuringiensis,* properly timed and applied (preferably as a dust), can destroy the young larvae in one to four days, before they cause damage. It was found to be nearly as effective as 5 per cent DDT dust, the standard commercial insecticide.[23] These are the larvae that develop from eggs laid mainly on the silk; older larvae developing on the whorls are less susceptible, and although they may eventually die from the disease, are able to migrate downward and enter the ears. For this reason the pathogen is not likely to be so effective in heavy infestations. Spray dusts on the silk do not interfere with pollination. The investigators believe that this pathogen should be considered as a means of control for insects of low economic threshold, even the

[22] William T. Wilson, "Observations on the Effects of Feeding Large Quantities of *Bacillus thuringiensis* Berliner to Honey Bees," *Journal of Insect Pathology,* June 1962.

[23] Y. Tanada and C. Reiner, "The Use of Pathogens in the Control of the Corn Ear-worm *Heliothis zea* (Boddie)," *Journal of Insect Pathology,* June 1962; "Microbial Control of the Artichoke Plum Moth, *Platyptilia carduidactyla* (Riley) (Pterophoridae, Lepidoptera), *ibid.,* Sept. 1960. Their comparison is at variance with tests made by Anderson et al. between 1959 and 1961, indicative that *B. thuringiensis* preparations were not as effective against the corn earworm on sweet corn as DDT and the newer insecticides. See L. D. Anderson, H. Nakakihara, and I. M. Hall, "Toxicity of New Insecticides to Corn Earworms on Sweet Corn," *Journal of Economic Entomology,* Feb. 1963.

boring kind. (The same applies to a nuclear polyhedrosis virus which was tested at the same time but which was not quite as effective as the bacillus.) Similar results were obtained with the artichoke plum moth (*Platyptilia carduidactyla*). The earliest stage of the larvae can be killed in one to two days, before it mines into the plant tissue; a single larva can mean the loss of an artichoke. The nontoxic nature (to man) of these pathogens certainly recommends their use wherever practicable.

B. THURINGIENSIS AND THE CRUCIFERS

The crucifers—cabbage, cauliflower, and broccoli—are difficult to grow without insecticides; on the other hand, cauliflower and broccoli in particular are notorious for their insecticidal residues. An effective microbial insecticide therefore comes as a great boon in the growing of these crops. Tests conducted in California by Irvin Hall and Lloyd Andres showed that *B. thuringiensis* applied as a dust gave good control of the cabbage looper (*Trichoplusia ni*) on cauliflower and cabbage plants, and of the imported cabbageworm (*Pieris rapae*) on cabbage plants. The tests showed that dusts were superior to sprays (water suspensions of the spore material), suggesting that thorough coverage of the plants was essential for the best results. Control varies with the worm population and size of both the larvae and the plants. (The effective dosage as determined from these tests was .5 to 1.5 pounds of 100 billion spores per gram concentration, applied in about 30 pounds of total dust per acre.)[24] Hall *et al.* concluded that the better of the *B. thuringiensis* formulations were as effective as the best of the chemical insecticides in controlling cabbage loopers on lettuce. These studies of the cabbage looper led to the development and use of dust formulations. *B. thuringiensis* is effective against the larger larvae of cabbage loopers, which are difficult to control with most insecticides; its greatest drawback has been

[24] Irvin M. Hall and Lloyd A. Andres, "Field Evaluation of Commercially Produced *Bacillus thuringiensis* Berliner Used for Control of Lepidopterous Larvae on Crucifers," *Journal of Economic Entomology*, Oct. 1959.

the lack of standardization of the various commercial formula-tions.[25] (Preparations called Bakthane 5 and Biotrol 5D have given good control of the cabbage looper on lettuce.[26])

Tests by McEwen and Hervey in New York have shown that good control of the imported cabbageworm can be obtained with *B. thuringiensis* spore dust applied at a rate of .3 pounds per acre at a concentration of 100 billion spores per gram.[27] A mixture of one-half to one pound in 100 gallons of water—a concentration of 75 billion spores per gram—applied to one acre of crop, is recom-mended for control of the imported cabbageworm by one of the manufacturers of the spore dust; one to two pounds are recom-mended for the cabbage looper—two to four pounds if they are large.[28] The tobacco hornworm, *Protoparce sexta,* can be con-trolled by the same concentration as that used for the imported cabbageworm. Two to four times this dosage was found to be required to control the cabbage looper in the New York tests. These pests are also susceptible to virus infections (granulosis and polyhedrosis) and indications are that a combination of the polyhedrosis virus and the bacillus might be more effective. The virus can be produced economically on a commercial scale.

Stickers made from skim milk powder and a latex preparation increase the effectiveness of the bacillus sprays in control of the cabbage insects on cabbage; otherwise the suspension does not adhere well to the smooth, waxy surface of the cabbage and washes off easily.[29] Fungicides and most insecticides added to the

[25] I. M. Hall, R. L. Hale, H. H. Shorey, and K. Y. Arakawa, "Evaluation of Chemical and Microbial Materials for Control of the Cabbage Looper," *Journal of Economic Entomology,* Feb. 1961.

[26] H. H. Shorey and I. M. Hall, "Effect of Chemical and Microbial In-secticides on Several Insect Pests of Lettuce in Southern California," *Jour-nal of Economic Entomology,* April 1962.

[27] F. L. McEwen and G. E. R. Hervey, "Microbial Control of Two Cab-bage Insects," *Journal of Insect Pathology,* May 1959.

[28] Bakthane L-69 Microbial Insecticide, produced by Rohm & Hass Co., Philadelphia, Pa.

[29] R. P. Jaques and C. J. S. Fox, "The Influence of Stickers on the Effec-tiveness of Sprays of *Bacillus thuringiensis* var. *thuringiensis* Berliner and *Bacillus entomocidus* var. *entomocidus* Heimpel and Angus," *Journal of Insect Pathology,* March 1960.

spore mixture do not reduce the effectiveness of the bacillus except when the mixture is allowed to stand for three hours or more. The chemicals could therefore be applied at the same time as the bacillus if needed.

B. THURINGIENSIS AND APPLE PESTS

Tests of the bacillus on the codling moth (*Carpocapsa pomonella*) did not give what is considered commercial control, though it was quite effective. The product used was a 25-billion spore (per gram) preparation applied at the rate of 4 pounds per 100 gallons of water. The same preparation applied at the rate of 6.7 pounds per 100 gallons of water gave satisfactory control of the red-banded leaf roller (*Argyrotaenia velutinana*). These dosages would be rather expensive, but more concentrated preparations than the one tested are available, and would give better results at less cost in both cases.

Studies by R. P. Jaques in Nova Scotia show that the winter moth (*Operophtera brumata*) and fall cankerworm (*Alsophila pometaria*) can be controlled successfully with *B. thuringiensis* at economically acceptable dosages. In some areas these pests are serious defoliators of apple trees in the spring, when the trees are in bloom and chemical insecticides cannot be applied because they interfere with pollinating insects—a situation in which the pathogen would be especially welcome. Two pounds of spore dust per 100 gallons of water (at a concentration of 70 billion spores per gram) were used—considerably less than the amount required to control the red-banded leaf roller. The eastern tent caterpillar (*Malacosoma americanum*) can be controlled at the same dosage as the winter moth and fall cankerworm. The lesser effectiveness in controlling the eye-spotted bud moth (*Spilonota ocellana*) and gray-banded leaf roller (*Argyrotaenia mariana*) is due to the protection afforded the insect by its habit of pulling the leaves together.[30]

[30] R. P. Jaques, "Control of Some Lepidopterous Pests of Apple with Commercial Preparations of *Bacillus thuringiensis* Berliner," *Journal of Insect Pathology*, June 1961.

B. THURINGIENSIS AND FOREST PESTS

Some interesting field tests on the effects of *B. thuringiensis* on the spruce budworm (*Choristoneura fumiferana*) were conducted in Quebec and New Brunswick in 1960. In Quebec, under natural conditions in the forest area where the tests were conducted, mortality of the spruce budworm population is about 26 per cent from various causes—about 6 per cent from a protozoan (microsporidian) disease, 1 to 2 per cent from a virus disease, about 1 per cent from fungus diseases; the rest is due to parasites and predators. A commercial preparation of *B. thuringiensis* (30 billion spores per gram concentration) was used in the tests, which were made with aqueous and oil suspensions and spore dust, applied from the ground. Best results were obtained with the aqueous suspension (80 grams of spore dust per gallon of water) applied at the rate of 10 gallons per acre. Larval mortality reached 80 per cent in eight days. The results varied considerably with temperature, which affects both the time required to kill the larvae and the number killed. *Bacillus cereus* was more effective at lower temperatures than *B. thuringiensis*. Because of the rains, applications do not persist on the trees for long—twenty days at most.[31]

In the New Brunswick test a formulation of 60 billion spores per gram was applied from an airplane. Suspensions in both water and oil, at the rate of two pounds of spore dust to one gallon of liquid, were applied at the rate of one gallon per acre. Some insecticidal effect was obtained from the bacillus, but not enough to be relied on as a control. The oil suspension was more effective; but a difference in larvae collected from the sprayed plots as against the check plots receiving no treatment was only 31 per cent after a little more than two weeks.[32]

[31] W. A. Smirnoff, "Tests of *Bacillus thuringiensis* var. *thuringiensis* Berliner and *B. cerus* Frankland and Frankland on Larvae of *Choristoneura fumiferana* (Clemens)," *The Canadian Entomologist,* February 1963.

[32] M. L. Prebble, T. A. Angus, A. M. Heimpel, R. A. Fisher, O. N. Morris, J. M. Kinghorn, "Tests of a Microbial Insecticide Against Forest Defoliators," *Bi-monthly Progress Report,* Canada Dept. of Forestry, May-June 1961.

Similar tests were conducted in British Columbia to determine the effect of aerial applications of *B. thuringiensis* on the black-headed budworm (*Acleris variana*). Laboratory tests show the budworm to be highly susceptible to the bacillus, but no definite conclusions could be drawn concerning the reduction of the population as a result of the aerial application because the population in the test area was too sparce. It was concluded, however, that lethal doses can be applied by aircraft and that efficiency will increase if "clumping" of the material can be overcome and residual life increased. Other forest pests showing varying degrees of susceptibility to *B. thuringiensis* are the green-striped forest looper (*Melanolophia imitata*), the western oak looper (*Lambdina fiscellaria somniara*), and the saddle-backed looper (*Ectropis crepuscularia*).[33]

Next to sawflies and budworms, bark beetles are the most difficult forest pest to combat. It is encouraging to note, therefore, that *B. thuringiensis* has been found in the western pine beetle (*Dendroctonus brevicomis*) and the Engelmann spruce beetle (*D. engelmanni*). Experiments in Utah show that the bacillus is an effective biological control agent against the Great Basin tent caterpillar (*Malacosoma fragile*), a pest of aspens and valuable browse plants growing on the range.

Besides those discussed, some other insect pests said to be susceptible to *B. thuringiensis* are as follows:[34]

GREATHER WAX MOTH	*Galleria mellonella*
OMNIVOROUS LOOPER	*Sabulodes caberata*
COTTON LEAF PERFORATOR	*Bucculatrix thurberiella*
BUCKEYE CATERPILLAR	*Junonia coenia*
VARIEGATED CUTWORM	*Peridroma saucia*
WESTERN YELLOW-STRIPED ARMY WORM	*Prodenia praefica*
INDIAN-MEAL MOTH	*Plodia interpunctella*
DIAMONDBACK MOTH	*Plutella maculipennis*

[33] O. N. Morris, "Comparative Susceptibility of Four Forest Insects to a Commercial Preparation of *Bacillus thuringiensis* (Berliner)," *The Canadian Entomologist*, July 1962.

[34] Thuricide, Experimental Microbial Insecticide: Technical Information, Research and Development Laboratories, Stauffer Chemical Co., Omaha, Nebraska (Jan. 1959).

CABBAGE WEBWORM	*Hellula undalis*
CELERY LEAF TIER	*Phlyctaenia rubigalis*
SPHINX MOTH (TOMATO HORNWORM)	*Protoparce quinquemaculata*
LEAF ROLLER	*Amorbia essigana*
WESTERN GRAPE LEAF SKELETONIZER	*Harrisina brillians*
EGYPTIAN ALFALFA WEEVIL	*Hypera brunneipennis*
COCONUT PALM RHINOCEROS BEETLE	*Oryctes rhinoceros*
CONFUSED FLOUR BEETLE	*Tribolium confusum*

The need for standardization of commercial spore dust formulations of *B. thuringiensis* has been pointed out by several investigators.[35] Some preparations of lower spore concentration are more effective than others of higher concentration, apparently because of a difference in the number of crystals. The point is made that since the crystalline inclusions in the bacteria account for its insecticidal properties, the material should be standardized according to the concentration of crystals rather than of spores, so that proper distinctions can be made as to its potency and effect on various pests. On the other hand, the crystals do not seem to be essential so far as the spruce budworm (*Choristoneura fumiferana*) is concerned. Tests subjecting this pest to a *B. thuringiensis* formulation containing spores and crystals, and to one mostly of spores, both produced mortality in three or four days, whereas a suspension of pure crystals failed to cause any deleterious effect.[36]

SOME OTHER BACTERIAL DISEASES [37]

Some forms of "septicemia" classed as "coliform infections" are common among a variety of insects. An epizootic of one of these

[35] Vernon M. Stern, Irvin M. Hall, and George D. Peterson, "The Utilization of *Bacillus thuringiensis* Berliner as a Biotic Insecticide to Suppress the Alfalfa Caterpillar," *Journal of Insect Pathology*, Aug. 1959; Y. Tanada and C. Reiner, "The Use of Pathogens in the Control of the Corn Earworm, *Heliothis zea* (Boddie)," *ibid.*, June 1962.

[36] W. A. Smirnoff, Tests of *Bacillus thuringiensis* var. *thuringiensis* Berliner and *B. cerus* Frankland and Frankland on Larvae of *Choristoneura fumiferana* (Clemens)," *The Canadian Entomologist*, February 1963.

[37] Edward A. Steinhaus, *Principles of Insect Pathology* (New York: McGraw-Hill Book Co., 1949).

diseases was discovered by F. d'Herelle in a swarm of migrating locusts (*Schistocerca*) at the border between Mexico and Guatemala, where the disease had become so devastating as to halt the migration. F. d'Herelle named the bacterium *Coccobacillus acridiorum*, but it is now called *Cloaca cloacae* var. *acridiorum,* or cloaca Type A. After isolating and propagating the bacteria, d'Herelle applied it to control of the grasshopper populations in various parts of Mexico, with apparent success, and was asked to try his technique elsewhere. Some success seems to have been attained in Argentina and Colombia, and to a lesser degree in Algeria and Tunisia. A grasshopper afflicted with the disease loses its appetite, becomes listless, is unable to jump, and may have convulsions. Soon it develops diarrhea and falls on its side; in a few hours death ensues, and the remains become putrefied. A cool to warm temperature favors the disease, and the cannibalistic habit of these insects is an important factor in its spread.

Hornworms are subject to a disease commonly referred to as "hornworm septicemia," caused by a bacterium considered to be an achromogenic strain of *Serratia marcescens.* It is found in the tobacco hornworm (*Protoparce sexta*) and in the closely related tomato hornworm (*Protoparce quinquemaculata*). After the usual symptoms—loss of appetite, and sluggishness—appear, the feces change to a watery substance and there is some discharge from the mouth; the caterpillar dies either lying on its side in a curved position or hanging from a leaf to which it is hooked by a leg, with the now liquid contents of the body gravitating toward the head. Epizootics are not common, and the use of the organism as a means of control does not seem to be practical. Cutworms (*Feltia*) are subject to a similar disease—"cutworm septicemia"—caused by a similar organism. Still another closely related species of bacterium—the cause of "potato-beetle septicemia"—infects the Colorado potato beetle (*Leptinotarsa decemlineata*). The symptoms are generally the same as those already described, except that infected larvae change from their reddish tint to brownish gray, later becoming darker or almost black. The disease is an important factor in natural control, and epizootics are not uncommon.

Silkworms, the European corn borer, and the gypsy moth are all susceptible to a pathogen called *Serratia marcescens.* The potato tuberworm (*Gnorimoschema operculella*) is also subject to attack by this organism, which often causes epizootics among insects reared in insectaries. In nature it seldom causes an epizootic. Squash bugs (*Anasa tristis*) sometimes contract a form of septicemia which causes them to lose muscular power and to fall from the leaves to the ground. The bacteria give off a toxic substance which will quickly kill chinch bugs, flies, and certain other insects placed in a broth made from the diseased squash bugs. The affected insects stiffen—a condition referred to as "toxic rigor." Some insects suffer from streptococcus infections, one of which is sometimes associated with European foulbrood and another with gattine, a virus disease of silkworms. The gypsy moth suffers from an infection caused by *Streptococcus disparis*, which results in violent discharges of diarrhea. It can be distinguished from the "wilt disease," a virus infection, by the fact that the skin of the streptococcus-infected insect may be stretched without easily breaking it, whereas the skin of an insect infected with the virus breaks open at the slightest touch. Epizootics of the disease have been successfully initiated among gypsy moth populations in Massachusetts. A *Microccus* infection found in June beetle larvae (*Lachnosterna*) is quite common in soils of Michigan, Illinois, Maryland, and North Carolina. The joints of the legs and the soft white parts of the body are the focal points of infection. The body turns dark brown, but the insect continues to move about almost until it is dead. A peculiar sympom of the disease is its progress up the insect's leg: segment by segment it turns black and then falls off, leaving a stump.

In a three-year study of corn insects in Iowa, Earle S. Raun *et al.* found eight species of bacteria causing disease in the European corn borer; strangely, none of them was of the genus *Bacillus*.[38]

[38] Earle S. Raun and Derl L. Brooks, "Bacterial Pathogens in Iowa Corn Insects," *Journal of Insect Pathology*, March 1963.

They believe that numerous strains of bacteria exert a pressure on corn insect populations in Iowa—just how much is not known, but it is probably quite significant. This probably goes for many other insect pests as well.

RICKETTSIAL INFECTIONS

Rickettsiae, which are similar to bacteria, can be seen with an ordinary microscope but cannot be grown on artificial media. They are present in many insects as "symbiotes"—that is, they live in intimate relation with the insect without doing it harm. Some rickettsiae, however, are pathogenic to insects and to man, one of them (*Rickettsia prowazekii*) being the cause of typhus fever and responsible for some of the dreadful pestilences of the past. The disease is spread by the human louse (*Pediculus humanus*), which is not merely a carrier but also suffers from the disease.[39] The best known of rickettsial diseases affecting insects alone is the fatal "blue disease" of the Japanese beetle grub (and some other species). In the course of three weeks the infected grub becomes sluggish and turns a greenish blue from the effect on the fat body, while the blood becomes cloudy from the presence of numerous particles or "rickettsial bodies." Death ensues in from eight to sixteen weeks.[40]

FUNGUS DISEASES

Fungi belong to the subdivision of the plant kingdom known as thallophytes—organisms that grow as irregular masses or "thalli" and are not differentiated into roots, stems, and leaves as are the higher plants. Lacking the chlorophyll of green plants, they are characterized by interwoven threadlike masses of filaments called "mycelia." Molds and yeasts are fungi, and those that cause disease in insects are referred to as "entomogenous" fungi.

As might be expected, the first written reference to disease in

[39] Steinhaus, *Principles of Insect Pathology.*
[40] T. A. Angus, "Some Effects of Microbial Pathogens on Insects," *Proceedings of the Entomological Society of Ontario, 1960* (pub. Sept, 1961).

insects is by Aristotle, who observed certain abnormalities among bees that are almost certainly the familiar diseases found in bee colonies today. Other early writings dealt with abnormalities in silkworms. One of the earliest observations on microbial disease organisms in insects describes a vegetable growth emerging from the "Chinese plant worm"—apparently the larva of a cutworm. In 1749 Terrubia, a Franciscan monk in Cuba, found dead wasps which he referred to as "vegetable wasps" because of the "little trees" growing out of their bodies; it is now known that these growths were *Cordyceps* fungi. Early references were also made to a disease of domestic flies which was quite probably due to an *Entomophthora* fungus. These observations did not amount to a recognition of the microbial nature of the organisms. That recognition took place in 1834, when Agostino Bassi, an Italian and the first insect pathologist, showed experimentally that an infectious disease had been caused by a microorganism. This was the fungus infection commonly known in France as "muscardine," which was a serious disease of silkworm menageries at the time and is now known to be caused by *Beauveria bassiana*.[41]

SOME ENTOMOPHTHORA INFECTIONS

The Phycomycetes or "algal fungi" are a large group found in either aquatic or terrestrial habitats, or as amphibians in both. The members of the genus *Entomophthora* are primarily entomogenous and contain many species important in natural and biological control of insect pests. The life cycle and the nature of the infections are quite similar for all the species in this group.

Fungus infections in insects occur via the skin or "integument" —rarely through the mouth and digestive tract. The point of entry of the "hypha" is usually through the thinner parts between the body segments or around the appendages. The fungus spores or "conidia," after they become attached to the insect, germinate to produce "conidial hyphae" which penetrate the skin and grow

[41] E. A. Steinhaus, "Microbial Control—The Emergence of an Idea," *Hilgardia*, October 1956.

into the body cavity. Here they branch out as mycelia or become segmented, breaking apart into "hyphal bodies" which multiply by budding or fission until they fill the body cavity. If conditions of temperature and moisture are just right, the hyphae continue development; if not, they form the "chlamydospores" of the resting stage. When the hyphal bodies and chlamydospores "germinate" they may grow directly to the outside of the insect and produce a single conidium or a set of conidia. With germination the hyphal bodies produce conidia-bearing resting spores ("conidiophores"). The conidia vary in size and form with the species. If, upon being discharged, they come in contact with a suitable host, germination takes place, the hyphae are sent out to penetrate the host's integument, and the cycle is repeated. Those of the conidia that do not fall on a suitable host, or on a moist surface, produce secondary conidia which discharge their spores in the usual manner; if these do not land on a suitable host, they form tertiary conidia; and so on until it loses vitality or a host is found. The germination of the spores takes place soon after they are discharged; the time varies, but is seldom as long as a week.

The *Entomophthora* infections are found mostly among the Diptera, followed by the Hemiptera, Lepidoptera, Coleoptera in that order. However, some species of Hymenoptera, Orthoptera, and Neuroptera are also susceptible to these fungi. Adult insects are more often affected than the larvae or pupae; nymphs, where metamorphosis is incomplete, are almost as susceptible as the adults. The infected insects often climb to the top of their food plants—which helps spread the discharged spores over a wider area. Very few species of these fungi have been successfully cultivated on other media than their natural host. A simple way to propagate the fungi is to divide a jar by means of a wire netting, placing healthy insects in the bottom of the jar and infected insects in the top part, and putting the lid on tight; the discharged spores will pass through the wire net and infect the insects below.

The common housefly (*Musca domestica*) is quite susceptible to the fungus *Entomophthora muscae*. Infected flies seek ceilings and windows indoors, where the dead ones are often seen adhering; the halo effect around those attached to the glass is produced by the discharged spores. *Entomophthora grylli*, a common infection of grasshoppers, was brought to the United States from Africa in 1896. Good results attended the early releases of infected material, but the exacting requirements of temperature and moisture made it impractical to continue distribution. Infected grasshoppers succumb to the disease about five or six days after being contaminated. Before dying they crawl to the top of the plant; unable to hold on with their claws, they grasp the blade of grass with their legs, which stiffen and hold them to the plant until the rains or wind knock them off.

Entomophthora sphaerosperma ranges through practically all orders of insects, and was first found in the cabbage butterfly, *Pieris brassicae*. It has been grown artificially on a medium of swordfish and potatoes. Epizootics of the disease have been noted among the larvae of the diamondback moth (*Plutella maculti-pennis*) in South Africa, where it is at times an important factor in control. In advanced stages of the disease the larvae become sluggish and gradually turn from green to yellow. The body becomes slightly enlarged, and before the hyphae protrude to the outside it becomes very brittle. There is little if any body fluid left and the cadaver disintegrates if lightly pressed. The pathogen was artificially disseminated in Nova Scotia apple orchards, with considerable success, to combat the apple sucker, *Psylla mali*. Leaves with diseased insects attached were pinned on the leaves of trees where the infection was not present, and diseased insects still able to fly were released in the infested but disease-free orchard. The contagion was spread throughout the orchards two or three weeks after "planting." This made it possible to produce the effects of biological control sooner than could have been done by building up material in cages early in the season.

At least fourteen described species of entomophthoraceous fungi attack various species of aphids throughout the world, according to Hall and Dunn,[42] who have isolated five new species

[42] Irvin M. Hall and Paul H. Dunn, "Entomophthorous Fungi Parasitic on the Spotted Alfalfa Aphid," *Hilgardia*, Sept. 1957.

from the spotted alfalfa aphid (*Therioaphis maculata*), occurring in California; two of these were found in specimens collected in India, Iraq, and Israel. The most important species for control of the spotted alfalfa aphid in California is *Entomophthora exitialis.* The spread of these fungi by natural and artificial means in a number of counties in California was spectacular, and resulted in "widespread control of the aphids by fungi." During the summer of 1956 over 1,800 cultures were placed in infested fields in twelve counties. It was believed that as these fungi become more evenly distributed, they would "become an important part of the predator-parasite-disease complex in the biological control of the spotted alfalfa aphid."[43]

The "browntail fungus," *Entomophthora aulicae,* attacks several species of insects besides the browntail moth (*Nygmia phaeorrhoea*). Epizootics occur naturally in browntail moth caterpillar populations and have been induced artificially with success. Another of these infections, *Entomophthora fumosa,* is believed to be the reason why the citrus mealybug (*Pseudococcus citri*) is less of a problem in Florida citrus groves than it has been in California. Climatic conditions—especially temperature and humidity—during the growing season in Florida are more suited to the development of the fungus than in California.

In 1923 an uncommon but interesting fungus called *Entomophthora erupta* was first observed in the apple-growing area of Nova Scotia on the green apple bug (*Lygus communis*); the only other report of this fungus came twenty-five years later from the opposite shores of the continent. Hall discovered an epizootic of the disease in a large population of the black grass bug (*Irbisia solani*) on the grounds of the University of California Citrus Experiment Station in Riverside.[44] The black bug is common in the

---

[43] Hall and Dunn, "Fungi on Spotted Alfalfa Aphid: Spread of fungi by natural and artificial means is resulting in excellent biological control of aphid in many countries," *California Agriculture,* Feb. 1957.

[44] Irvin M. Hall, "The Fungus *Entomophthora erupta* (Dunstan) Attacking the Black Bug, *Irbisia solani* (Heidemann) (Hemiptera, Miridae), in California," *Journal of Insect Pathology,* May 1959.

western states, and had apparently developed to large numbers in response to the high rainfall and lush grass in the spring of 1958. It is believed that the fungus may be specific to the bug family Miridae. A characteristic feature of the disease is a grotesque swelling of the bug's abdomen as a result of the pressure of the growing mass of fungus, resulting in a breaking apart of the body segments.

A new species of entomophthoraceous fungus, *Entomophthora creatonotus* was recently found by David Yen in Taiwan after he had observed an epizootic among a population of tiger moth larvae (*Creatonotus gangis*).[45] A characteristic of the fungus is its large conidia. It was also found at this time that the armyworm, *Pseudaletia unipuncta,* was highly susceptible to the disease; in field trials, effective control of the pest was obtained with *Creatonotus* material produced on an artificial medium. This is one of the few entomophthoraceous fungi that can be cultivated outside their hosts. The medium consisted of nutrient agar, maltose agar, fresh pork, fish, egg yolk, and potatoes. At the University of California Biological Control Laboratories in Riverside, eight or more entomophthoraceous fungi are under continuous culture.

CORDYCEPS INFECTIONS

According to Steinhaus, there are over 200 known species of fungi belonging to the genus *Cordyceps*, about 40 of which occur in the United States.[46] Most of them are parasitic on insects. They produce the familiar stemlike growths (hyphae) that are seen protruding from the dead insect; the stem and the club or head at the end—which is often brightly colored—are called the "stroma." The "head" contains the spores or fertile portion of the fungus; as these mature the head swells and breaks open, releasing them. The stem and head take on various odd and often

[45] David F. Yen, "An Entomophthora Infection in the Larva of the Tiger Moth, *Creatonotus gangis* (Linnaeus)," *Journal of Insect Pathology*, March 1962.

[46] Steinhaus, *Principles of Insect Pathology*.

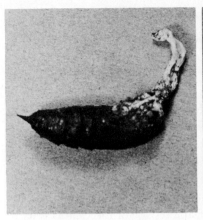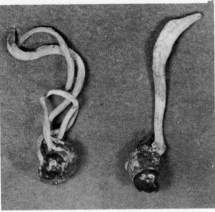

Two species of *Cordyceps* fungi: *left, Cordyceps militaris* growing from pupa of the orange-striped oakworm (*Anisota senatoria*); *right, Cordyceps melolonthae* growing from unidentified scarabaeid beetle larvae, collected from a garden in Guatemala City, Guatemala. (*E. A. Steinhaus* and *G. A. Marsh*)

grotesque shapes; in many instances they resemble mushrooms or "toadstools." These are the "vegetables" and "trees" described by early observers of fungus infections which they could not explain.

Not the least of the interesting things about *Cordyceps* is that they are used as food in some parts of the world. In China, caterpillars infected with this fungus are considered a delicacy and a tonic food, and at least until recently they could be purchased in herb shops in San Francisco's Chinatown.[47] The caterpillars are made into a broth. Szechwan Province in China is—or at any rate used to be—the trade center for the product, where infected caterpillars with long strands of fungus growth were wrapped in neat little packages of a dozen or so and sent to all parts of China. Their relative scarcity made them expensive, and only the well-to-do or those of the middle class could afford them. Whether the Peoples' Republic sanctions this traffic we have no way of as-

[47] Edward A. Steinhaus, "Microbial Control—The Emergence of an Idea: A Brief History of Insect Pathology Through the Nineteenth Century," *Hilgardia*, Oct. 1956.

certaining. An American scientist, W. E. Hoffman, sampled the delicacy while traveling in China and described it as "quite tasty." Perhaps the flavor and therapeutic properties of this gourmet's delight are the result of some mysterious transformation inherent in the predigestion twice over of the insect's plant food—first by the insect and then by the fungus—before it reaches the human consumer.

SOME FUNGUS INFECTIONS OF SCALE INSECTS

Many species of fungi are parasitic on scale insects and are an important factor in their control, especially in the tropical countries, where temperature and humidity are often conducive to their development. Several *Sphaerostilbe* infections are important in control of various scales in North and South America and in the Orient. In Florida and the West Indies, S. *aurantiicola* is found on a multitude of scales, such as the Florida red scale, California red scale, Spanish red scale, Putham scale, San Jose scale, green scale, purple scale, black scale, snow scale, ivy scale, thread scale, chaff scale, rufous scale, and Glover scale. (The importance of these fungi has been questioned by some specialists in this field.) Infections by two species of *Nectria* are important in control of scale insects. One with pink stroma, called the "pink fungus" (*N. diploa*), is found in Florida as well as many other parts of the world. It is an important factor in control of the Florida red scale and has been disseminated artificially with success. *Podonectria coccicola* was one of the first fungi to be recognized in Florida as parasitic on scales; found on purple scale, Glover scale, and chaff scale, it occurs in South America and the Orient as well. It was believed to have saved the citrus industry in Florida when the Glover scale was introduced there in 1830.

SOME COELOMOMYCES INFECTIONS OF MOSQUITOES

Twenty-three species of the genus *Coelomomyces* are known, chiefly as causing diseases of mosquitoes; in some instances they have been very effective in controlling mosquito populations, and are generally recognized as having considerable potential for biological control. Coelomomyces infections are found in mosquitoes of the genera *Aedes, Anopheles,* and *Culex,* as well as *Psorophora* and *Uranotaenia.* It is not definitely known whether the disease is transmitted to the mosquito larvae by way of the mouth and digestive tract or through the integument; at any rate, it develops within the body cavity, with mycelia and spores often growing within the head. Although development is usually completed in the larvae, it is not uncommon for an infection occurring in the late larval stage to carry over into the pupal or adult state. In the surviving adult females the fungus generally develops in the ovaries.

Coelomomyces psorophorae has been recently found to occur in *Aedes taeniorhynchus* and *Psorophora howardii* in Florida.[48] Infected females appear normal in that they continue to bite and to take their blood meals, but their eggs fail to mature, owing to the rapid growth of the mycelia and the development of spores. The larvae of *P. howardii,* are predaceous in certain stages, but whether they spread the disease is not known. It is clear that rapid dissemination of the fungus can occur, since in the experimental plots used in Lum's studies it established itself within a year. The adults are believed to be one of the disseminating agents since resting bodies of the fungus are found in them.

SOME FUNGUS DISEASES OF WHITE FLIES

Five species of fungi infect the whiteflies, which are serious pests of citrus.[49] They are of course not true flies but homopterans, along with aphids, scale insects, treehoppers, leafhoppers, and the like, and do not have a complete metamorphosis; the nymphs are the stage commonly attacked by the fungi. The citrus whitefly (*Dialeurodes citri*) and the cloudy-winged whitefly (*Dialeurodes*

[48] Patrick T. M. Lum, "The Infection of *Aedes taeniorhynchus* (Wiedemann) and *Psorophora howardii* Coquillett by the Fungus Coelomomyces," *Journal of Insect Pathology,* June 1963.
[49] Steinhaus, *Principles of Insect Pathology.*

citrifolii) are the most important of their kind in Florida. A whitefly nymph infected by the fungus *Aschersonia aleyrodis,* commonly called "red aschersonia," becomes swollen and secretes more honeydew than usual; after it dies, the hyphae break through to the outside of its body, forming a fringe around its edge, and develop red pustules containing spores. The fungus has been cultivated using sweet potatoes as a medium, and large quantities were distributed by a fairly simple process. Sterilized slices of sweet potato were inoculated and placed in pint bottles; in from thirty to forty days matured cultures were ready and bottles were sent out to growers, or kept in storage if not immediately needed. Growers simply added water to the jar and then shook and filtered its contents through cheesecloth to obtain a suspension for spraying. One pint was sufficient for an acre of orchard in the moist period of June and July.

Aschersonia goldiana, the "yellow aschersonia," resembles the red aschersonia fungus except for the color of the spore pustules, and can be cultivated in the same way. "Webber's brown fungus" —*Aegerita webberi*—attacks the *Dialeurodes* flies in Florida; it is also found in the West Indies, Ceylon, India, and New Zealand, and in Cuba it attacks the citrus blackfly. Dark brown stroma cover the entire insect, and later in its development the hyphae extend over the entire leaf, exposing large quantities of spores to be carried away by the wind. For this reason the fungus is one of the most efficient natural controls of the whiteflies. It has not been successfully grown on cultural media, so artificial dissemination has been by such more direct methods as pinning fungus-bearing leaves on infested trees not having the fungus, or making a suspension from the spores washed off fungus-bearing leaves.

SOME MUSCARDINE DISEASES

The word "muscardine" was first applied to the silkworm fungus that plagued French and Italian sericulturists in the early part of the last century. It comes from a French word for the bonbon or comfit, a confection covered with powdered sugar, to which the dead silkworms covered with white fungus have a certain resemblance. Diseased insects are easily recognized by the characteristic thick, white covering composed of the fruiting bodies. "Muscardine" is now generally applied to all those diseases characterized by the appearance of the fruiting bodies on the exterior of the insect to produce such a covering. The fungi themselves, because they are known principally in their imperfect stages, are spoken of as "fungi imperfecti."

Beauveria bassiana, like most other entomogenous fungi, enters the insect through the integument, not more than two days after the spores or conidia have become attached to the skin. With warm temperatures and proper humidity, the spores germinate and send out mycelial filaments or conidial hyphae that penetrate the skin. Development in the body is generally the same as that already described; in the blood, short hyphal bodies form, gradually consuming the blood cells and reducing its volume. Solid tissues such as the fat body are not attacked until after the insect dies; following death, the body takes on a reddened or pinkish hue and gradually hardens. Death is believed to be due in part at least to the toxic effects of the disease; it was found that under conditions of high humidity, houseflies could be knocked out quickly by dusting with germinating spores. Silkworms do not appear to possess any natural immunity to the disease.

According to Steinhaus, at least thirty species of insects on the North American continent are susceptible to *Beauveria bassiana.*[50] Of these one of the most sensitive to the disease is the European corn borer (*Ostrinia nubilalis*). Although infection is largely by way of the integument, as it is in the silkworm, there is some evidence that it may be contracted by way of the alimentary tract as well. Externally, manifestations of the disease are about the same as in the silkworm. The larva becomes sluggish and turns pink or red soon after infection; when the hyphae or mycelial filaments have filled the body cavity and penetrated the various tissues, the body becomes rigid. Mummification takes

[50] *Ibid.*

Adults of *Brachyrhinus cribricollis*, a beetle of the destructive Curculionidae family, killed by infection with a fungus, *Beauveria bassiana*. The beetles were killed in the soil and not able to emerge. The fungus reduced the beetle population in an artichoke field near Castroville, California, in a period of one week, and "appeared to give effective control." (*W. H. Lange*)

place and the body becomes crisp and easily broken, and can be crumbled into a chalky white powder. The fungus is not apparent so long as the mummified body remains dry, but when it is moistened the white mycelia can be seen. After a time in a moist atmosphere, conidia develop in great numbers, giving the mummified remains a powdery look.

Some other important insect pests are also susceptible to *Beauveria bassiana*. The codling moth (*Carpocapsa pomenella*) is very sensitive to the disease, which occasionally exerts a significant natural control over this pest. Cool, wet seasons are most conducive to the development and spread of the disease. In New Jersey artificial dissemination of the fungus in field trials was successful in controlling the codling moth. Larvae infected with the disease exhibit dark brown lesions of the skin. *B. bassiana* can be grown on almost any of the artificial media commonly used for such purposes. Soy-bean mash and moistened wheat bran have been used with success. Spores have been produced on a large scale in Petri dishes using dried beans (or various bulk vegetables) as a medium. Hall obtained a yield of 35 grams of spores from a European corn borer strain of the fungus grown on fifty-one large Petri dishes—or about .7 gram per dish.[51] The fungus grew well on several media, including the ordinary breakfast variety of rolled oats, nutrient agar, and wheat bran. The fungus retains it virulence for long periods of time when kept on artificial media or as pure spores at temperatures near or below freezing.

Metalnikov and others have reported successful attempts to control the European corn borer in Europe with *B. bassiana*. Tests in the United States also show the fungus to be a potential biological control agent for this insect. Other important insect pests susceptible to *B. bassiana* are the Japanese beetle (*Popillia japonica*), Colorado potato beetle (*Leptinotarsa decemlineata*), Mexican bean beetle (*Epilachna varivestis*), housefly (*Musca domestica*), rice weevil (*Sitophilus oryza*), confused flour beetle (*Tribolium confusum*), black carpet beetle (*Attagenus piceus*), bean weevil (*Acanthoscelides obtectus*) American cockroach (*Periplaneta americana*), and cabbage butterfly (*Pieris brassicae*). In tests made in New York the Mexican bean beetle was successfully controlled by artificial dissemination of the disease.

In California Hall demonstrated that one of the sod webworms, *Crambus bonifatellus,* an important pest of lawns, is very susceptible to *B. bassiana.* In field trials, good control of the webworm was obtained from spore dust applications, the right conditions of temperature and moisture being present. (*Bacillus thuringiensis* was more effective because it is not limited in this way.) The

[51] Irvin M. Hall, "Studies of Microorganisms Pathogenic to the Sod Webworm," *Hilgardia*, Feb. 1954

bassiana spores do not mix well with water, but require a wetting agent; a spore-talc dust, however, was a more effective method of application. Two different strains of the fungus were used, one from the corn borer and the other from a species of *Crambus;* the latter was more effective against the late-stage larvae.

Weevils (Curculionidae) are generally susceptible to *Beauveria bassiana.* Investigations in Texas using a spore dust preparation showed that *B. bassiana* can infect the larvae, pupae, and adults of the boll weevil (*Anthonomus grandis*) under conditions of high moisture.[52] In Iowa similar results were obtained with *Calomycterus setarius,* a weevil indigenous to Japan but now widespread in the United States.[53]

WHITE MUSCARDINE AND THE CHINCH BUG

The chinch bug, *Blissus leucopterus,* one of the most important insect pests of cereal crops, is susceptible to at least six species of fungus, the most important being *Beauveria bassiana.* The white muscardine fungus almost covers the infected insect with a white, cottony growth. Infection is through the integument; when humidity is high, the conidial spores on the insect's skin germinate and send germ tubes through the body wall. The hyphae fill the body cavity and finally penetrate to the outside wall, covering the insect with a cottony white mycelium. All stages of the bug are susceptible but the older ones are especially so; death usually comes about three days after infection.

In Kansas and some other western states, large-scale propagation and distribution of *B. bassiana* for control of the chinch bug was carried on from 1890 until 1900, when the programs were generally abandoned. These programs were sometimes quite effective during the first two years, according to reports, but ap-

[52] Roy Earl McLaughlin, "Infectivity Tests with *Beauveria bassiana* (Balsamo) Vuillemin on *Anthonomus grandis* Boheman," *Journal of Insect Pathology,* Sept. 1962.

[53] Richard D. Frye and Earle S. Raun, "Preliminary Laboratory Tests Utilizing *Beauveria bassiana* (Balsamo) Vuillemin on *Calomycterus setarius* Roelofs," *Journal of Insect Pathology,* Sept. 1961.

peared not to make much difference after that—apparently
because once the infection is present naturally in the insect population, little is to be gained by adding more spores to the field.
The fungus is generally present where chinch bugs are found,
and is probably the most important natural enemy of the insect;
but its effect depends on the weather and is not increased by
artificial dissemination of additional spores.

Beauveria bassiana also attacks the pupae and adults of the elm
leaf beetle (*Galerucella xanthomelaena*) in late summer, especially during moist seasons, and is at times a very important
natural control factor operating against this pest.[54]

GREEN MUSCARDINE

Seventy-one species of insects in the United States and possibly
as many more in other countries are susceptible to *Metarrhizium
anisopliae,* commonly called "green muscardine" because of its
dark green conidia or spores. It is closely related to *Penicillium.*
Both the silkworm and the European corn borer are susceptible
to the disease. After the discovery in 1879 by investigators in
Russia that the wheat cockchafer (*Anisoplia austriaca*) and the
sugar-beet curculio (*Cleonus punctiventris*) could be infected artificially, the fungus, was widely used as a control agent; methods
were devised to produce and distribute it on a fairly large scale.
Much later (1931) in Europe the fungus was used experimentally
to control the corn borer, with some success, but it has not been
tried on a large scale. It was used successfully in Trinidad (1910)
against the froghopper (*Tomaspis varia*), a pest of sugar cane.
Large quantities of the spore material were cultured in specially
constructed cabinets, and a mixture of spore dust and flour were
dusted on the plants at the rate of two or three pounds per acre.

An interesting application of *Metarrhizium anisopliae* to biological control of the rhinoceros beetle (*Oryctes rhinoceros*), a
pest of the coconut, was reported (1913) to be very successful

[54] *The Elm Leaf Beetle* (Washington: USDA Leaflet No. 184, Dec.
1952).

in Java. Traps baited with rotted coconut husks and other debris, and containing beetles infested with the fungus, were scattered throughout the coconut groves. Beetles in the area were attracted to the traps, where they laid their eggs, and the hatching larvae promptly acquired the contagion. *M. anisopliae* is very widely distributed and is on the whole a valuable control agent. Where it is not established, introductions of the pathogen can be useful, but in most cases they do not appear to help disseminate the spores where the disease is already present.

The so-called fungi imperfecti include a multitude of species besides those already mentioned, and the references to them can only be very brief. Six species of *Penicillium* are known to be infectious for North American insects. The genus *Spicaria* includes a number of entomogenous species. *Spicaria farinosa* attacks insects in several orders—Coleoptera, Lepidoptera, Hymenoptera, Diptera, and among the Homoptera, the Aphididae. *Spicaria heliothis* is parasitic on the corn earworm; *S. canadensis* on the larvae of the satin moth; and *S. rileyi* on several Coleoptera and Lepidoptera.

L. W. Getzin observed an epizootic caused by *S. rileyi* among the cabbage loopers (*Trichoplusia ni*) in the lower Rio Grande valley of Texas during the winter of 1958 and 1959, a period of high humidities and abnormally heavy rainfall.[55] The progress of the disease is similar to that of other muscardine fungi. The infected insect turns yellowish or brown as the hyphae of the germinated spores penetrate the integument of the looper and ramify throughout its body. The diseased larva becomes sluggish, and after death is stiff and mummified. Under conditions of sufficient moisture green conidia develop in great abundance on the body of the insect. Investigations were undertaken to determine the effectiveness of the pathogen as a control agent for the cabbage looper. Spores of *Spicaria rileyi* were grown on a medium

[55] L. W. Getzin, "*Spicaria rileyi* (Farlow) Charles, an Entomogenous Fungus of *Trichoplusia ni* (Hubner)," *Journal of Insect Pathology*, March 1961.

composed of ground potatoes, egg yolk, yeast, Bacto-peptone, and agar, and distributed artificially in a field where no natural infection of the fungus was apparent. *Bacillus thuringiensis* and a polyhedrosis virus were also distributed for comparison. The mortality produced by *B. thuringiensis* was the earliest—beginning three or four days after treatment—but its total (60 per cent) was not the highest. The virus disease produced a mortality of 86 per cent, but required thirteen days to reach its peak. *S. rileyi* produced a 67 per cent mortality but required sixteen days to reach its peak. These observations and tests show that high humidities and rainfall are required for the fungus to be really effective, but that artificial dissemination under favorable conditions would be practical.

> . . . *There is reason to believe that the use of microorganisms*
> *may have a significant place among the efforts of man to*
> *protect himself from the ravage of insects—his number one*
> *competitor on earth.*
>
> —EDWARD A. STEINHAUS

VIRUS AND OTHER INFECTIONS

11

Viruses are so small that they can't be seen with an ordinary microscope and will pass through a thick porcelain filter. They first attracted interest around the turn of the century, when it was noticed that the mosaic disease of tobacco could be transmitted to another plant from filtered juices that were free of bacteria. The name "filterable virus" was first applied to these, but *filterable* was dropped when it became known that certain bacteria and other agents were also capable of passing through filters in the same way. Viruses are "obligate parasites"—that is, they cannot be grown on ordinary cultural media, apart from living cells, as bacteria can. Some question has been raised as to whether they are actually living substances; the electron microscope shows them at any rate to be distinct entities and to have various shapes not unlike those of the bacteria.

VIRUS INFECTIONS

Viruses found in insects are similar to other viruses that cause disease in higher animals and plants, except that some insect viruses produce peculiar crystal-like polyhedral (many-sided) bodies in the cells of infected tissues; these "inclusion bodies" are found only in insects. Not all insect viruses are of this kind, however; some of them produce a granular inclusion body, and others are "free viruses," which produce no inclusion bodies at all. The virus infections that produce polyhedral inclusions are called "polyhedroses"; those producing granular inclusions are called "granuloses." The polyhedral crystals are still something of a mystery. They are not the virus itself but contain the virus particles; they have the nature of protein and can be separated from the virus, which remains infectious without them.[1]

Polyhedroses are of two types: those whose polyhedral inclusions develop in the cellular nuclei of the host tissues, and those that develop in the cytoplasm (the contents of the cell surrounding the nucleus). Nuclear polyhedrosis is the most common insect virus and is found mainly in the Lepidoptera, although some Diptera and notably some Hymenoptera (chiefly sawflies) are susceptible. The infection is an important natural control factor in populations of the latter; from all indications it also has potentialities as a biological control.

Insects infected with polyhedrosis may become limp and slightly swollen, and often turn paler in color as a result of the large number of inclusion bodies in the blood serum; the skin may become fragile, and if it is broken a milky-white substance oozes out. Death occurs within a few days, or at most a week or two, where dosage, temperature, the condition of host, and other factors have been favorable to the development of the disease. Within the cell, small granules first appear in the nucleus, which gradually increases in size as the polyhedra develop; these increase in size and number until the nucleus bursts. Gradually the cell also is filled and then disintegrates, releasing the polyhedra; as more cells are destroyed the infected tissues and organs deteriorate.[2] The polyhedra and viruses produce distinct char-

[1] Edward A. Steinhaus, *Principles of Insect Pathology* (New York: McGraw-Hill Book Co., 1949).

[2] T. A. Angus, "Some Effects of Microbial Pathogens on Insects" (Symposium: Insect Pathology), *Proceedings of the Entomological Society of Ontario*, Sept. 1961.

acteristics in each insect species—the jaundice of the silkworm, for example, being distinct from the "wilt disease" of the gypsy moth.

In the granulosis type of virus, the small inclusion bodies that develop in the cytoplasm of the cell are ellipsoidal in shape. Double infection—both granuloses and polyhedroses in one insect—although rare, is known to occur. The armyworm *Pseudaletia unipuncta* is attacked by three different viruses—a nuclear polyhedrosis, a granulosis, and a noninclusion virus—and may become infected with the nuclear polyhedrosis and the granulosis at the same time. It is believed that the two together have a synergistic effect, making the combination more effective than either alone, and that this plays an important part in virus epizootics in field populations of the armyworm.[3]

Noninclusion or free viruses appear to be scarce in insect populations, but one of special interest was found in 1958 in the citrus red mite (*Panonychus citri*) near Oxnard, California.[4] These mites have developed resistance to chemicals and have become increasingly difficult to control. The virus infection may be introduced into colonies of mites with a very dilute aqueous suspension made from diseased mites, or by releasing inoculated mites; severe infections and mortality have been produced in laboratory colonies by either method. Mites must ingest the material to become infected. Suspensions of the material are not very stable when exposed to sunlight; gelatin appeared to have the greatest promise as an additive to prolong the infective period. Field trials have been difficult to evaluate, and no definite conclusions as to the biological control potential of the virus can be drawn at this time.

The list of insect species susceptible to viruses grows as research

[3] Y. Tanada, "Descriptions and Characteristics of a Nuclear Polyhedrosis Virus and a Granulosis Virus of the Armyworm, *Pseudaletia unipuncta* (Haworth) Lepidoptera, Noctuidae"; also "Synergism between Two Viruses of the Armyworm," *Journal of Insect Pathology*, Oct. 1959.

[4] J. E. Gilmore and F. Munger, "Stability and Transmissibility of a Virus-like Pathogen of the Citrus Red Mite," *Journal of Insect Pathology*, June 1963.

in this field continues. About fifteen years ago Steinhaus indicated that approximately 100 species of insects were known to be susceptible to viruses;[5] in 1957 Kenneth Hughes listed nearly 200 species of insects harboring insect viruses, as indicated by published reports.[6] (For a partial list of these insects see the Appendix.) Martignoni and Langston have expanded this list to well over 200 species and have added numerous references.[7]

TRANSMISSION OF VIRUS DISEASES

Although no virus will grow on a cell-free medium, successful mass production techniques for biological control of the alfalfa caterpillar and other insects have been worked out, using infected caterpillars for propagation. Suspensions in water can be applied with low-volume sprayers and even mist blowers, or sprayed from airplanes. The nuclear polyhedroses have certain properties that lend themselves to natural and biological control. The fact that they attack the cells of the fat body, blood, skin, and tracheae, producing a tendency for the body to become liquefied and the skin to become fragile and to erupt, is important in the dissemination of the disease. With the rupture of the skin, the polyhedra containing the virus particles are well spread out over the plant or tree and the chances for contagion are thus increased. In the cytoplasmic polyhedroses there is a tendency for the body to become desiccated; but the virus is excreted in the feces and is spread partly by this means. The polyhedra are important in the dissemination of the disease since they help to protect the virus and enable it to survive long periods of exposure in a viable state. They can persist in an insect environment for many years, remaining inactive until the susceptible host increases in sufficient numbers to initiate an epizootic. For the same reason, they can be produced in quantities and stored easily.

[5] Steinhaus, *Principles of Insect Pathology*.

[6] Kenneth M. Hughes, "An Annotated List and Bibliography of Insects Reported to Have Virus Diseases," *Hilgardia*, May 1957.

[7] Mauro E. Martignoni and Robert L. Langston, "Supplement to an Annotated List and Biblography of Insects Reported to Have Virus Diseases," *Hilgardia*, June 1960.

Another interesting attribute of viruses—and one important for biological control—is that they can be transmitted from one generation of the susceptible insect to the next, thus assuring the survival of the population and its spread from one area to another. Insects infected late in the season can harbor the virus and transmit it by way of the egg to their progeny the following season. The technical name for this phenomenon is "transovarial transmission," and is applied both when the virus merely becomes attached to the surface of the egg and is thus communicated to the offspring, and when it is actually transmitted within the egg. The same thing occurs in the vectors of microorganisms causing diseases in man and animals, and to some extent in those transmitting plant diseases. According to Steinhaus, certain protozoa and viruses are transmitted in this way but there is no evidence that it occurs in any of the bacteria or fungi that cause diseases in insects.[8]

The classic example of disease transmission by this means occurs in "pebrine" (*Nosema bombycis*), a microsporidian (protozoan) disease of the silkworm, *Bombyx mori,* which Pasteur was able to control only by preventing the use of contaminated eggs. This type of transmission occurs in both polyhedral and granular viruses. According to K. M. Smith, the granulosis viruses are transmitted to progeny of the white butterflies (*Pieris brassicae* and *P. rapae*)*,* and the polyhedral viruses are transmitted from parent to offspring in the European pine sawfly *Neodiprion sertifer.* As an interesting sidelight he also reports that the semi-liquid remains of *P. brassicae* larvae that have succumbed to granuloses appear to have an attraction for the healthy larvae, a predilection that proves fatal.[9] F. T. Bird noted that of the polyhedrosis virus controlling the European spruce sawfly *Diprion*

[8] Edward A. Steinhaus, "The Effects of Disease on Insect Populations," *Hilgardia,* December 1954.

[9] Kenneth M. Smith, "Some Factors in the Use of Pathogens in Biological Control with Special Reference to Viruses," in *Report of the Seventh Commonwealth Entomological Conference,* 6th-15th July 1960 (London: Commonwealth Institute of Entomology, December 1960).

hercyniae in Ontario, nearly all that remained on the trees was washed off by the rains during the winter, and that the initial infection each year was due to transmission of the virus via the eggs of infected adults. Similar conclusions were drawn from his studies of the epizootics of the virus disease in the European pine sawfly, *Neodiprion sertifer*.[10]

Some insects possess a natural immunity to diseases, in part as a result of nutritional factors, but they are not known to develop resistance to viruses or other diseases as they are able to do against chemical insecticides. By the time an epizootic dies out the survivors have completed their metamorphosis or migrated, or are dead from some other cause. As biological control agents, a combination of two viruses or bacteria and a virus seems to have a synergistic effect in some cases, making them more effective than either one alone. Alfalfa caterpillar populations can be reduced faster than is otherwise possible with a mixture of a polyhedral virus and bacteria, but the effect appears not to last as long. A mixture of *Bacillus thuringienis* and a polyhedral virus has been suggested as being more effective against the cabbage looper than either alone.

LATENT INFECTIONS

Another interesting thing about viruses—and one of some significance for biological control—is that many insects have latent virus infections which may be triggered by such stress factors as crowding or changes of temperature and humidity. A latent infection can sometimes be stimulated artificially by the use of another virus. Smith was able to do this experimentally with larvae of the winter moth (*Operophtera brumata*) by feeding them on leaves coated with a nuclear polyhedrosis from diseased larvae of the painted lady butterfly (*Vanessa cardui*). The winter moth larvae died—not from the *Vanessa* virus but from

[10] F. T. Bird, "The Use of a Virus Disease in the Biological Control of the European Spruce Sawfly, *Diprion hercyniae* (Htg.)," *Bi-monthly Progress Report,* Canada Dept. of Agriculture, Jan.-Feb. 1954.

a latent *cytoplasmic* polyhydrosis. The virus obtained in this way was now infective for other winter moth larvae. According to Smith, cross-transmission of a virus disease from one insect to another not already susceptible to virus attack is another interesting possibility. He has succeeded in producing this with a new virus known as the *Tipula* iridescent virus, found in the larvae of a fly called the leatherjacket (*Tipula paludosa*). The virus produces crystals with a blue or violet iridescence in the infected larvae, making for positive identification in its new host. The disease has been successfully transmitted to many species of Lepidoptera and Coleoptera, as well as Diptera; these include the blowfly or bluebottle fly (*Calliphora vomitoria*), the white or European cabbage butterfly (*Pieris brassicae*), the gypsy moth (*Porthetria [Lymantria] dispar*), and a mealworm (*Tenebrio molitor*). Large-scale production methods have been perfected for the *Tipula* iridescent virus, using *Pieris brassicae* caterpillars and a technique similar to that used for mass-producing granulosis viruses.

SOME POLYHEDRAL VIRUSES

The first virus disease to attract attention was polyhedrosis of the silkworm (*Bombyx mori*). For many years, however, it was confused with other diseases of the silkworm, and identification did not occur until the polyhedral bodies were observed. The disease is called "jaundice" in America because of the diseased insects' yellowish hue and "grasserie" in France because of their swollen bodies. Although the matter is not settled, other insects do not appear to be susceptible to silkworm jaundice under normal conditions; however, the gypsy moth and others have been infected experimentally.

Polyhedrosis of the nun moth (*Lymantria monacha*) was first observed in Europe around 1890, when it took a heavy toll of the pest larvae at the height of a severe infestation of the spruce forests. Epizootics occur after a population buildup, about every two or three years. Early attempts to initiate epizootics artificially included releases in the forest of larvae that had been fed diseased material, the spraying of suspensions made from infected insects, and the shooting of infectious material to the top of the trees with a mortar—none of which were very successful. Later attempts in Bavaria that consisted of bringing in heavily infested forest litter were reported to have been successful. It has been observed that tachinid parasites tend to migrate from areas heavily infested with the virus; normally they attack the older larvae, but late stages of diseased larvae are ignored. Infectious material, if kept dry, will remain viable for as long as three years.

Perhaps the best known of the virus diseases is the so-called "wilt disease" of the gypsy moth (*Porthetria dispar*). It first attracted attention in this country in 1907 when large numbers of dead, half-grown larvae were observed in various places where moth infestations were high. It was not recognized as a virus until 1913. The distinctive pattern of the disease makes recognition relatively easy: the virus spreads rapidly, leaving numerous dead caterpillars hanging limp from the trunk and branches of the tree; if disturbed slightly the skin breaks and the dark brown, liquefied body contents ooze out. The tendency of the diseased larvae to seek a higher position on the tree tends to favor the spread of the disease to the rest of the population. The liquefied larvae are odorless until attacked by bacteria and putrefaction sets in. The virus retains its viability for two years, and can be transmitted via the egg from one generation to the next. It appears to be specific to the gypsy moth, but has been transmitted experimentally to the silkworm and nun moth.

It has been demonstrated in Egypt that a serious pest, the cotton leafworm (*Prodenia litura*), can be successfully controlled by a spray suspension made from an indigenous polyhedrosis virus.[11] In tests the leafworm was held to noneconomic levels even though the timing was not ideal, the spray having been applied to early stages of the caterpillar. (Growers are advised to

[11] Salah Abul-Nasr, "Further Tests on the Use of a Polyhedrosis Virus in the Control of the Cotton Leafworm, *Prodenia litura* Fabricus," *Journal of Insect Pathology,* Aug. 1959.

apply the spray three days after the egg masses are laid.) An interesting phenomenon noted in the test was that the larvae in nearby untreated plots were attracted by the stench of the diseased larvae in the test plots, producing a large migration from one to the other.

On three occasions in recent years—in 1942-1943, in 1953-1954, and in 1961—severe outbreaks of the linden looper (*Erannis tiliaria*) have occurred in the sugar maple stands of eastern Quebec.[12] A natural epizootic of nuclear polyhedrosis was found to be the cause of a sudden collapse of the outbreak in 1961, and is believed to have been the controlling factor of the other two instances as well. The first signs of the latest outbreak were noted in mid-May. On the basis of a survey of 5,000 square miles of the hardwood area, two zones of infestation were mapped: a moderate-to-severe area, ellipsoidal in shape, 50 miles long and 30 miles across at its widest part, and one of light infestation comprising the remainder of the surveyed area. In all, over a million acres of forest area were involved. The first signs of the disease were noted in one locality about mid-June.

During early stages of the disease it is difficult to distinguish the infected larvae from the healthy ones, and they continue to feed until a few hours before death. When feeding stops, the larvae become sluggish and wander about aimlessly on the leaves. The skin pigment lightens and the body contents turn to a thick, creamy white liquid which is released and causes the disintegrated carcass to stick to the leaves. The disease is highly contagious, and mortality soon becomes severe. One yardstick of infestation—the number of larvae collected per hour—showed a drop of from 600 to 100 per hour in a period of 20 days. All indications are that the virus would be effective for biological control of an outbreak of the linden looper when the disease does not occur naturally to check it.

[12] W. A. Smirnoff, "A Nuclear Polyhedrosis of *Erannis tiliaria* (Harris) (Lepidoptera: Geometridae)," *Journal of Insect Pathology*, Dec. 1962; also René Martineau, "A New Looper Infestation in Sugar Leaf Maple Stands in Quebec," *Bi-monthly Progress Report*, Canada Dept. of Forestry, Sept.-Oct. 1961.

As was mentioned in the discussion of *Bacillus thuringiensis,* the cabbage looper (*Trichoplusia ni*) is also susceptible to a polyhedrosis virus disease. In addition to crucifers, the cabbage looper attacks cotton and lettuce; in the southwestern states, young lettuce plants and maturing heads are often severely infested in the fall, and cotton plants are attacked in the summer months. The virus is found in many parts of the United States, and natural epizootics of the disease occur in cabbage looper populations on crucifer and cotton crops—although not, so far as has been observed, on lettuce—in Arizona and California. Hall has shown that a virus epizootic can be artificially induced in field populations of the cabbage looper on lettuce.[13] Virus material for his tests was produced by collecting naturally infected loopers from cotton fields, and rearing them on a variety of plant materials —cotton leaves, lettuce, cabbage, and alfalfa.

In the field tests conducted on lettuce, with a virus suspension of 300,000 polyhedra per ml. concentration, applied at the rate of 75 and 37.5 gallons per acre, dead larvae were observed twenty-five days after application, and a reduction of 80 per cent in the cabbage looper population was noted. In later tests, 10, 5 and 1 million polyhedra per ml. applied at the rate of 12 gallons per acre were more effective and showed that the higher concentrations—or two applications of a lower concentration— were necessary to produce 100 per cent mortality. It was noted that temperature played an important part in spread of the virus: mortality of the cabbage loopers sprayed with the suspension was 100 per cent on the ninth day at a temperature of 22° C.; a drop of 6.5° C. doubled the time for the same effect.

BIOLOGICAL CONTROL OF SAWFLIES

Polyhedrosis infecting the European spruce sawfly (*Diprion hercyniae*) is the most important control factor affecting this pest in Canada and the northeastern states. Its sudden ap-

[13] Irvin M. Hall, "Use of a Polyhedrosis Virus to Control the Cabbage Looper on Lettuce in California," *Journal of Economic Entomology,* Oct. 1957.

pearance during the height of the sawfly outbreak in eastern Canada between 1930 and 1938, and the dramatic effects of the virus disease on the pest population, have already been mentioned in connection with parasites. The first sign of the disease in the sawfly larva is a change from the normal green color to a faint yellow; sluggishness and cessation of feeding are also early symptoms. A dark brown fluid may exude from the anus and glue the larva to the needle; the skin erupts easily, causing the liquefied body contents to ooze out, and after a time the body shrivels and dries up. The disease is transmitted from one larva to another by means of contaminated food; the transmission of the virus to the next generation via the egg, and its effect on the winter carryover of the virus, have already been mentioned. In the field the virus will remain virulent for many years; an aqueous suspension made from virus-killed larvae and stored at ordinary room temperature will retain its virulence for three months.

Tests made by F. T. Bird and others show that this aqueous suspension, used as a spray, is very effective in controlling the sawfly. In a carefully controlled experiment, seven trees in the center of a moderately infested, disease-free area four miles square were treated from a hand sprayer; although the operator climbed into the tall trees to spray, only partial coverage of the foliage was possible. At the end of the second generation the next year the disease had spread to a radius of about one-half mile from the central sprayed area. A follow-up and study of this area for ten years showed that the artificial dissemination of the virus had succeeded in keeping the sawfly under sufficient control to prevent economic damage in the absence of any appreciable parasitism. It was concluded that "epizootics occur year after year if there is a sufficient number of insects for virus propagation; and in areas where it is not present, epizootics can be initiated by spraying virus on a few infested trees."[14]

[14] F. T. Bird and J. M. Burk, "Artificially Disseminated Virus as a Factor Controlling the European Spruce Sawfly, *Diprion hercyniae* (Htg.) in the

The European pine sawfly (*Neodiprion sertifer*) can also be effectively controlled by artificial dissemination of a virus to which this pest is susceptible. The pathogen actually came from Sweden, having been imported by the Canada Department of Agriculture in 1949. From the few infected larvae that were imported a sufficient stock was built up so that 100 gallons of spray material could be shared with the United States Department of Agriculture in 1951. Ground and aerial treatments of Scots and red pines in New Jersey proved very successful, as did later ground treatments in Illinois.[15] In a test made in Canada by F. T. Bird, the virus suspension was applied with a mist blower; best results were obtained at night, when the relative humidity was high and the virus-laden mist remained suspended in the air for a fairly long period of time.[16] Tests in Ohio have shown that a suspension of the material will remain virulent for five years. A virus bank has been established at the Forest Insect Laboratory in New Haven, Connecticut; from this material "starters" can be supplied to state pest control organizations or others equipped to mass-produce and disperse it. One gallon of material is sufficient to treat an acre of trees, and if timed properly in the spring, will give protection for six or seven years.

In 1954 USDA entomologists isolated a virus from the Virginia pine sawfly in Maryland. Starting with thirty infected larvae, they developed a spray that proved very effective in reducing the sawfly population; in one instance it was estimated that the larval population had been reduced by 77 per cent in eleven days.

A virus disease of Swaine's jack pine sawfly (*Neodiprion swainei*), a serious defoliator of jack pines in Canada, was found in Quebec and northeastern Ontario. Tests were made to deter-

---

Absence of Introduced Parasites," *The Canadian Entomologist*, March 1961.

[15] *Use of Diseases to Kill Plant Insect Pests: A Research Progress Report* (Washington: USDA Agricultural Research Service, ARS 22-74, Oct. 1961).

[16] F. T. Bird, "On the Artificial Dissemination of the Virus Disease of the European Pine Sawfly, *Neodiprion sertifer* (Geoffr.)," *Bi-monthly Progress Report*, Canada Dept. of Agriculture, May-June 1952.

mine the feasibility of spraying the virus from an airplane for biological control of the pest.[17] A suspension of virus material in water and one in oil were both used. Since the oil formulation was more easily atomized, it was more effective at lower rates of application and in the drift area. The year following application the test plots and surrounding area within one-quarter of a mile were under complete control, and the disease had spread two miles beyond the plots. Smirnoff *et al.* concluded that it was feasible to "disperse a specific polyhedrosis disease as a biological control agent of a forest pest by aerial spraying"; that good results could be obtained with intermittent spot or strip application; and that dissemination of infected larvae in the forest would be both practical and inexpensive. Weak dosages are preferred in spot treatments so that enough individuals will survive to spread the disease.[18] Carryover of the disease from year to year is insured through transovarian transmission—that is, from the infected adult to her progeny via the egg.[19] Predatory wasps, which were numerous in the area, also assisted in spreading the disease.

DOUBLE INFECTIONS

Another instance of a double infection, where an insect is susceptible to both a polyhedrosis and a granulosis virus, is found in the spruce budworm (*Choristoneura fumiferana*). From some interesting studies made by Bird, it appears that a cell will not accept both viruses, but that adjacent cells may each have a different virus; more commonly, however, blocks of cells will be infected with the same virus. Double infection is possible only if the granulosis virus is given the advantage of a head start or a

[17] W. A. Smirnoff, "A Virus Disease of *Neodiprion swainei* Middleton," *Journal of Insect Pathology*, March 1961.

[18] W. A. Smirnoff, J. J. Fettes, and W. Haliburton, "A Virus Disease of Swaine's Jack Pine Sawfly, *Neodiprion swainei* Midd., Sprayed from an Aircraft," *The Canadian Entomologist*, May 1962.

[19] W. A. Smirnoff, "Trans-ovum Transmission of Virus of *Neodiprion swainei* Middleton (Hymenoptera, Tenthredinidae)," *Journal of Insect Pathology*, June 1962.

greater concentration.[20] Field tests to determine the effects of
these infections on forest populations of the spruce budworm
were made by spraying virus suspensions on infested trees.
Suspensions of each of the viruses alone, and a mixture, were
both used. The greatest larval mortality (26.2 per cent) resulted
on the trees sprayed with both viruses; the incidence of infection was highest (61.5 per cent) on those sprayed with the
granulosis virus alone, but the rate of mortality was greater from
the polyhedrosis virus alone.[21] The practical use of these viruses
in control of the spruce budworm awaits further study, but it is
believed that an effective combination of pathogens for use as
sprays against the spruce budworm may yet be found. This has
been one of the most troublesome forest pests in Canada and
the northern states, and has not responded well to biological control measures employing parasites. An effective microbial spray
would be a major breakthrough.

BIOLOGICAL CONTROL OF THE ALFALFA CATER-
PILLAR

One of the most serious pests of alfalfa in the west and southwest—the alfalfa caterpillar (*Colias eurytheme*)—is also subject to attack by a nuclear polyhedrosis. The disease is one of
the most important natural checks on the pest; once started, it
acts swiftly and with great devastation. One infestation was reported to have reached the point that at the end of June 14,000
larvae were collected with each hundred sweeps of the field with
a net—and at just this point the polyhedrosis disease appeared.
Three days later each hundred sweeps of the net yielded only
40 caterpillars—and hundreds of thousand of dead ones were
seen clinging to the alfalfa plants. By the first week in August,

[20] F. T. Bird, "Polyhedrosis and Granulosis Viruses Causing Single and
Double Infections in the Spruce Budworm, *Choristoneura fumiferana*
Clemens," *Journal of Insect Pathology*, Dec. 1959.
[21] G. R. Stairs and F. T. Bird, "Dissemination of Viruses Against the
Spruce Budworm, *Choristoneura fumiferana* Clemens," *The Canadian
Entomologist*, Sept. 1962.

Alfalfa caterpillar dead of polyhedrosis virus, hanging by prolegs from plant. Body contents have become fluid and have gravitated to anterior end of the larva. (*K. M. Hughes,* courtesy *G. A. Marsh*)

the number of larvae collected with each hundred sweeps had dropped to only 13.

A peculiar thing about these epizootics, as observed by Thompson and Steinhaus in the San Joaquin Valley of California, is the fact that they strike the entire population of a field at one time, while an adjoining field with the same caterpillar population and other conditions may be almost free of the disease.[22] Temperature and humidity have been dismissed as direct factors in the start of an epizootic or in accounting for its uniformity. Aside from population density, irrigation and the stage of growth of the alfalfa are believed to be important factors, since the epizootics always occur one or two weeks after the fields are irrigated, and since the virus is generally widely spread throughout

[22] Clarence G. Thompson and Edward A. Steinhaus, "Further Tests Using a Polyhedrosis Virus to Control the Alfalfa Caterpillar," *Hilgardia,* Feb. 1950.

the field litter, in the surface soil, and in the irrigation water standing in the field.

The first symptoms of polyhedrosis appear four or five days after infection. The caterpillars turn a lighter green or pale yellow and become sluggish; they die anywhere from five to ten days—but usually about seven—after infection. With the posterior end clinging to the alfalfa stalk, the larva hangs in a wilted mass as the body contents "melt down" and flow to the anterior end. The skin breaks easily and the contents ooze out over the plants. Thousands of larvae may be seen hanging in this way following an epizootic.

A braconid parasite, *Apanteles medicaginis,* which is often responsible for control of the alfalfa caterpillar, is also important along with predatory insects in spreading the disease. Dissemination of the virus by these and other insect vectors is aided by the extreme virulence of the disease. Its value is further enhanced by being able to withstand exposure and to survive up to two years outside its host. Tests show that the virus can be effective as a biological control agent if timed properly, and that application by airplane is feasible. The larvae will continue to feed at least four days after the application of the virus; thus careful timing is necessary to prevent the population from reaching damaging levels. One day can make the difference between adequate control and economic loss.

It is relatively easy and inexpensive to build up a supply of the virus for biological control purposes. Healthy larvae can be brought into the laboratory and infected, or dead and dying larvae can be collected in the field. The easiest and least expensive way to build up a large supply of the virus is to spray a field containing a high population of caterpillars, and collect them with a sweeping net the day before they die. The supply can be maintained by collecting diseased larvae in the field at the proper time after each succeeding application. To prepare a spray suspension, the dried-up caterpillars are simply crushed and stirred in water. One caterpillar in a gallon of water will give a standard concentration of about 5 million polyhedrons per quarter of a teaspoon; each polyhedron contains several hundred virus particles.[23]

The alfalfa caterpillar is also susceptible to a cytoplasmic polyhedrosis. Some interesting possibilities involving this microorganism are suggested by experiments carried out in California by Y. Tanada, who found that by feeding the caterpillars some microsporidian (protozoan) spores from the armyworm (*Pseudaletia unipuncta*), a cytoplasmic polyhedrosis could be developed in the alfalfa caterpillar. (As we have seen, Smith used the same kind of trick on the winter moth when he induced a cytoplasmic polyhedrosis with a *nuclear polyhedrosis.*)[24] It would appear that suspensions of these microsporidian spores might be used to activate latent cytoplasmic polyhedrosis in the alfalfa caterpillar.

As has been noted, the alfalfa caterpillar is also susceptible to the pathogen *Bacillus thuringiensis,* and in some ways this is a more effective agent for biological control purposes. It is not as virulent as the polyhedral virus and does not reduce the caterpillar population so greatly, but it does have a shorter incubation period and hence takes effect much sooner than the virus. When the bacillus is used, the caterpillar populations are effectively reduced by the second day as compared to the five or six days required for the virus to take effect. In one experiment, at the end of three days the larva count was reduced from 44 to 11 for every two sweeps of the net; 20 is an economic level.[25] Another advantage of the bacillus is that it does not disintegrate the body of the caterpillar to liquid form, and the skin usually remains intact; the dead insects drop to the ground without smearing the plants.

[23] Edward A. Steinhaus, "Living Insecticides," *Scientific American*, Aug. 1956.

[24] Y. Tanada, "Effect of Microsporidian Spore Suspension on the Incidence of Cytoplasmic Polyhedrosis in the Alfalfa Caterpillar, *Colias eurytheme* Boisduval," *Journal of Insect Pathology*, Dec. 1962.

[25] Edward A. Steinhaus, "Possible Use of *Bacillus thuringiensis* Berliner as an Aid in the Biological Control of the Alfalfa Caterpillar," *Hilgardia*, Feb. 1951.

(The smearing caused by the virus sometimes makes hay un-palatable for cattle.) The bacillus has a further advantage in that it can be reared on nutrient agar and is thus easier to pro-duce.[26]

Field tests made by Stern et al. in 1958 show that commercial preparations of B. thuringiensis applied with ground or airplane equipment will provide commercial control of the alfalfa cater-pillar as satisfactory as can be obtained with chemicals. With ground equipment, good control was obtained two days after making an application of 7.8 ounces of spore material per acre (having a formulation of 40 billion spores per gram), and excel-lent control four days after using only 1.8 ounces per acre. Sur-prisingly, the larger larvae were killed sooner than the smaller ones—the opposite of what happens when chemicals are used—possibly because they move about more and consume more of the infested leaves, and hence more of the toxic crystals in the bacteria.

Satisfactory results were obtained by spraying with aircraft, using 4.3 ounces of spore material per acre. It was concluded that from 3 to 4 ounces of spore material per acre (at 40 billion viable spores per gram) would give satisfactory control if applied with ground equipment, and from 4 to 5 ounces per acre if applied with aircraft.[27]

SOME PROTOZOAN INFECTIONS

Protozoa are one-celled animals, as distinguished from the plant-like bacteria, yeasts, and fungi. Most protozoa are free-living rather than dependent on another organism as host, but many live in association with other animals, either as parasites or in a "com-mensal" relationship—that is, one that affords mutual benefit, as

[26] Edward A. Steinhaus and Elizabeth A. Jerrel, "Further Observations on Bacillus thuringiensis Berliner and Other Spore Forming Bacteria," Hilgardia, May 1954.

[27] Vernon M. Stern, Irvin M. Hall, and George D. Peterson, "The Utiliza-tion of Bacillus thuringiensis Berliner as a Biotic Insecticide to Suppress the Alfalfa Caterpillar," Journal of Insect Pathology, Aug. 1959.

for example the protozoa that live in the gut of the termite and on which the latter depends absolutely for the digestion of the wood that is its food. Protozoa have a variety of shapes, and are classified according to their form of locomotion. Infections by the flagellates and amoebae are believed to cause insects some harm, but they are not fatal. Some species of the flagellate *Leptomonas* invade the gut, body cavity, and salivary glands of certain plant bugs; others infect the Malpighian tubules and alimentary tract of the European corn borer and the dog flea (*Ctenocephalides canis*). No outward sign of infection is apparent, but the invaded tissue undergoes damage. Several species of flagellates also invade the intestinal tract and Malpighian tubules of drosophila flies. Some flagellates that cause infection in vertebrate animals also invade the cells of the insect vector (their means of reaching the host) in the course of their development. For example, a trypanosome that causes a mild infection in the rat also invades the stomach wall of the flea that brings it to the host.[28]

Probably the most serious amoebic infection among insects is *Malpighamoeba mellificae*, which affects the honeybee, *Apis mellifera*. It invades the Malpighian tubules, filling them with encysted amoebae, and also the large intestine, from which the excreted cysts spread the infection to other bees. When it occurs along with the nosema disease, the combination is generally fatal; the amoebae alone are not likely to be fatal in the first year, but the next spring the infection becomes more severe. A malpighamoeba also parasitizes certain grasshoppers of the genus *Melanoplus*. The invaded Malpighian tubules become filled with cysts and may swell to the point of bursting, thus liberating cysts throughout the body. These tubules open into the hind gut of insects and perform an important excretory function; if the amoebic disease is not fatal it seriously affects the physiology of the insect. In mild cases the disease is not apparent; but in severe cases the grasshopper becomes sluggish and loses its appetite, and

[28] Edward A. Steinhaus, *Principles of Insect Pathology* (New York: McGraw-Hill Book Co., 1949).

as the disease advances the insect is unable to keep itself upright. In an attempt to disseminate an amoebic infection (*Malameba locustae*) found in grasshoppers, spore cysts of the disease were collected by scraping up the feces of infected grasshoppers reared in cages; mixed with bran and molasses, and scattered along the road and fences, they produced significant results.

SOME MICROSPORIDIAN INFECTIONS

The zoological class of the Sporozoa includes more protozoans pathogenic to insects than any other. All members of this group are parasitic on a wide range of animals, and all form spores at some time during their development. Among them are the gregarines, coccidians, and microsporidians. The most important of these for insect control are the Microsporidia, and among them the genus *Nosema* includes the most prominent. Of the 131 known species of Microsporidia listed and described by H. M. Thomson in 1960, well over a third belonged to the genus *Nosema*.[29]

The life cycle of these protozoans is very complex. The "amoebula," as the parasite is called, surrounds itself with a spore, a membranous covering which plays an important part in its career by enabling it to survive for long periods between hosts. Spores even in the same species vary in size and form; a typical one contains a "sporoplasm" or amoebula and a "polar filament." When the spore is ingested by an insect, what is known as the vegetative stage takes place: the host's digestive fluids cause the polar filament to pierce the spore wall and detach itself, leaving an opening for the amoebula. Propelled by amoeboid movement, it makes its way into the hosts gut and penetrates the intestinal wall; from there it migrates to a particular part of the body, where it enters the cytoplasm of a cell. Here multiplication (by division) and sporulation (forming of new spores) ensue in the chosen tissues, until eventually the cytoplasm of the invaded cells has been consumed and replaced by what at this stage are called

[29] H. M. Thomson, "A List and Brief Description of the Microsporidia Infecting Insects," *Journal of Insect Pathology*, Dec. 1960.

"schizonts" and "meronts"; the latter are then transformed into new spores. The entire life cycle of *Nosema bombycis*—the cause of the so-called "pebrine" of the silkworm—is completed in about four days.

Some microsporidian species parasitize only one host species, others more than one. Some are distributed in practically every country where the host species are found; others seem to be restricted to one locality. Outwardly, infection may be indicated by any of various changes in the color, size, and form of the insect, according to the severity of the infection. Frequently the body takes on a dull, milky appearance owing to the collection of spores underneath the skin; areas of dark brown spots may appear, giving a mottled effect. Changes of body form are varied in the extreme; the insect may remain small and dwarfed, or it may become swollen and enlarged. Decreased activity may be due to deterioration of the muscles or to the swelling of the infected tissues—especially in the fat body, which is the usual area of infection. Great enlargement of the invaded cells, with replacement of the cytoplasm and deterioration of the nucleus, is a characteristic feature of the disease; whether this is the effect of a toxin is not known.

Pebrine, the most famous of all diseases associated with insects, is so named because of the telltale spots found on the skin of the infected silkworms (*Bombyx mori*). A century ago the infection all but wiped out the silk industry in France and all over Europe, producing so serious a threat to the French economy that the government commissioned Louis Pasteur to make a study of the disease. As Steinhaus has pointed out, from this investigation of a mere insect stemmed the important later discoveries concerning anthrax, rabies, and other infectious diseases that plague man and animals.[30] Bees also suffer from a microsporidian, *Nosema apis,* which is not as serious as the foulbroods for the colony as a whole.

[30] Edward A. Steinhaus, *Principles of Insect Pathology.*

OF CABBAGES AND CORN

The importance of the microsporidian *Glugea pyraustae* in controlling the European corn borer (*Ostrinia nubilalis*) has already been discussed in connection with the parasites and biological control measures involving this insect. All stages of the host are subject to attack. After the amoebulae are released from the spores in the corn borer's digestive tract, they find their way to the Malpighian tubules, causing them to swell and to turn an opaque white. The disease is transmitted by the ingestion of contaminated food, and is also passed on from one generation to the next by way of the egg, as viruses are.

Four species of Microsporidia have been found in the cabbage butterfly, *Pieris brassicae*. Two of these, *Glugea pieris* and *Glugea mesnili*, invade the Malpighian tubules and silk glands, and can be artificially transmitted; neither of these infections appears to be fatal to the insect. *Glugea legeri* and *Thelohania mesnili* (a very rare infection) develop only in the fat tissues and apparently cannot be transmitted orally through the digestive tract. Certain of these infections seem to be entirely specific as to tissues attacked. It is believed that those infections that cannot be contracted orally are carried either through transovarial transmission or by insect parasites. The fact that the incidence of *Glugea legeri* is high in the years that parasitization by *Apanteles* is high seems to support the latter hypothesis.

SOME NOSEMA INFECTIONS

A microsporidian, *Nosema heliothidis*, that attacks the digestive tract of the corn earworm (*Heliothis zea*) and the tobacco budworm (*Heliothis virescens*), has been found in California, Illinois, Maryland, and North Carolina, as well as Brazil. John Paul Kramer believes the disease is a significant factor in the natural control of the corn earworm and tobacco budworm.[31] The codling

[31] John Paul Kramer, "On *Nosema heliothidis* Lutz and Splendor, a Microsporidian Parasite of *Heliothis zea* (Boddie) and *Heliothis virescens*

moth (*Carpocapsa pomonella*) is parasitized by a microsporidian (*Nosema carpocapsae*), and in some regions of France has infected as much as 40 per cent of the larvae. In general, however, it is not considered an important factor in natural control of this insect. It may attack almost any of the cells of the host but does so most often in the silk glands, Malpighian tubules, and fat tissues. Its development is remarkably well synchronized with that of the host; during the moth larva's diapause the microsporidia do not multiply, and remain in the spore stage.

Certain locusts (or grasshoppers) are susceptible to the microsporidian *Nosema locustae;* these include the migratory locust (*Locusta migratoria migratorioides*), the two-striped grasshopper (*Melanoplus bivittatus*), the migratory grasshopper (*Melanoplus mexicanus*), the clear-winged grasshopper (*Camnula pellucida*), and some others.[32] Infected grasshoppers show considerable damage in the fat tissue, which loses its bright yellow color and takes on a pink pigment. Nymphs are highly susceptible to the infection, the highest mortality occurring at the final molt. Impairment of flying ability in the surviving adults is a significant effect of the disease. Since most of the infected locusts die before becoming adults, the difficulty of rearing stocks sufficient to produce the necessary quantity of spores seems to make its use as a biological control agent impractical at the present time.

The gypsy moth (*Porthetria dispar*) and browntail moth (*Nygmia phaeorrhoea*) are susceptible to a microsporidian infection caused by *Plistophora schubergi,* which may on occasions be as important as the wilt (polyhedral) disease in natural control of the gypsy moth. Although the reduction of population by this pathogen is gradual, in contrast to the explosive nature of the wilt disease, it is often very significant. Mosquitoes as a

(Fabricius) (Lepidoptera, Phalaenidae)," *Journal of Insect Pathology,* Oct. 1959.

[32] Elizabeth U. Canning, "The Life Cycle of *Nosema locustae* Canning in *Locusta migratoria migratorioides* (Reiche and Fairmaire), and Its Infectivity to Other Hosts"; also "The Pathogenicity of *Nosema locustae* Canning"; *Journal of Insect Pathology,* June 1962.

group are quite susceptible to the microsporidia; however, though using the spores as a biological control measure has been considered, it has not been tried.

THE MICROSPORIDIA AS CONTROL AGENTS

Little has been done by way of artificial distribution of microsporidian spores for biological control, presumably because they cannot be cultivated on artificial media. Nevertheless, this has not been an insurmountable obstacle in using such virus infections as the polyhedral diseases of the alfalfa caterpillar and the sawflies, for which adequate amounts of infective material have been made available at low cost.

It has been pointed out that disease may have a profound effect on the population of insects without causing mortality, by limiting their fecundity or reproductive capacity. This is especially true of microsporidian diseases because of their chronic nature. Where the adult insects do not consume any food and are dependent on reserves of nutrients built up by the larvae, any factor with an adverse effect on the nutrition of the larvae will also affect the adults. This was demonstrated by Veber and Jasic in experiments with the silkworm (*Bombyx mori*) and the fall webworm (*Hyphantria cunea*), in which sublethal doses of the microsporidian *Nosema bombycis,* fed to the larvae, had an adverse effect on the weights and egg-laying capacities of the adult females.[33] For this as well as for the more obvious reasons, the Microsporidia (and other pathogens) can be very important factors in regulating insect populations even where they do not "control" them.

NEMATODE INFECTIONS

Nematodes, also called roundworms, are found in vast numbers in the soil; many of them are harmless, but some are serious pests because they attack the roots of crop plants. Some nematodes are the cause of disease in man—for example the tropical disease

[33] J. Veber and J. Jasic, "Microsporidia as a Factor in Reducing the Fecundity in Insects," *Journal of Insect Pathology,* June 1961.

filariasis, caused by the nematode *Wuchereria bancrofti,* and transmitted by mosquitoes. For servicemen in the South Pacific, natives afflicted with this disease, popularly known as "ele-phantiasis," were a familiar sight; the immense swelling of af-fected parts is due to the roundworm's blocking off of the lymph channels. Other nematodes of medical importance include the hookworm, found in rural areas of the southeastern states, and the "trichina worm" (*Trichinella spiralis*), the cause of trichinosis, which is usually contracted after eating undercooked meat such as pork—or even bear! One of the largest nematodes, *Ascaris lumbricoides,* is a parasite that inhabits the human intestine and that is found chiefly in areas where sanitation is poor.[34]

The nematodes that concern us here—those parasitic on insects —are at times important in the natural control of insect pests. Some of them can be propagated in large numbers and disseminated for biological control in much the same way as is done with microorganisms. In a water suspension these amazing little animals can be poured on the ground from a sprinkling can for the control of soil insects—or sprayed on plants with a mechanical sprayer at pressures of 100 p.s.i., without being injured! They can also withstand the toxic effects of pesticides.

These tiny worms look like pieces of fine sewing thread— hence their name, *nema* being Greek for "thread." They all look alike: their elongated cylindrical bodies are pointed at one or both ends; they have no legs or cilia, are not segmented, and are covered with a tough cuticle or sheath. According to Steinhaus more than 1,000 species of nematodes have been reported to be as-sociated with insects.[35] A partial review of world literature noted fourteen families of nematodes associated with sixteen insect orders, and 3,300 individual nematode-insect occurrences.[36]

[34] Ralph Buchsbaum, *Animals Without Backbones: An Introduction to the Invertebrates,* Vol. I (Harmondsworth, Middlesex, England: Penguin Books, Ltd., 1957).
[35] *Principles of Insect Pathology.*
[36] H. E. Welch, "Nematodes as Agents for Insect Control," *Proceedings of the Entomological Society of Ontario,* 1961 (pub. Aug. 1962).

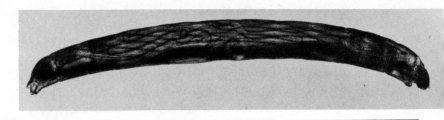

Effect of a nematode parasite. The larva of a chironomid fly with coils of a mermithid nematode inside. (*George O. Poinar, Jr., Rothamsted Experimental Station, Harpenden, England*)

Nematodes are bisexual, the male being generally smaller than the female, and have three stages of development—egg, larva, and adult. In most species the microscopic eggs are discharged before the embryos have completed their development; but in some species they hatch in the uterus, and are thus said to be "ovoviviparous." The embryos sometimes require several weeks or even months of development before they hatch. Nematodes that attack insects may live in the alimentary tract, the body cavity, or the tissues of the host; or they may be free-living for part of the time and parasitic for the rest. Those living in the alimentary tract generally cause little damage to the host; those with semiparasitic habits include some valuable control agents, notably in the group known as neoaplectanids. These nematodes harbor a bacterium which causes the death of the host insect, and are therefore actually "saprophytes" since they live on the dead remains rather than on the living animals as true parasites do.

The members of two groups, called tylenchoids and aphelenchoids, are equipped with stylets which they use to pierce the cuticle of the host so as to enter its body cavity; under the microscope they look like tiny darts driven into the side of the insect. Their life cycle is very complex; some live in the digestive tract, others in the genital tract. Injury to the host occurs when they emerge, and in the latter means an impairment of its reproductive capacity. A fourth group important as parasites are the mermithids, whose size causes a fatal injury to the host when they emerge.

Outward signs of the infection in grubs are loss of appetite and increasing lethargy; white grubs become mottled and gradually lose their pink tint, in random blotches at first, finally becoming a more or less uniformly rusty brown or some similar color. After the infective (second-stage) nematode larvae have been ingested by the beetle grubs, the nema mature and mate inside the insect. The eggs hatch within the uterus of the female nematode, the average number being about fifteen, and the larvae are discharged into the alimentary tract of the host. A generation is completed in a week or less, and the insect dies about eleven days after becoming infected. The nema now continue to feed on the cadaver, and two more generations are completed within it. The number of nematode larvae in a diseased grub averages about 1,500 and may run as high as 2,400; but a single one can infect and eventually kill the host. When the cadaver has been consumed the larvae invade the soil and become free-living until they are ingested by another grub, whereupon the cycle is repeated.

NEMATODES AS BIOLOGICAL CONTROL AGENTS

According to H. E. Welch, the Canadian nematologist, although nematodes in general play an insignificant role in the natural regulation of insects they are significant in the regulation of certain groups of insects. "They may be manipulated as both biological control agents and biological insecticides, and by altering the environment so as to increase parasitism, or may be used in conjunction with chemical pesticides." Welch lists four kinds of biological manipulation for pest control: (1) biological control in the strict sense, namely, introduction of parasites and predators from the environment where they occur naturally; (2) regular release of large quantities of beneficial insects or microorganisms, using them in the same way as chemical insecticides; (3) manipulation of the environment so as to encourage the biological agents already present to increase their attacks; and (4) integration of chemical and biological agents. Since nematodes are resistant to chemicals, they can be used in conjunction with them. The mermithids, because of their relatively large size and their similarity to insect parasites, lend themselves best to "biological control" as it is defined here; the neoaplectanids, because of their high reproductive capacity, are best used as "biological insecticides."

One of the first attempts to use nematodes as a biological control agent was made in New Jersey following the discovery by R. W. Glaser and H. Fox in 1930 that the nematode *Neoaplectana glaseri* was a parasite of the Japanese beetle (*Popillia japonica*). The infected beetles seem to have been found naturally in only one restricted area of the state. Glaser was able to cultivate *Neoaplectana glaseri* on an artificial medium of veal-infusion agar and dextrose placed in a Petri dish and flooded with a pure culture of baker's yeast. Fermented potato mash and later infused veal pulp proved more productive and easier to handle. A square centimeter of this culture surface, inoculated with 600 nematodes, yielded from 9,000 to 12,000 nematodes in seven days. Before 1940 an extensive program of disseminating the nematodes was undertaken in New Jersey, with introductions into infested areas at 3½-mile intervals throughout the state. The resulting parasitization ranged from less than 1 per cent to 81.5 per cent, depending on moisture, temperature, nematode dosage, and the density of the beetle grub population. The nematodes were able to maintain themselves under natural conditions for a period of six and one-half years, during five of which the host population was low. It was noted that the infection is spread by migrations of the nematodes and infected grubs in the soil, and by flights of infected adult beetles. The results were very encouraging, but have since been obscured by Glaser's introduction of milky-disease spore dust and by the spectacular success of the latter program in controlling the Japanese beetle.

In 1955 a neoaplectanid nematode was discovered by S. R. Dutky in the codling moth (*Carpocapsa pomenella*), and was given the mathematical name DD 136. Nematodes of this species are ingested by the codling moth larva and penetrate the wall of the digestive tract to enter the body cavity, where they release bacteria which in turn kill the insect. Several generations then feed on the cadaver until eventually they become free-living, carrying the bacteria with them. In this stage they do not feed and can survive for long periods of time, during which the bacteria are retained in a viable state. In laboratory tests Dutky found more than 100 species of insects susceptible to neoaplectanid infections, and he was able to control many pests in the field using the nematodes as a biological insecticide. He succeeded in reducing codling moth larvae 60 per cent by spraying the trunk and main branches of apple trees, and the tobacco budworm (*Heliothis virescens*) by from 80 to 85 per cent under conditions of ample moisture and high humidity.

In 1960 George Poinar and George Gyrisco discovered a new species of mermithid nematode (*Hexamermis arvalis*) in the alfalfa weevil (*Hypera postica*) in New York State. Their studies have shown parasitism to reach 33 per cent in some fields; but the nematodes do not appear to be numerous enough at this time to constitute any over-all economic importance.[37]

It is very significant that some species of nematodes are parasitic on bark beetles, since the latter are difficult to control by artificial means. *Aphelenchulus reversus* has greatly reduced egg production by females of the Englemann spruce beetle (*Dendroctonus engelmanni*). *A. elongatus* likewise affected the egg-laying capacity of females of the California five-spined engraver (*Ips confusus*), a serious pest of pinyon in Arizona and New Mexico, which also attacks ponderosa pine in California. Controlled studies by Calvin Massey showed a 70 per cent reduction in broods produced by infected female beetles. It is interesting to note that the construction of egg galleries is also affected; in the study it was found that the length of galleries constructed by

[37] George O. Poinar, Jr. and George G. Gyrisco, "A New Mermithid Parasite of the Alfalfa Weevil, *Hyper postica* (Gyllenhal)," *Journal of Insect Pathology*, June 1962; "Studies on Bionomics of *Hexamermis arvalis* Poinar and Gyrisco, a Mermithid Parasite of the Alfalfa Weevil, *Hyper postica* (Gyllenhal)," *ibid.*, Dec. 1962.

nema-infected beetles averages 4.5 inches as compared to 7.1 inches for the noninfected beetles.[38]

Extensive tests of the neoaplectanid nematode DD 136 as a biological control agent have been made by Welch and L. J. Briand at the Belleville, Ontario biological control laboratories. Field tests using a nematode suspension applied to the soil against the cabbage root maggot *Hylemya brassicae,* produced results indicated protection intermediate between chemical treatments and none at all.[39] Nematodes seem to be best adapted for use against soil pests, however, since there is ordinarily no problem of moisture; indications so far are that they will survive at least a year in sandy soils. Tests directed against the Colorado potato beetle (*Leptinotarsa decemlineata*) indicate that the nematode does not lend itself to protection of open leaf plants except where the temperature and moisture are ideal.[40]

The results of test applications to corn plants against the European corn borer (*Ostrinia nubilalis*) were as good with the nematodes as those obtained with chemical pesticides; the tightly whorled leaves of the corn plant preserve enough moisture to protect the nematodes from desiccation.[41] Similar results were obtained, for the same reasons, with cabbage plants after the heads were well formed. There is a good possibility that nematodes applied to mosquito pools may afford biological control of woodland species of *Aedes* and of the yellow fever vector, *Aedes aegypti.* Mermithid nematodes show promise as control agents for black flies, which vie with mosquitoes as tormentors of man in

[38] Calvin L. Massey, "Life History of *Aphelenchulus elongatus* Massey (Nemotoda), an Endoparasite of *Ips confusus* LeConte, with a Description of the Male," *Journal of Insect Pathology,* March 1962.

[39] H. E. Welch and L. J. Briand, "Field Experiment on the Use of a Nematode for Control of Vegetable Crop Insects," *Proceedings* of the Entomological Society of Ontario, 1960, (pub. Sept. 1961).

[40] H. E. Welch and E. J. Briand, "Tests of the Nematode DD 136 and an Associated Bacterium for Control of the Colorado Potato Beetle, *Leptinotarsa decemlineata* (Say)," *The Canadian Entomologist,* Sept. 1961.

[41] H. E. Welch, "Nematodes as Agents for Insect Control," *Proceedings* of the Entomological Society of Ontario, 1961, (pub. Aug. 1962).

northern woodlands. Both of these interesting possibilities are being investigated at the Belleville laboratories.

Some nematodes are beneficial because they prey on other nematodes (commonly called "eelworms") that attack crop plants. Roland Mulvey has described a family of free-living predaceous nematodes that live in the soil and in fresh water, and that prey on protozoa, rotifers, and other nematodes.[42] It is believed that one of these, *Mononchus papillatus,* a predator of the sugar-beet nematode (*Heterodera schachtii*) in Utah, would be a valuable control agent if large populations could be maintained in infested fields. *M. papillatus* kills its prey by sucking out the body contents, or by swallowing the whole nematode head first, sometimes excreting the whole undigested cuticle from the anal opening. A single laboratory specimen was observed to kill 1,332 nematodes in a twelve-week period. Another species (*Iotonchus brachylaimus*) cultured in the laboratory was observed to devour large numbers of *Heterodera* eggs and larvae.

Among the ubiquitous and formidable nematodes (which are actually complex animals in spite of their size) are some that attack the stems, leaves, and flowers as well as the roots of plants. Fortunately, their enemies include other soil inhabitants, among them certain fungi, in whose delicate threadlike hyphae they become ensnared and are unable to escape.[43] Some species of these predaceous fungi give off a viscid fluid, which holds the nematode fast just as flypaper holds a fly, so that as it struggles it only becomes more enmeshed in the mass of hyphae that eventually consume it. In some species of fungi the mycelia form loops that act in the same way as the snares that are used to catch rabbits; in others a refinement of this method produces rings of mycelium that are triggered by contact with the nematode into constricting until the victim is strangled.

[42] Roland H. Mulvey, "The Mononchidae: A Family of Predaceous Nematodes," *Canadian Journal of Zoology,* Oct. 1961.

[43] C. L. Duddington, *The Friendly Fungi* (London: Faber and Faber, 1957).

We must study the modes of action of parasites, predators, and pathogens in much the same way that others at present study the modes of action of insecticides. At the same time, we should try to assess the general role that one can expect certain types of natural enemies to play and to determine the way in which we may expect these to interact with their environments.

—A. L. TURNBULL and D. A. CHANT

CONTROL OF INSECTS BY ARTIFICE

12

The control measures to be considered here include the sterilization of male insects, attractants (with traps) and repellants, the simulation of insect and other sounds, and the manipulation of electrical fields, as well as such cultural practices as the breeding of insect-resistant varieties of plants, making the plant environment more favorable to the beneficial insects and less favorable to the insect pests, altering nutrient levels in the plants (through the soil) to make them less palatable to the insects, and increasing soil fertility to produce healthier plants resistant to insect attack.

THE STERILE-MALE TECHNIQUE[1]

Certainly the most dramatic attack on insects is the sterile-male technique, a weapon first used against the screwworm (*Cochliomyia hominivorax*), a serious pest of cattle and wild animals in

---

[1] For an account of the research that led to this method of control, by the originator of the idea, see E. F. Knipling, "Control of Screwworm Fly by Atomic Radiation," in *Biological and Chemical Control of Plant and Animal Pests* (Washington: American Association for the Advancement of Science, Publication No. 61, 1960); also *The Scientific Monthly*, Oct. 1957.

southeastern United States. The female of this fly lays a mass of about 200 eggs in a wound or other break in the animal's skin; the navel of a newborn animal is especially attractive to these flies. After only a day the eggs hatch, and the larvae bore into the flesh and feed on the tissues, often causing the death of small or young animals. After feeding from five to seven days, the larvae drop to the ground and pupate in the soil; this phase lasts about a week in warm weather. The idea of controlling these flies by releasing sterilized males to compete with the natural population of males was conceived by E. F. Knipling, director of the USDA's Entomology Research Division, and stems from a discovery made by geneticists working with fruit flies: researchers using X rays and gamma rays emitted by isotopes of cobalt, the standard technique for inducing mutations (sudden changes of hereditary characteristics in the genes), noted that overuse of irradiation made the flies sterile.

In winter the screwworms in Florida are scattered, but are isolated from those of adjoining areas where temperatures are too severe for overwintering; this situation, and the fact that winter populations in Florida are greatly reduced, suggested that it might be possible to release sterile flies in sufficient quantities greatly to outnumber the natural population. Accordingly, experiments were begun by R. C. Bushland in 1950 to determine whether screwworms could be sterilized without adversely affecting such factors as adult emergence, mating, or longevity.[2] Subjecting the pupae to irradiation a day or two before the adult flies emerged produced no detrimental side effects. Laboratory tests also indicated that the adult female screwworm is monogamous, and that sterile males can compete successfully with fertile males. From this it is apparent that if the sterile males outnumber the fertile males, the latter stand a poor chance of reaching the females ahead of their

[2] Raymond C. Bushland, "Insect Eradication by Means of Sterilized Males," in *Handbook on Biological Control of Plant Pests* (Brooklyn Botanic Garden, 1960). For their outstanding achievement, Knipling and Bushland received the $10,000 Hoblitzelle National Award in the Agricultural Sciences for 1960.

Sterilized-male technique for control of the codling moth. (a) Rearing larvae of the codling moth on immature apples. (b) Sorting pupae of the codling moth for irradiation; only mature (dark) pupae are irradiated as young pupae (light color) are too susceptible to radiation injury.

(c) Placing codling moth pupae in the gamma irradiator. (d) Examining emergence cage for adult codling moths; the rate of moth emergence in the cage determines the number and rate of release of sterilized moths. Note milk bottle on right scaffold limb; sterilized moths can be seen leaving the open bottle. (S. R. *Cannings,* courtesy *M. D. Proverbs,* Canada Department of Agriculture) sexually altered competitors. If the number of sterile males is maintained by mass releases with each succeeding generation, the fertile males, in the face of a diminishing natural population, face increasing odds and overwhelming competition, until only infertile eggs are laid by the females. This "progressive increase in efficiency as the natural population declines" is a unique feature of the technique; as a USDA publication remarks, "All other systems of population control achieve about the same degree, or perhaps a lesser degree, of effect as the population declines."[3]

Before field testing, a successful technique was worked out for mass propagation of the flies in the laboratory, using a warm attractant composed of a mixture of ground meat, blood, and water, on which the females readily laid their eggs and which served as a suitable nutrient for the larvae. It was also necessary to design equipment for irradiation of the flies on a large scale. In 1954 the possibility of eradicating the screwworm by this method was established conclusively on Curaçao, an island with an area of 170 square miles in the Netherlands Antilles, forty miles off the coast of Venezuela, where native goats were badly infested with the pest. Sterilized flies, both male and female, were released on the island at the rate of 400 per square mile each week. In less than a week 69 per cent of the egg masses were failing to hatch, and after thirteen weeks complete control had been achieved. In 1957, with the development of a cobalt-60 gamma ray machine capable of irradiating 14 million flies per week, the trials were extended into Florida. Here it was found that sustained releases, consisting of millions of sterilized flies, could be maintained over thousands of square miles of infested area, and that the released males survived and mated with most of the natural population of female flies. In 1958 the research facilities at Orlando, Florida were expanded, and new facilities capable of producing 50 million sterilized flies each week were constructed at Sebring. Mass distribution was made from twenty-one airplanes, covering all of

[3] *Research on Controlling Insects Without Conventional Insecticides* (Washington: USDA Agricultural Research Service, ARS 22-85, Oct. 1963).

Florida and parts of adjoining states each week in two-mile swaths. By late 1959 the screwworm was completely eradicated from Florida, at a total cost of about one-third the annual losses (estimated to be $20 million) previously sustained by the cattle industry in the area. Careful inspection of cattle shipments into the region is maintained to prevent reinfestation, and a stand-by colony of screwworms to provide breeding stock where necessary, is maintained at the USDA's Kerrville, Texas laboratory.

OTHER APPLICATIONS

There is a good possibility that this technique may be successfully applied against many other crop pests. Extensive investigations are now underway. The main requirements of the sterile-male technique are (1) a cheap method of mass-rearing the insect, (2) sterility without adverse effects, (3) female monogamy, or the production by sterile males of sperm competitive with the sperm of fertile males, (4) low population, and (5) absence of harmful or noxious qualities in the sterile insects to be released.[4] This technique could be useful against many native crop pests when the populations are low, and might be successfully applied against introduced species before they become too numerous. It is also possible to outnumber the natural population of fertile males with sterile males after first reducing the population with insecticides. Experiments in 1962 and 1963 on the 33-square-mile island of Rota in the Pacific by the USDA's Hawaii Fruit Fly Laboratory, demonstrated that the melon fly can also be eradicated by the new technique. After reducing the natural population by 75 per cent with poison bait, anywhere from 4 to 10 million sterile melon flies were released on the island each week, and in three months the melon fly population was completely eradicated! This is the second important insect pest to have been eliminated by the sterile-male technique. Tests have

[4] Codling Moth Experiments: Exhibit at the Centennial of Entomology in Canada, Ottawa, Sept. 3–6, 1963 (Research Station, Research Branch, Canada Department of Agriculture, Summerland, British Columbia).

shown that the release of sterile insects will have adverse effects on the reproductive potential of the Mediterranean fruit fly, the Mexican fruit fly, and drosophila fruit flies.[5] The release of chemically sterilized males led to elimination of the boll weevil from a small isolated field. Chemical sterilization, now under intensive investigation, is believed to offer the possibility of inducing continuing sterility in the natural insect population, thus avoiding the expense of laboratory rearing and sterilization with subsequent release of the insects. Many insects have been treated with chemosterilants in laboratory tests; and limited field tests with the housefly show that it can be greatly reduced by using fly baits containing chemosterilants. However, it could well be that certain reserves of resistance built into these animals over the millions of years of their existence would be summoned to combat such a threat to their survival.

Laboratory and field tests in British Columbia show considerable promise for control of the codling moth in apple-growing areas by the release of sterile males.[6] The codling moth females are polygamous, and laboratory tests show that the sperm of irradiated moths does not compete with that of the normal moths, apparently because they are less motile and (probably) less numerous. It is believed, however, that since the female moth lays most of her eggs within a week after mating, this disadvantage can be overcome by flooding the orchard with sterile males; it is likely that a large proportion of the eggs deposited will then be nonviable. In the test orchard where releases of sterile males are being tried, the number of wormy apples and of trapped moths indicates a steady decline in the population of normal codling moths. The Canadian researchers point out that eradication of the codling moth by the sterile-male technique "would alle-

[5] *Research on Controlling Insects Without Conventional Insecticides* (ARS 22-85).

[6] M. D. Proverbs and J. R. Newton, "Some Effects of Gamma Radiation on the Reproductive Potential of the Codling Moth, *Carpocapsa pomonella* (L) (Lepidoptera: Olethreutidae)," *The Canadian Entomologist*, Nov. 1962.

viate or avoid insecticide resistance, mite injury, destruction of beneficial insects, and many other problems caused by or associated with the use of chemicals for codling moth control."[7] A cooperative experiment with the USDA, with possible release of sterile moths at the United States–Canadian border, is planned for 1965.

SEX ATTRACTANTS AND TRAPS

According to USDA researchers, attractants offer "the greatest possibilities for the development of effective and highly specific ways to control key insect species."[8] Attractants may be in the form of insect lures (extracts from adult virgin females), chemicals, and light or other means of evoking a visual response. Sex lures and traps have been used mostly to sample insect populations and to determine the presence of insect infestations or population density, but they are also being studied as a means of controlling or eradicating insect pests. Because attractants are highly specific, they have an advantage over insecticides in being harmless to other animals, including beneficial insects and man. Sex attractants may be used to lure male insect pests into traps, where they can then be killed by poisons; or they might be used to attract large numbers of males, which would then be collected, sterilized, and released—a variation of the sterilized-male technique.

Some of the earliest studies and uses made of sex attractants have been in connection with population studies of the gypsy moth. The sex attractant of the gypsy moth was the first such lure to be synthesized in the United States. A similar substance, called "gyplure," has also been synthesized and used in traps for population studies, and its use for control purposes is under study. The pink bollworm, a pest of cotton, has been raised in large numbers for extraction of the female sex lure, in order to determine the possibility of synthesizing the substance and using

[7] Codling Moth Experiments, *ibid.*
[8] ARS 22-85.

it as a control measure. Lures also have possibilities in control of cockroaches and certain beetles (dermestids, which are a pest of stored products, May beetles, mealworms, and wireworms, for example).

OTHER ATTRACTANTS

Certain chemicals also have a strong attraction for some insects. A mixture of nine parts anethole and one part eugenol by volume has been used to attract and trap Japanese beetles. Traps painted yellow and baited with these chemicals—or with geraniol substituted for anethole—have been used to control the Japanese beetle, but are not satisfactory if the population is high or if the traps are not used in the immediate neighborhood.[9] Methyl eugenol has a strong attraction for males of the oriental fruit fly, which will devour materials smeared with the chemical. Fiberboard squares impregnated with this substance and with a poison, distributed by plane in some areas of Hawaii, led to reductions of the oriental fruit fly populations by from 60 to 82 per cent. The same attractant mixed with a poison called "naled" was used successfully to eradicate the oriental fruit fly from the small Pacific island of Rota. Terpinyl acetate attracts the oriental fruit moth, and has been used in traps for population studies of that insect; the chemical also attracts males of the Natal fruit fly, a citrus pest in South Africa, and traps baited with the attractant are recommended for control of this insect.

After spending several millions of dollars in the South on an ill-advised attempt to "eradicate" the fire ant with conventional insecticides, causing widespread losses of wildlife, a new bait was developed consisting of corncrib grits mixed with soybean oil and an insecticide called Mirex. ARS scientists report that "only 1/7 ounce of the toxicant is applied per acre in a single treatment, thus practically eliminating the hazards involved in previous treatments that called for much higher dosages of an insecti-

[9] *Controlling the Japanese Beetle* (Washington: USDA, Farmers' Bulletin No. 2004, Jan. 1949).

cide."[10] The possibility of controlling certain bark beetles by using chemical attractants is suggested by the accidental discovery that a scolytid beetle (*Dolurgus pumilus*) in a British Columbia forest was attracted to a barrel previously containing a commercial preparation of BHC (benzene hexachloride). Of three empty barrels that had been filled with water for fire protection, it was noted that one—strongly smelling of BHC—contained thousands of dead beetles, almost all of them belonging to this one species, though numerous others had been seen flying about at the time.[11]

Experiments in the state of Washington showed that of fruit from a baited block of trees in an orchard 12 to 16 per cent more was without codling moth damage than those from the unbaited trees that had received the same chemical treatments. In another instance all the trees in an orchard were given sticky bands, and in one block of trees a baited trap was placed in each tree; in the fall the bands on the unbaited trees had captured six times as many larvae as those on the baited trees. Vincent Dethier concluded that baited traps are a useful adjunct to spraying as a means of controlling the codling moth for the following reasons: many of the trapped insects are females (90 per cent of them may be gravid, and 5 per cent may have deposited all their eggs); the larvae are reduced accordingly: thus there is little immigration into the orchard, and more fruit is worm-free.[12]

Some growers of dates and figs use the simplest kind of trap— a bucket of fermenting fruit—to control the dried-fruit beetle (*Carpophilus hemipterus*). The small, shiny black beetles of this species are good fliers, whose wings don't quite cover the abdomen; they prefer fermenting fruit but attack ripening dates and figs by boring into the fruit. They often carry bacteria, yeasts, or fungi on their bodies, causing smut and souring of the fruit. The

[10] ARS 22-85.

[11] J. A. Chapman, "Attraction of the Bark Beetle, *Dolurgus pumilus* Mannerheim, to a Barrel Previously Containing Commercial BHC," *Bi-monthly Progress Report*, Canada Department of Forestry, Jan.–Feb. 1963.

[12] Vincent G. Dethier, *Chemical Insect Attractants and Repellents* (Philadelphia: The Blakiston Co., 1947).

buckets are baited with peach culls, melon rinds, souring dates, and so on (with a little water to hasten fermentation) and placed where they may be conveniently tended. The bait is more attractive after it has become infested with larvae, which are prevented from escaping by greasing the top three inches inside the container.[13] Weekly collections are made, and the insects are destroyed by hot water or other means. Pigs are sometimes used to remove the drops;[14] they have no trouble removing the pits, do a better job of sanitation than human employees—and demand much less for their services.

LIGHTS AND OTHER VISUAL ATTRACTANTS

Light traps are also valuable for population studies and control of insect pests. In a vineyard on the Moselle River in France more than 18,000 moths were collected with light traps in five nights; in another vineyard of 13.5 acres, 275,000 moths were trapped in the period of a month—an average of more than 20,000 moths per acre.[15] Not all species of insects respond in the same way to colors; some react more readily to those in the greeen and blue bands of the spectrum, others to the blue-to-violet band and least of all to the red-to-yellow. *Aedes* mosquitoes have been observed to vary their rate of attack according to the color of clothing. One insect-electrocuting light trap per acre, using a clear blue light, was sufficient to control grape leafhoppers in the vineyards of San Joaquin Valley, California.[16] Clear blue attracted twice as many leafhoppers as white, and a greater proportion were females. Increasing the intensity of the light from 60 to 150 watts more than doubled the number of leafhoppers trapped.

---

[13] C. L. Metcalf and W. P. Flint, *Destructive and Useful Insects* (New York: McGraw-Hill Book Co., 1951).

[14] This method of controlling the dried-fruit beetle, and the use of pigs for sanitation, are practiced in the Lee Anderson date grove at Coachella, California.

[15] Charles T. Brues, *Insect Dietary* (Cambridge: Harvard University Press, 1946).

[16] William B. Herms, "Some Problems in the Use of Artificial Light in Crop Protection," *Hilgardia,* April 1947.

Black-light trap hanging from tree near greenhouses of the Agricultural Experiment Station, University of California, Berkeley, where they are used for study of insect populations and flight habits. (*Harold F. Madsen*)

Unfortunately the light also attracted leafhoppers carrying Pierce's disease from nearby fields, and its use had to be discontinued. (The concentration of diseased plants around the light led to the discovery that certain leafhoppers—*Carneocephala fulgida* and *Draeculacephala minerva*—are vectors of this disease.) The same trap—with a pale blue light, the most effective color in this instance—gave something less than adequate protection against the codling moths in an apple orchard; the resulting worminess was about 50 per cent of that occurring where there was no chemical protection. The height of the traps makes a difference in their efficiency, as do climatic factors such as temperature, humidity, and wind direction.

Black light—found in the ultraviolet region of the spectrum, and invisible to man—is an effective attractant for many insects. In North Carolina 370 traps in a 113-square-mile area caught what was estimated to be from 50 to 60 per cent of tobacco hornworm moths in the area. Other adult insects attracted by black light are the codling moth, oriental fruit moth, corn earworm, European corn borer, cabbage looper, cotton leafworm, pink bollworm, European chafer, fall armyworm, and some species of cutworms. Deay and Hartsock at Purdue University devised a trap equipped with three 15-watt black light fluorescent lamps mounted over a cylinder flared like a funnel at the top; inside the cylinder is an electric fan, which draws the hovering insects into the trap, and below this is a separate collecting chamber. One trap protected corn, potatoes, and cucumbers in a 50 x 60-foot garden plot from damage by such insects as the corn earworm, European corn borer, potato leafhopper, tomato hornworm, and striped and spotted cucumber beetles. Bacterial wilt, a troublesome disease of cucurbits, also ceased to be a problem with the control of the spotted cucumber beetle, a vector of the disease. In these experiments one trap with a single 15-watt black light gave adequate protection to an acre of tobacco against the tobacco hornworm.[17]

Visual response to moving patterns is another principle of insect attraction on which the design of traps may be based. An interesting trap operating on this principle was designed by Canadian researchers for population studies of mosquitoes.[18] Illuminated by night, this type of trap can give samplings around the clock, and must have a pattern offering sufficient contrast to compete with environmental patterns by day. It consists of a cylinder painted with twelve black and white spiral stripes 1 5/8 inches wide, hung from a tripod. The cylinder rotates on ball bearings and contains a motor with a fan to draw the mosquitoes into the collecting chamber. The early model tried out in Manitoba in

[17] Eldon E. Fredericks, *Insects See the Light* (Lafayette, Indiana: Purdue University Agricultural Experiment Station, Summer 1959). The trap was designed by entomologist H. O. Deay and agricultural engineer J. G. Hartsock.

[18] W. O. Haufe and L. Burgess, "Design and Efficiency of Mosquito Traps Based on Visual Response to Patterns," *The Canadian Entomologist*, Feb. 1960. The trap was designed at the Lethbridge, Alberta research station of the Canada Department of Agriculture.

1951 was rotated by the air stream generated by the fan and striking against vanes attached to the inside of the cylinder; in a later and more satisfactory model tried out in Quebec, the cylinder is rotated by a belt from a motor mounted on the outside. At the top is a horizontal disk extending a little beyond the cylinder, with a hole slightly smaller than the cylinder and painted with the same number of stripes. The mosquitoes are first oriented toward the black and white contoured lines and then directed toward the opening at the top by the inward-spiraling pattern on the cylinder, while they are guided into the air stream by the revolving horizontal disk. The trap is illuminated at night with three 60-watt bulbs placed 25 feet away. It is very efficient in capturing large numbers of mosquitoes where light traps would not be satisfactory.

BARRIERS AND OTHER TRAPS

Barriers of various kinds, which are in effect traps without the attractant feature, can sometimes afford good protection for plants. Ditches and fences were used as early as 1894 to prevent migrating Mormon crickets—which do not fly—from invading farmers' fields.[19] A board fence about six inches high with a strip of tin on the top edge bent at an angle, was sufficient to stop them; after climbing as far as the strip they fell back and accumulated in heaps along the inside of the fence. Sticky bands make another form of trap that does not depend on an attractant to lure the insect; they may be used to trap insects that hatch in the ground or litter and crawl up the trunk of the tree to feed, as well as crawlers that climb the trunk to lay their eggs on the limbs or in the bark. Sticky bands work quite well for the fall and spring cankerworms (*Alsophila pometaria* and *Paleacrita vernata*), pests of apple and shade trees.[20] Their larvae are referred to as loopers, inchworms, or measuring worms because the larvae crawl by

[19] Claude Wakeland, *Mormon Crickets in North America* (Washington: USDA Technical Bulletin No. 1202, Aug. 1959).

[20] T. H. Jones, *Cankerworms* (Washington: USDA Leaflet No. 183, Aug. 1953). Rev. by J. V. Schaffner Jr.

arching their bodies high and pulling the hind legs forward; they spin threads of silk like those of spiders, by which they are often seen hanging from the trees. The adult female moths do not have wings and must crawl up the tree to lay their eggs; they can be prevented from doing so by putting a strip of cotton batting two inches wide around the tree trunk (to protect the bark), wrapping a strip of tar paper around this, and applying the sticky substance to the paper. The bands are applied in the middle of October to prevent the female fall cankerworms from climbing the trees to lay their eggs, and renewed in early spring, if necessary, to control the spring cankerworms.

Jarring the limbs with a padded pole, and catching the insects in sheets spread on the ground under the trees, amounts to a form of trapping. This method is effective for beetles in peach orchards, especially near woodlands or other places where the insects are concentrated after coming out of hibernation in the spring.[21] When disturbed by jarring the beetles fold their legs and fall immediately; in the early morning they are less active and can be jarred loose more easily than at any other time. Jarring is quite effective with the plum curculio, a small, black beetle with a snout, which is one of the worst pests of peaches.

REPELLENTS

Repellents, in contrast to attractants, are not specific—what repels one insect is likely to repel another. The repellent quality can be physical rather than chemical; many nontoxic dusts are repellents—for example, wood ashes can be used effectively on such plants as cucumbers and cabbages. A protective film of a nontoxic material, an acrylic resin, has been tried in Florida on citrus trees and is said to hold sufficient promise to warrant further research.[22] Almost any odor is repellent if sufficiently con-

[21] Oliver I. Snapp, *Insect Pests of the Peach in the United States* (Washington: USDA Farmers' Bulletin No. 1861, Feb. 1954).

[22] J. R. King, M. Cohen, and R. B. Johnson, "Filmforming Sprays on Citrus in Florida," *Florida Entomologist,* 43: (1960) 59-64.

centrated. It is a common practice among gardeners to protect young cabbage plants from the cabbage maggot by means of a disk or square made of tar paper with a hole in the center, slit so the paper can be slipped around the plant; the female butterfly is repelled by the smell of tar and avoids laying her eggs near the plant. Since a repellent must in most cases compete with an attractant, and may be effective alone but not when the competition is present, an extract made from a plant avoided by a certain insect will not necessarily repel that insect when applied to another plant; its repellency may not be sufficiently strong to overcome the attraction. Actually, some repellents are deodorizers that counteract attractive odors.

Many repellents have insecticidal qualities; oil of clove kills ants quickly, and camphor and napthalene act more slowly. The search for repellents among plants, on which man's first efforts in this direction were concentrated, led to the discovery of four substances that are now more famous for their insecticidal properties than as repellents: derris (rotenone), pyrethrum, nicotine, and oil of citronella. Pyrethrum is an effective repellent of fullgrown codling moths when applied to trees in the form of corrugated paper bands impregnated with a 5 per cent extract, to which a proportion of from 5 to 10 per cent of cottonseed oil, emulsified with blood albumen, has been added. Pyrethrum mixed with vanishing cream and applied to the skin is said to give six-hour protection against a species of tsetse fly (*Glossina palpalis*) on the Gold Coast of Africa, provided the person does not sweat too much. It is also effective against biting midges (*Culicoides* spp.). Oil of citronella has been used since 1882 as a mosquito repellent. Derris repels the Japanese beetle and the Mexican bean beetle; a mixture of derris powder and Bordeaux mixture is an effective combination against many insects. Nicotine sulfate combined with Bordeaux mixture repels the melon fly. A tree spray containing rotenone, pyrethrum, and ryania mixed with a finely divided (colloidal) clay, sprayed on the trees in a water suspension, is said to give good protection against many orchard pests.[23] The colloidal clay forms a protective film on the trees, similar to the acrylic resin mentioned above, and is also used as a dormant spray.

Perhaps the most important use of repellents is to protect man against mosquitoes, biting flies, and ticks. In 1957 the USDA announced that its scientists at the Beltsville, Maryland laboratories had developed the best all-round repellent to date—an organic compound called diethyl toluamide, which gives long-lasting protection against mosquitoes, chiggers, ticks, fleas, and biting flies. It is said to be safe for the skin and clothing, and to resist wear. Claims are made that it is the best repellent against all mosquitoes, as well as the stable fly, the rat flea, and ticks, and that it is as good as any against the deer fly, sand fly, and chiggers.[24]

SOUND IN INSECT CONTROL

Most insects react to sound. Their response has a range of about thirteen octaves, many of which are beyond the sensitivity of the human ear, in frequencies above 20,000 cycles per second. Experiments show that the auditory nerves of moths will respond to 200,000 cycles per second. Sound vibrations are not received by ears on the side of the insect's head, but rather by organs located in various parts of the body, which vary enormously in complexity—from simple hairs with a single cell to the paired "Johnson's organs" located in the second segment (counting forward from the head) of the *male* mosquito's antennae. The most familiar of these hearing organs are the tympana of grasshoppers —two oval plates on each side of the first abdominal segment. Similar tympana are found in crickets and katydids, consisting of slits on the side of the tibia (the leg segment next to the tarsus or foot.) Tympanal organs occur in pairs, and range in complexity from those found in the thorax of noctuid moths to the elaborate

[23] The product, called B.D. (for Bio-dynamic) Tree Spray, was developed by Peter A. Escher and Ehrenfried E. Pfeiffer at Threefold Farms, Spring Valley, N. Y.

[24] Entomology: 'Best' Insect Repellent Ready for Spring Sale," *Science News Letter*, March 16, 1957.

abdominal form (with some 1,500 sense cells) found in the cicadas.[25] The antennal organs found in mosquitoes are of special interest. Male mosquitoes orient themselves toward their mates by adjusting their direction of flight until the two antennae are equally stimulated or in phase with one another.

It is believed that insects use sound to attract their own species for mating, and probably as an isolating mechanism to keep the species separated. In two species of grasshoppers, however, the females seem to be most attracted by the mating call of a male of the *other* species. The song of the males of *Ephippiger bitterensis*, a longhorned grasshopper (Tettigoniidae), is more attractive to the females of *E. ephippiger* than to those of their own species; and the females of *E. bitterensis*, as though to even the score, pay more attention to the singing of *E. ephippiger* males than to the stridulating of males of their own kind. The attraction, which does not result in cross-mating, is believed to be due to a similarity in the frequency and pulse rate of the two songs. It is also possible that sounds may serve as a means of spacing the males; in some species of crickets that confine themselves to a restricted area, the male gives out warning chirps when another male enters his domain.[26]

The first attempt to turn insect sounds to practical use was in detecting infestations of wood-boring insects in trees and house timbers by their chewing noises. Around 1935 an amplifying apparatus was used to detect larvae of the house longhorn beetle in samples of wood. More recently feeding noises have been used to locate infestations of the granary weevil, *Colandra granaria*. There is a possibility of using sound to repel moths by simulating the ultra high frequencies emitted by bats in search of their prey.

It has been suggested that sound might be used to kill insects directly or to interfere with mating by breaking up swarms of

[25] Peter Belton, "The Physiology of Sound Reception in Insects," *Proceedings,* Entomological Society of Ontario, 1961 (pub. Aug. 1962).
[26] P. T. Haskell, *Insect Sounds* (London: H. F. & G. Witherby, Ltd., 1961).

Time exposure showing moth tracks. Simulated bat cry (beyond range of the human ear) causes moths to turn sharply as they come within range. (Sound-emitting device out of view.) Moths are flying toward the observer. (*Peter Belton,* Canada Department of Agriculture)

insects; but the current cost of such equipment appears to be prohibitive. "Jamming," as in radio communication, by broadcasting sounds that would interfere with the mating sounds of females and throw the males into confusion, is being investigated. Belton sees practical possibilities in attracting female insects toward "electronic mates," or in assembling parasites by "simulating the noises of their hosts."[27] A "sonic-baited" trap for mosquitoes was tried as early as 1945, with partial success. A loudspeaker was used to broadcast the recorded sound of a female mosquito in flight; 90 per cent of the mosquitoes attracted were males of the same species. One of the limitations of this device was in amplifying the sound enough to cover a given range without making it repellent; another is the fact that since mosquitoes are oriented

[27] Peter Belton, "Sound and Ultrasound in Insect Control" (Symposium on Unconventional Approaches to Insect Control, Annual Meeting, Entomological Society of Ontario, Hamilton, Ontario, Nov. 17, 1961).

toward sound only when in flight, the inactive ones were not attracted to the trap.

ELECTRICAL FIELDS AND INSECT CONTROL

The increased activity of insects before a storm, reflected in high trap catches, and the increased foraging activities of bees at such times, have been noted; but until quite recently no work had been done on how atmospheric electricity affects insects. Storms and cold fronts have a decided effect on caged insects living under controlled conditions in the laboratory, as well as on those in the natural state. It has been observed in the laboratory that the common vinegar fly *(Drosophila melanogaster)* produced more progeny when the barometric pressure had been rising, and less when it had been decreasing, during the mating period. When the flies are subjected to an imposed electrical field, the atmospheric effects were offset in some way, and the progeny increased. These differences are believed to be due to changes in the ionization levels in the air. The increase in the number of ions as the atmospheric pressure decreases, has a depressing effect on insects; and the imposed electrical field is believed to act as a shield against the atmospheric ions. The ionic content of the air is closely associated with potential gradients; an increased ionization level increases the conductivity of the air, and reduces the potential gradients.[28]

M. G. Maw found that the ichneumonid wasp *Scambus buolianae* deposited more eggs when shielded from atmospheric fields, and concluded that "fluctuating electrical fields, either of artificial or natural origin, disturb the insects while ovipositing and so the oviposition rate is suppressed."[29] There is also evidence to show that molting rates, adult emergence, and the flight of insects are associated with atmospheric electrical fields.

[28] M. G. Maw, "Some Biological Effects of Atmospheric Electricity," *Proceedings,* Entomological Society of Ontario, 1961 (pub. Aug. 1962).

[29] M. G. Maw, "Suppression of Oviposition Rate of *Scambus buolianae* (Htg.) (Hymenoptera: Ichneumonidae) in Fluctuating Electrical Fields," *The Canadian Entomologist,* July 1961.

An interesting experiment to test the effect of electrostatic fields on insects was conducted by Maw at Belleville, Ontario.[30] He placed ten females of an ichneumonid wasp (*Itoplectis conquisitor*) on one side of a lucite plastic box, with a 25-watt yellow incandescent bulb on the other side to attract them. Between the sides, waving lines of electrostatic charges varying from 30 to 100 volts were imposed on the floor of the box by stroking it with the bare end of a wire connected to a power source. Since the plastic is a nonconductor, the charges remained well defined as lines. The insects' movements were plotted on a sheet of squared paper on the floor of the box. They moved rapidly toward the light until the first line (30-volt potential) was reached, whereupon they stopped; considerable turning and tapping of antennae took place before they proceeded to the next line (40 volts), and again until the third line (100 volts) was reached. The highest voltage produced the longest delay. After crossing the 100-volt line, barriers of decreasing voltages (40 and 30) were encountered; the same behavior took place here as when the potentials were increasing. Presumably the delay each time was long enough for the insects to pick up the higher potentials and to discharge them as the voltages decreased. From this experiment it appears that insects are influenced in their movements by electrostatic fields. Although these potentials—which did not harm the wasps—were higher than are encountered in nature, it would appear that lower potentials also have an influence on the activity and flight patterns of insects and are a factor in their distribution. It is well known that trees, shrubs, and other plants are surrounded by electrostatic fields. It was observed that swarming flights of mosquitoes (*Aedes trichurus*) in a glade concentrated in rather well defined flyways bounded by the steep potential gradients surrounding the trees.

The influence of electrical fields on the behavior of insects is demonstrated by the effect of electrical charges accumulating

[30] M. G. Maw, "Behaviour of an Insect on an Electrically Charged Surface," *The Canadian Entomologist*, May 1961.

on a trap net made of synthetic fibers. A revolving net brushed against a leaf collected considerably fewer hymenopterous parasites than its counterpart swung freely; it is believed that this difference was due to electrical charges accumulating on the net as a result of the leaf's brushing against it. Among the possible applications of electrical field phenomena to crop protection, the use of electrical fields to induce insect pests to lay their eggs where they would be exposed to attack by predators and parasites, to provide a protective electrical field over plants by means of a system of small wires, and to predict future insect populations by sampling the ion content of the air, has been suggested.[31]

High-frequency electric fields—not to be confused with the electrical fields associated with the atmosphere—offer an inexpensive way of protecting stored grains from insects, and appear to be more desirable than fumigation. When such relatively poor conductors as insects or grain are subjected to an alternating electric field of several million cycles per second, an effect known as dielectric heating is produced. The heating is very rapid: an exposure of only a few seconds will raise the temperature of the conductor (the grain and insects in this case) by from 50 to 100 degrees; all the material is heated simultaneously, since the heat energy is developed by the field and absorbed from it. Tests of HF electric fields as a means of protecting stored grains were conducted by the Stored-Grain Insects Laboratory at Manhattan, Kansas in 1956–1957. One HF power oscillator of 39 mc. with an output of 3 kw., and one with a frequency range of 1.5 to 11 mc. and an output of 1 kw. were used.[32] Hard red winter wheat (mostly Pawnee) was used in the tests, except for three employing wheat shorts, with various stages of the rice weevil (*Sitophilus oryza*), granary weevil (*Sitophilus granarius*), confused flour

[31] M. G. Maw, "Some Biological Effects of Atmospheric Electricity."
[32] HF=high frequency; mc.=megacycles (millions of cycles); kw.=kilowatts (thousands of watts); kv.=kilovolts (thousands of volts); kv./in., r.m.s.=kilovolts per inch, root mean square; kw.-hr.=kilowatt hours.

beetle (*Tribolium confusum*), red flour beetle (*Tribolium castaneum*), lesser grain borer (*Rhyzopertha dominica*), and dermestid beetle (*Trogoderma parabile*).

It was found that in some stored-grain insects all stages can be killed by HF electrical treatments of a few seconds' duration, without damage to the grain; different species and stages within a species showed differences in resistance to the treatment. A field intensity of 3.6 kv./in. r.m.s. was more effective in killing adult insects than lower intensities; field intensities over 4.8 kv./in. were apt to cause arcing and to burn the kernels. Resistance to HF treatment was in the following order of increasing resistance at 3.6 kv./in. intensity in wheat: rice weevil adults, granary weevil adults, confused flour beetle adults, lesser grain borer adults, dermestid larvae, immature rice weevils, and immature lesser grain borers. Temperatures required for a 90 per cent kill were (in the same order) 94, 98, 108, 122, 130, 127, and 134 degrees Fahrenheit. Insects not killed by treatments were injured at higher field intensities; most of the injured insects died within a week after exposure. Higher-level treatments are required for control of adult insects in wheat shorts. Treatments at 102° F. were required to give 80 per cent mortality in wheat; the same mortality in shorts required 127°. The estimated cost of large-scale treatments of grain using this method is from 2.8 to 3.7 cents per bushel, including depreciation, interest on investment, maintenance, and a power cost of 2 cents per kw.-hr.[33]

BREEDING INSECT-RESISTANT PLANTS

A fruitful approach to insect problems is in the breeding of plants resistant to insect attack. Reginald Painter comments that the newer insecticides developed during and since World War II have been given such wide acclaim that there is a tendency to overlook the many other ways of controlling insects. "Informa-

[33] W. K. Whitney, S. O. Nelson, and H. H. Walkden, *Effects of High-Frequency Electric Fields on Certain Species of Stored-Grain Insects* (Washington: USDA, Market Quality Research Division, Agricultural Marketing Service, March 1961).

tion of these other ways is not broadcast by highly paid advertising staffs. Yet there are large areas where certain crops could not be grown profitably because of insects without the use of biological or cultural control measures."[34] Control of the wheat stem sawfly in the western plains region, for example, is not feasible with chemicals. According to Painter, the development of resistant varieties of wheat—notably Rescue and Chinook spring wheats—have made it possible to grow wheat profitably on 1.8 million acres in Canada and more than 600,000 acres in the north central wheat-growing area of the United States. The pioneer in developing insect-resistant plants has been the Kansas Agricultural Experiment Station (in cooperation with the USDA) at the University of Kansas, where projects for developing resistant varieties of crop plants have been carried on continuously for over thirty-five years. Out of this have come some eleven varieties of crop plants, including corn, wheat, barley, alfalfa, and sorghums, that are resistant to various insects.[35]

When confronted with an insect problem, the plant breeder looks for host plants that appear resistant, selecting them from infested fields or from adapted varieties and imported plants; these are brought into the greenhouse for study, hybridization with other varieties, and further selection from subsequent generations. It normally takes from ten to fifteen years to develop a resistant plant, but after the spotted alfalfa aphid first invaded the western states in 1954, three resistant varieties of alfalfa were ready for use within three years. Resistance may consist of one or more of the following factors: preference (the number of insects attracted to the plant), tolerance, and antibiosis (the effect of the plant on such things as the egg-laying capacity of the female insect). Resistance of sorghum varieties to chinch

[34] Reginald H. Painter, *Insect Resistance in Crop Plants* (New York: The Macmillan Company, 1951).

[35] Reginald H. Painter, "Breeding Plants for Resistance to Insect Pests," in *Biological and Chemical Control of Plant and Animal Pests* (Washington: American Association for the Advancement of Science, Publication No. 61, 1960).

bugs comprises all three factors; the resistance of corn to grass-hoppers is primarily a matter of their preference for one variety of plant as against another. The resistance of corn to the European corn borer consists mainly of tolerance and antibiosis, preference also being a factor; that of wheat to the Hessian fly is largely antibiosis, and that of wheat and barley to the green bug is principally tolerance.

RESISTANCE TO WHEAT STEM SAWFLY

The varieties of wheat resistant to the wheat stem sawfly are solid-stemmed; that they resist development of the eggs as well as the larvae has been shown by W. D. Holmes and L. K. Peterson.[36] The eggs are laid in the pith or cavities within the internodes of the stem, and the survival both of the egg and of the larvae that succeed in hatching are related to the space available. The only thing the eggs require of the plant is moisture; but the larvae must bore their way down through the ripening stems if they are to survive and reach the ground for overwintering. Only one larva can survive in a stalk; the others, along with the unhatched eggs, become food for the survivor. The solidity of the stems, and thus the degree of resistance, will vary with environmental factors. The amount of moisture available and the time of planting are important factors in the survival of the eggs and larvae, since both affect the size of the cavities available in the stems at critical times in egg and larval development. Where wheat is irrigated, the sawfly is never a problem.

WHERE RESISTANCE PAYS OFF

Most successes with insect-resistant plants have been in field crops such as corn, wheat, barley, sorghum, alfalfa, and sugar cane. The earliest record of insect resistance in a plant that can be identified dates back to 1831, when the winter Majetin apple

[36] N. D. Holmes and L. K. Peterson, "Resistance of Spring Wheats to the Wheat Stem Sawfly, *Cephus cinctus* Nort. (Hymenoptera: Cephidae), I. Resistance to the Egg; II. Resistance to the Larva," *The Canadian Entomologist,* April 1961, April 1962.

was reported to be resistant to the woolly apple aphid (*Eriosoma lanigerum*); this resistance is still present. The resistance of sorghums to *Melanoplus* grasshoppers was first reported in 1877. The resistance of certain varieties of corn to the corn earworm (*Heliothis zea*) was first noted in Kansas around 1919, and numerous hybrids of varying resistance to the earworm have been developed; several varieties grown in the South are resistant to the earworm and the rice weevil. Certain varieties of corn grown in the central United States have led to reduced injury by this pest to the point where insecticides are no longer used to control it. Five varieties of alfalfa resistant to the spotted alfalfa aphid are now being widely used in alfalfa-growing areas, and insecticides are seldom required where these resistant varieties are grown. Control of the Hessian fly by development of resistant varieties of wheat has been very successful. "Seventeen Hessian fly resistant wheats are now being grown on 4½ million acres in 26 states," according to the USDA.[37] Previous to this, delayed seeding was the only effective means of controlling the fly (and then only the fall generation) on winter wheats. More recently, potato varieties have been developed which are said to be resistant to some fourteen species of insects, including such notorious potato pests as the Colorado potato beetle, the leafhoppers, and the tuber flea beetle.

Some of the advantages of building resistance into plants are that it is "cumulative and continuing" (Pawnee, a variety of wheat resistant to the Hessian fly, and Atlas, a variety of sorghum resistant to the chinch bug, are outstanding examples of long continued resistance); that it does not create a residue problem; that it increases yield and improves the quality of plants; that it often reduces the population of the resisted insect throughout the area (notable examples are the Hessian fly, spotted alfalfa aphid, and the European corn borer); that it does not reduce the beneficial insect populations, and that it reduces cost of production to the grower.

[37] ARS 22-85.

CULTURAL PRACTICES AND INSECT CONTROL

Probably the best place to begin plant protection is with the plant itself and its environment. Walter Fleming points out that "plants grown in fertile soil are usually hardier, healthier, and more resistant to insects than those in poor soil. Barnyard manure, green manure crops, and commercial fertilizers are of value in assisting plants to outgrow damage by insects."[38] Fertilizing field crops is often the best way to combat infestations of corn root aphids, the southern corn rootworm, the Hessian fly, the white-fringed beetle, the wheat stem sawfly, the sugar cane beetle, and white grubs; and in controlling tree-boring insects in apple orchards it is important to keep trees growing vigorously. Cultural practices which help keep insects under control include crop rotation, tillage, attention to the time of planting and harvesting, strip cropping, and intercropping.

CROP ROTATION

Growing the same crop year after year tends to encourage insect pests. Rotating immune crops such as legumes with corn, wheat, barley, oats, and rye will control the chinch bug. Oats, buckwheat, corn, or sorghum rotated with wheat will break the cycle of wheat pests such as the Hessian fly, false wireworm, wheat jointworm, winter grain mite, and wheat stem sawfly. Grubs of the Japanese beetle, the European chafer, the Asiatic garden beetle, the oriental beetle, and native white grubs are pests of garden and field crops, grasses, and nursery plants; legumes in rotation with these crops will greatly reduce the damage done by the grubs. Wireworms cause the greatest damage to cultivated crops in the irrigated fields of the Pacific northwest; they can be controlled if alfalfa is grown for three or four years, followed by one year of potatoes and one or two years of truck

[38] Walter E. Fleming, "Soil Management and Insect Control," in *Soils: Yearbook of Agriculture,* USDA (Washington: Government Printing Office, 1957).

crops such as corn, beans, peas, and sugar beets. East of the Rockies, wireworms cause the greatest damage to hay and small grains, and can be controlled by rotation with legumes and by not planting susceptible crops to the same land two successive years.

TILLAGE

Plowing or disking at the right time will destroy many insects. Fall or early spring plowing of stubble will expose grasshopper eggs to freezing or drying, or bury them too deep for the nymphs to reach the surface after hatching. When crop residues are needed to protect the soil from erosion, tillage with a subsurface blade or shovel type of implement is recommended. Disking in the summer months will destroy many white grubs, including those of the Japanese beetle, white-fringed beetle, and European chafer. Disking orchards in early summer will destroy many pupae of the plum curculio. Plowing or disking just before planting will scatter and destroy enough corn-root aphids, and the ants associated with them, to give corn and cotton a chance to become well established before being attacked. Plowing immediately after harvest will help to control some insects; this is recommended for pea crops, to prevent development of weevils in peas left in the field.[39] In some areas the same advice applies to grain cutworms as well.

STRIP CROPPING

Strip cropping (planting alternate rows of different crops in the same field) conserves moisture, prevents soil erosion, and complements other good farming practices. It also helps to control insect populations, as do other cultural practices associated with it. Growing corn and meadow, or small grain and meadow, in alternating strips in separate fields will often avoid crop damage by chinch bugs. It has been found in the eastern United States that strip-cropped fields have larger populations of ground-nest-

[39] T. A. Brindley, J. C. Chamberlin, and Ralph Schopp, *The Pea Weevil and Methods for its Control* (Washington: USDA, Farmers' Bulletin No. 1971, Jan. 1956).

ing birds; hence strip cropping aids in insect control by increasing the population of these consumers of insects.[40] In Peru cotton is generally interspersed with rows of corn at regular intervals to reduce the damage of *Heliothis virescens* (known here as the tobacco budworm), which attacks the corn as well as cotton. The pest is attracted to the corn, where eggs and larval stage are attacked by a predatory anthocorid bug, *Paratriphleps laeviusculus,* which is attracted to corn but avoids cotton. Another bug—the mirid *Rhinacola carmelitana*—and some other predators attack the pest on cotton, avoiding the corn.

ATTRACTING INSECT PARASITES

Strip cropping and intercropping—growing a variety of crop plants in close proximity—tend to build up a more complex "ecosystem," which has been defined as "the complex of organisms and physical factors that forms a more or less natural community."[41] Our system of monoculture—the growing of field or orchard crops singly in large unbroken expanses—tends to increase the population of insect pests. The idea of a more varied environment is not only to reduce the pest population by having fewer of their preferred plants where large populations build rapidly, but also to make the environment more suitable to their natural enemies. An investigative team who visited the Soviet Union a few years ago reported that much emphasis was placed there on intercropping.[42] This extends to the growing of plants specifically to attract parasites. Corn is interplanted with pumpkins, for example, to attract parasites of the European corn borer to the fields. It is well known that different pollens have varying effects on the longevity and egg production of parasites and that they are attracted to some plants more than others. Tests made by

[40] Howard E. Tower and Harry H. Gardner, *Strip Cropping for Conservation and Production* (Washington: USDA, Farmers' Bulletin No. 1981, June 1960).

[41] Walter Ebeling, "Biological Control," in *Subtropical Fruit Pests* (Berkeley: University of California Press, 1959).

[42] *Entomology in the Soviet Union: Report of a Technical Study Group* (Washington: USDA, Agricultural Research Service, June 1961).

K. Leus show that the longevity and egg production of *Scambus buolianae*, an ichneumonid wasp, varies considerably with the kind of pollen available to the females. Tulip, poppy, and snapdragon pollens gave the highest egg production, and those of birch, apple, and Scots pine gave the lowest. The addition of wild carrot and tulip pollen to the diet resulted in the greatest longevity and egg production.[43] From this it is apparent that parasites have a better chance of becoming established in an area where there is a rich variety of pollen and nectar-producing plants, and that they will be more effective in such an environment.

TIME OF PLANTING

The time of planting—and of harvesting too—can affect the damage done by insects. In the north central and northeastern United States the earliest plantings of corn are injured the least by corn earworms (*Heliothis zea*). On the other hand, early planting gives an advantage to the European corn borer, so the planting of corn in these areas must be according to the best practice for the particular locality. In the southern states, where the European corn borer is less numerous, early plantings of corn are more subject to corn earworm infestation because the moths concentrate their egg-laying in these fields in the absence of cotton or other crops. Planting the corn according to the best practice for a given locality, so that it comes into silk when cotton and other plants are also available, keeps earworm damage to a minimum.[44] Early planting of corn and sugar cane in the southeastern states reduces the damage caused by wireworms and the sugar cane beetle.

[43] K. Leus, "Influence of Food on Fecundity and Longevity of Adults of *Itoplectis conquisitor* (Say) (Hymenoptera: Ichneumonidae)," *The Canadian Entomologist*, Sept. 1961; also "Effects of Pollens on Fecundity and Longevity of Adult *Scambus buolianae* (Htg.) (Hymenoptera: Ichneumonidae)," *ibid.*, Feb. 1963.
[44] R. A. Blanchard and W. A. Douglas, *The Corn Earworm as an Enemy of Field Corn in the Eastern States* (Washington: USDA Farmers' Bulletin No. 1651, Nov. 1953).

If seed-corn maggots are present, the planting of beans, corn, peas, and melons should be delayed to avoid sprouting until danger from the maggots, which are most active in early spring, and in cool, wet soils, is past. Wheat is generally planted on so-called "fly-free dates"—that is, seeding is delayed in the fall until most of the fall brood of the Hessian fly has disappeared. These dates are determined by experiment stations for each of the wheat-growing states. Delayed sowing also reduces damage from wireworms, false wireworms, and white grubs. Delayed planting on cutover forest lands is advisable in some areas to avoid insect problems in new plantations. A weevil, *Steremnius carinatus,* has become very destructive to new Douglas fir plantations in the coastal region of British Columbia, killing or damaging as much as 40 per cent of the seedlings. It is believed that the trouble is the result of rapid replanting of cutover lands, where logging, slash burning, and replanting have all taken place within a two- or three-year period. This is described by R. R. Lejeune as "a logical sequence of events for beating the brush to the site."[45]

TIME OF HARVESTING

"Strip farming" is a term applied to the planting and harvesting of a field crop in alternate strips rather than all at one time. It was found in California that harvesting alfalfa in strips, so that two different ages of hay growth were present in the field at one time, helped to maintain a better balance between pest species of insects and their natural enemies. When a set of alternate strips is cut, the others are about half grown, so the field is never bare. By conserving the natural enemies of the spotted alfalfa aphid and other pests, it is possible to maintain pest population densities "below the economic level throughout the year and minimize the need for applying any kind of insecticide."[46]

[45] R. R. Lejeune, "A New Reforestation Problem Caused by a Weevil *Steremnius carinatus* Boh.," *Bi-monthly Progress Report,* Canada Dept. of Forestry, Nov.–Dec. 1962.

[46] E. I. Schlinger and E. J. Dietrick, "Biological Control of Insect Pests Aided by Strip-farming Alfalfa in Experimental Program," *California Agriculture,* Jan. 1960.

A controlled pattern of harvesting hardwood has been used successfully in the Soviet Union to eliminate a forest pest, *Cerambyx cerdo*. This beetle has a three-year life cycle. Under the old practice the trees were cut in alternate strips, with the result that high beetle populations developed along the margins of the strips. By harvesting adjacent strips in successive years the immature beetles at the edge of the previously harvested strips are prevented from developing into adults. Almost complete eradication of the pest has resulted from this method.

Although the spruce budworm (*Choristoneura fumiferana*) is attacked by thirty species of primary parasites in North America, neither they nor various predators prevent occasional severe outbreaks of the pest. The greatest injury occurs in overmature stands of balsam and of red spruce, and in mixed stands where balsam predominates. Rapid utilization of overmature trees, and harvesting of the oldest stands first, "in order to produce fast growing balsam forests handled on a short rotation," is recommended.[47] The susceptibility of the mature trees appears to be related to the increased exposure of the crowns (and increased evaporation rate), and to the flight behavior of the adult female moths; more eggs are deposited on the taller, more exposed trees.[48]

Two-stage harvesting of wheat is practiced in the Soviet Union to control thrips and two bugs (*Eurygaster integriceps* and *Aelia acuminata*) on grain. The wheat is cut when it reaches the wax stage and is allowed to stand in windrows for some time before threshing, to restrict the feeding periods of these insects. The thrips are curtailed by being deprived of the high moisture content of the wheat, whereas with the bugs it is a matter of preventing the fat storage required for successful hibernation. The formation of fat bodies in these insects occurs in the ten-day

[47] J. M. Swaine (rev. by C. E. Atwood), *The Spruce Budworm* (Ottawa: Canada Dept. of Agriculture, Dec. 1944).

[48] D. G. Mott, "The Forest and the Spruce Budworm," in *The Dynamics of Epidemic Spruce Budworm Populations*, R. F. Morris, ed. (Memoirs of the Entomological Society of Canada, No. 31, 1963).

period following transformation from the nymph to the adult stage, and normally coincides with the wax stage of the wheat; deprived of this essential food at a critical period, they are short of the requirements for withstanding winter temperatures.

SOME OTHER CULTURAL PRACTICES

Trap crops can be effective in controlling some insects. In some pea-growing areas a strip of early blooming peas is sown around the margin of a large field to control the pea weevil, *Bruchus pisorum* (Bruchidae). The peas are planted to bloom a week or ten days ahead of the main crop. The weevils concentrate in the trap and are destroyed. A similar device, the planting of nurse crops, is sometimes used where insects will feed on a variety of crops, to divert pests from valuable planted seedlings. Pruning practices are sometimes the key to pest control. Michigan State University foresters found that delayed shearing of scots and red pines in Christmas tree plantations eliminates the pine shoot moth. Most growers shear in late June to improve the shape of the trees. Delaying the pruning for two weeks means that the buds are clipped off with the moth larvae inside or while the latter are still on the twigs; in either case the pest is eliminated. With spraying costs running about four dollars an acre, this pays good dividends without increased pruning cost or effort.[49]

INSECT CONTROL THROUGH NUTRITION

There is a good possibility that some major insect pests can be controlled through depriving them of their nutritional requirements. According to Leonard Haseman, "there is definite evidence that we may be able, by stepping up the major and minor soil minerals and other nutritional factors, to produce larger crops providing optimum balanced rations for man and livestock, but which may prove either distasteful or even harmful to the well-

[49] *Shearing Delay Controls Pine Shoot Moth* (News Release, Dept. of Information, Michigan State University, East Lansing, July 3, 1961). The foresters are Walter A. Lemmien and Victor J. Rudolph.

being of some of our insect pests."[50] He believes that by controlling their diet it may be possible to affect their reproductive
potential, and possibly to bring about anatomical changes, for example in wing development. The worker bee is not a queen
simply because she has received a different diet in the larval
stage; but she can become a queen if necessary by being given
the proper diet. Experiments showing that the pollens of different plants vary in their effect on the reproductive capacity and
longevity of certain parasites have already been cited.

The chinch bug is influenced by the amount of nitrogen in its
diet, and passes up the nitrogenous legume crops in favor of the
grasses, which are richer in carbohydrates. It thrives best on the
stunted crops of eroded slopes, rather than on the more vigorous
plants in more fertile soil; and it is favored by the dry years when
lack of soil moisture deprives the plants of minerals, and especially of nitrogen. Laboratory tests have shown that thrips live
longer and lay more eggs when the diet is low in nitrogen. Greenhouse thrips also pass up the more vigorous plants, which are high
in nitrogen, for inferior plants. Some pests, such as the European
corn borer, seem to thrive best on crops grown on more fertile
soils, but Haseman believes it might still be possible to affect
them adversely by shifting the relative levels of soil minerals.
The Colorado potato beetle and the tuber flea beetle, which have
shifted from weeds to potatoes and have shown a marked response to the new diet, might well be held in bounds by a shift
in nutrient levels. Some blood-sucking parasites of domestic animals and man also respond to changes in their host's diet which
affect their well-being and reproductive potential. Scrawny, un-
derfed animals seem to be more susceptible to lice and other insect infestations.

In laboratory experiments, Smith found that the development,
survival, and fecundity of the migratory grasshopper, *Melanoplus
bilituratus,* was greater on wheat low in phosphorus (0.17 per cent

[50] Leonard Haseman, "Controlling Insect Pests Through Their Nutritional
Requirements," *Journal of Economic Entomology,* June 1950.

dry weight) than on wheat high in phosphorus (1.86 per cent dry weight). Development was much more rapid on the low phosphorus; at a time when 70 per cent of the insects on the low phosphorus diet were in the fourth instar stage of larval development, only 25 per cent of those on the high phosphorus diet had reached this stage. Survival was nearly three times as great on the low phosphorus diet as on the high phosphorus diet. The survival rate was about the same for both sexes in each case, but the twenty-seven surviving females on the low phosphorus diet laid thirty-three egg pods, whereas none were laid by the surviving females on the high phosphorus diet.[51] In tests made by N. E. Daniels with winter wheat, the number of greenbugs (*Toxoptera graminum*) per gram of plant varied inversely with the amount of nitrogen applied,[52] and Dahms reported that the chinch bug, *Blissus leucopterus*, produced more eggs when fed on seedling sorghum plants grown in a medium deficient in phosphorus.[53]

In a controlled experiment, William A. Albrecht found that as the nitrogen and calcium levels in the soil increased, injury to spinach plants from thrips decreased. Spinach in soil offering 10 milligram equivalents and less of nitrogen was attacked by thrips, whereas plants offered 20 milligram equivalents and more were free from attack. Even with low nitrogen (or "insufficient protein for self-protection"), as the 10 milligram equivalents were combined with increasing amounts of calcium, there was less attack from the thrips, showing that a better balance of calcium and nitrogen in the soil gave better protection to the plants. Albrecht has also shown that a better balance of nitrogen and phosphorus in the soil protected stored corn grown on that soil against attack by the lesser grain borer. This insect showed a decided prefer-

[51] D. S. Smith, "Effects of Changing the Phosphorus Content of the Food Plant on the Migratory Grasshopper, *Melanoplus bilituratus* (Walker) (Orthoptera: Acrididae)," *The Canadian Entomologist,* Feb. 1960.

[52] N. E. Daniels, "Greenbug Populations and their Damage to Winter Wheat as Affected by Fertilizer Applications," *Journal of Economic Entomology,* Dec. 1957.

[53] R. G. Dahms, "Oviposition and Longevity of Chinch Bugs on Seedlings Growing in Nutrient Solution," *Journal of Economic Entomology,* Dec. 1947.

Effect of fertilization of the soil on resistance of stored corn to attack by the lesser grain borer: *center ear*, representative ear of hybrid corn grown on soil fertilized with nitrogen only; *left ear*, representative ear of same hybrid grown on the same soil but fertilized with both nitrogen and phosphorus. Attack was only at point where the two ears were in contact for two years; *right ear*, open-pollinated corn fertilized by barnyard manure. This ear, which has only one borer hole, was in storage for two and a half years and in contact with the center ear for only six months, after latter was full of borers. (*William A. Albrecht*)

ence for the corn grown on soil fertilized with nitrogen only, to the corn grown on the same soil fertilized with both nitrogen and phosphorus.[54]

[54] Personal communication from Dr. William A. Albrecht, now Chairman Emeritus, Department of Soils, University of Missouri, July 23, 1963. He explains that in the experiment on the effect of minerals on thrips and spinach plants, instead of using nutrient solutions, the calcium and nitrogen were controlled "by using separated, colloidal clay, electrodialyzed to remove all nutrients and other cations, except to saturate it by hydrogen completely. Then the nitrogen as ammonium, and the calcium were titrated on the clay."

Results of free larval selection by fabric-eating insects: (a) check (no treatment), first consumed; (b) low-level antimetabolite treatment, third consumed; (c) treatment with full-level antimetabolite combination, not consumed; (d) cationic surfacant, second consumed; (e) treated with stomach poison, fourth consumed. (*Roy J. Pence*)

CONTROLLING FABRIC-EATERS BY NUTRITION

Clothes moths and carpet beetles can be controlled through their nutritional requirements. Exhaustive laboratory tests show that safe long-lasting, inexpensive protection against fabric insects can be obtained by depriving them of certain food factors. Clean fabrics alone do not have sufficient food value to maintain the fabric-eaters; they get some food factors (such as vitamins) necessary to their growth from contaminants added by simply handling, or from food and liquid stains, perspiration, body oils, urine, and even from cigar and cigarette ashes which have micronutrients that attract rather than repel them. Contamination can scarcely be avoided unless a fabric is sterilized and put into an airtight container. Fabric pests can be controlled by the use of what are called growth factor analogs, or antimetabolites. By omitting a single atom from the complex chemical structure that makes up a vitamin, an imitation can be constructed to resemble the real thing so closely that the insect readily accepts it as food. The antimetabolite, however, is antagonistic to the vitamin it resembles and quickly disrupts the processes of digestion and metabolism. By applying low-level antimetabolites to fabrics the young larvae are driven by hunger to eat more and more until they die of vitamin deficiency or starvation; the more they eat the more they want, and the faster they bring on the end. Older larvae, having reserves accumulated of adipose tissue, eat the impregnated fabric for only a short time, and the mature larvae will have none of it; both die of starvation. The fabric-eaters need not only vitamins—the principal one of which is nicotinic acid (niacin)—but also amino acids, principally phenylalanine, tyrosine, and lysine, which they derive from the protein fibers such as wool. Amino acid inhibitors are therefore also important in the insect-proofing process, and can be combined with the vitamin-antimetabolites. These substances are insoluble in organic solvents, and withstand repeated dry cleaning in pure benzene and carbon tetrachloride. Antimetabolites are inexpensive and are easy to prepare and use. A 2 per cent solution in water or 3 per cent in alcohol is sufficient to control fabric insects, and is harmless to human beings and pets; it is also not likely to foster the development of resistance in the pests as do the insecticides commonly used for this purpose.[55]

[55] Roy J. Pence, "Control of Fabric-Feeding Insects by Neutralizing Vitamins in Fibers," *California Agriculture*, Feb. 1960).

Mass destruction [by chemicals] and the casual releasing of predators and parasites may some day be looked back upon as we do upon the mistakes of the industrial age, the excesses of colonial exploitation or the indiscriminate felling of climax forests.

—CHARLES S. ELTON[1]

BIOLOGICAL CONTROL OF INSECT PESTS

13

A brief look at the history of biological control in the United States (more particularly California, where much of this activity has centered) and in Canada will be useful at this point.

Although the concept of biological control is as old as recorded history—the ancient Chinese having used ants to combat insect pests—its practice in the West goes back only about 75 years. The first published work reporting the transport of insects for biological control (predatory ants in Yemen) appeared in 1775. Erasmus Darwin, father of Charles Darwin, suggested the possibility of biological control in a book on agriculture and gardening published in London in 1800. In the United States the first suggestion, for importing insect enemies of a pest from its native country, in print at least, was in 1855, when Asa Fitch wrote to the president of the Royal Entomological Society in London requesting that parasites of the wheat midge be collected in Europe and shipped here. In 1864 the Reverend C. J. S. Bethune in Canada made a similar request, but nothing came of either one.

[1] *The Ecology of Invasions by Animals and Plants* (London: Methuen and Co. Ltd., 1958).

358

E. J. Wickson, editor of the Pacific Rural Press in California, wrote in 1879 that "it would seem wise to take measures to introduce . . . foes of the scale insects in places where the pest has full sway.' C. V. Riley, entomologist of the United States Department of Agriculture, first proposed the transfer of parasites from one part of the country to another in 1870, and in 1873 he made arrangements for the first international transfer of a beneficial species, with the shipment to France of an American predatory mite (*Rhizoglyphus phylloxerae*) which fed on the grapevine phylloxera. The following year a lady beetle (*Coccinella undecimpunctata*) was imported into New Zealand for control of aphids. The first shipment of a biological control agent into Canada was made in 1882 by William Saunders, who imported from New York some eggs of the currantworm that had been parasitized by *Trichogramma* wasps. The parasite is found throughout Canada today; however, it may have been present in some areas at the time of this introduction.

In 1883 Riley made the first intentional introduction of a foreign parasite into the United States with the importation of *Apanteles glomeratus,* a parasite of the imported cabbage worm, from England; the wasp spread rapidly and is present in this country today wherever cabbage plants are grown. Riley was also responsible for sending Albert Koebele to Australia in 1888 to search for enemies of the cottony cushion scale—a trip which resulted in the most successful biological control project in entomological history. The first attempt in this country to control pests biologically over a wide area was undertaken in 1905 by the United States Department of Agriculture, in cooperation with the Commonwealth of Massachusetts, against the gypsy moth and the browntail moth. An active biological control program had its beginning in Canada in 1910 when G. Hewitt took the post of dominion entomologist; he had studied the larch sawfly in England and was responsible for bringing the parasite *Mesoleius tenthredinis* to Canada to combat it. A large-scale importation and release program was undertaken and met with great success—an auspicious beginning not unlike our own project against the cottony cushion scale.

RIDING HIGH

In a way it is unfortunate that these initial projects were so successful, since the hopes for the technique were thereby raised too high, at least so far as the cottony cushion scale was concerned. At that time, which has been referred to as "a dangerous period in the entomological history of North America,"[2] all caution was thrown to the winds. Great numbers of insects were brought into this country without proper screening or quarantine, and it is a wonder that no greater harm ensued than the waste of time and effort. With the spectacular success of the vedalia beetle in controlling the cottony cushion scale, the enthusiasm of the fruit growers in California for biological control knew no bounds. There was contention between Riley and the state agricultural officials over sending Albert Koebele back to Australia for a second time in 1891. The quarrel between Riley and the State Board of Horticulture became so bitter that federal agents of the USDA's Division of Entomology were withdrawn from California, and Koebele, refusing to go to Washington, resigned. The controversy between the USDA and Elwood Cooper, commissioner of agriculture for California at the time, continued into the regime of L. O. Howard, Riley's successor, and did not end until Cooper's retirement under pressure in 1907.

Statements made by representatives of the two sides at the time reflect the extreme divergence of opinion concerning biological control. On the one hand it was the contention of Cooper that insect pests are controlled by predators and parasites in their places of origin, that to control a pest it was necessary only to determine its place of origin, find the parasite or predator controlling it, import and release the latter in the troubled area, and let nature take its course. The opposite view, as expressed by

[2] A. L. Turnbull and D. A. Chant, "The Practice and Theory of Biological Control of Insects in Canada," *Canadian Journal of Zoology*, Oct. 1961.

Riley, was that introduced pests could be controlled by introducing their enemies only in exceptional cases, that advance planning was necessary, with careful study of the history and systematics of the insects involved, and the conditions of climate and geography; that the introduction of miscellaneous enemies of the pest resulted in little if any gain, especially when they did not control the pest in its place of origin. He believed that the sudden decline of pest populations was often the result of disease, debility, and want of proper nutrition or of climatic conditions, and that such a decline was sometimes erroneously attributed to the action of parasites and predators. As Harold Compere points out, the two schools of thought still are with us —one advocating advanced planning and study, the other favoring mass releases over a broad area without delay.[3]

The indiscriminate introductions of insects came to an end in California with the appointment of a new state horticultural commissioner in 1911, and the appointment a little later of Harry S. Smith to take charge of the investigation, introduction, and liberation of beneficial insects in the state. Howard later said that this action on the part of the Commissioner was the only thing that kept the importation of insects from foreign countries from being stopped altogether. (The importation of foreign insects into the United States has always been restricted to the Entomology Division of the United States Department of Agriculture, with the single exception of the state of California.) After Smith's appointment as director of the Biological Control Laboratory at Riverside in 1923, and the transfer of the biological control program to the University of California, a staff of experts in this field was built up there and in Berkeley; their achievements in the biological control of many important insect pests in California, and their contributions to the techniques in this field and in the basic understanding of the parasitic Hymenoptera, has been outstanding.

[3] Harold Compere, "The Red Scale and Its Insect Enemies," *Hilgardia,* Nov. 1961.

Insectary at Riverside, Calif., operated by the University of California. One wing of the second floor in building in the foreground houses the quarantine section, where all beneficial insects imported from foreign countries into California are received and carefully screened before being propagated and distributed for biological control. (*T. W. Fisher*)

MASS RELEASES OF PARASITES

With the spectacular success of the imported parasite *Mesoleius tenthredinis* against the larch sawfly, biological control became firmly established in Canada as a weapon against insect pests. The period from 1929 to 1955 was one of tremendous activity in the insectary and field; over a billion parasites were released against sixty insect pests of forests and agricultural crops. The main attack was upon pests accidentally introduced into the country; the object was to introduce great numbers and a variety of the natural enemies of these pests, on the assumption that this was all that was necessary to bring about control of the intruders in their new haunts. Parasites were transferred from one area to the other, as well as from foreign countries.

Attempts to control agricultural pests by mass propagation and release of parasites and predators are regarded as warranted in Canada today only where a pest is giving trouble in several

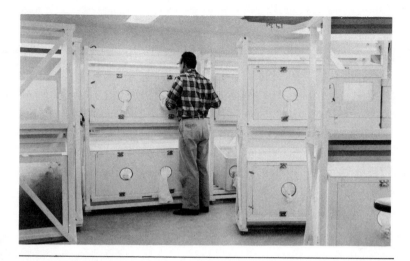

An insectary room at Riverside, showing sleeve cages. About 100 importations of beneficial insects and mites are screened through the quarantine facility annually and several million are reared in the 40 air-conditioned rooms of the insectary each year. (*T. W. Fisher*)

isolated areas; where there is no other satisfactory means of chemical control, and where saturation releases will prevent economic loss; and in limited areas such as greenhouses, where host and biological agents are wiped out at intervals and the pest returns. Under the new policy such projects as providing a continuous supply of parasites (for example the wasp *Encarsia formosa* for control of the greenhouse whitefly, *Trialeurodes vaporariorum*) to greenhouse operators has been discontinued. (The parasite was an effective control agent, but has now been replaced by fumigants.) But though mass propogation and release of biological control agents is not generally considered warranted, it is believed that the propagation and release of small numbers (100 or more) is often desirable.

The function of the Biological Control Laboratory at Belleville, where the mass release programs centered, has changed from the collecting, propagating and distributing of biological control agents to basic studies of the relations between insect pests and their enemies and of the interactions within their environment.

But the laboratory is still a center for the importation and distribution of biological control agents for all of Canada. In 1960 and 1961 over 500,000 live insects were imported from sixteen foreign countries; approximately 92,000 were shipped to the provinces for liberation and about 46,000 were exported to a total of six foreign countries.[4]

IMPORTATION OF PARASITES AND PREDATORS

It has long been a rule that insect predators and parasites must be quarantined and screened before they are distributed, to ensure that no new pests or hyperparasites are brought in with them. Since the hyperparasites attack the primary or beneficial parasites, their presence would tend to nullify any benefits derived from the importation of the parasites, or they might be enemies of those already established. Considering the large quantities of this material that are handled—and even a small quantity could do great harm—there is a real risk involved.

After a French amateur naturalist brought the gypsy moth into Massachusetts, the invasion started with only a few eggs' going astray. The path of entry can be very devious, as it was in the case of the little beetles that hatched from the shirt buttons of a man who returned to England from Egypt. The buttons turned out to have been made from a nut of a certain kind of palm tree, and the larvae had survived the manufacturing process. As Charles Elton remarks, "It takes so few individuals to establish a population, and such a lot of work to eradicate them later on."[5]

After screening at the quarantine station, pure colonies are released to field stations for rearing and colonization, followed by recoveries to determine whether the insect has become established. In the United States this part of the program has generally been handled by the USDA's Entomology Research Branch (or

[4] Bryan P. Beirne, Foreword, *Research Report 1960 and 1961, Entomological Research Institute for Biological Control, Belleville, Ontario* (Ottawa: Canada Department of Agriculture, Dec. 1961).
[5] Charles S. Elton, *The Ecology of Invasions by Animals and Plants.*

its equivalent in earlier years) in cooperation with state organizations; more and more, however, the states have been taking on the entire phase of rearing and colonization.

The one exception has been the state of California, which has excellent quarantine facilities of its own and since 1899 has been authorized to make its own importations. The work there is now a cooperative effort on the part of the University of California, the state department of agriculture, and the federal organization; the scale of operations has been about equal to that of the federal organization alone, and about one-third of the predators and parasites to become established in the United States have been those imported into California. Large-scale programs such as those to control the Japanese beetle and the European corn borer have been handled by the federal bureau alone; the gypsy moth program was a joint effort with the Commonwealth of Massachusetts, and the Maine Forest Service and the New Jersey Department of Agriculture have carried on their own large rearing and colonization programs against the European sawflies, using material provided by the Canada Department of Agriculture.

RESULTS OF IMPORTATIONS

According to C. P. Clausen, during approximately sixty years of search by collectors throughout the world for the enemies of insect pests of agricultural crops and trees, a total of 660 species have been imported into the United States.[6] Of these 175 were never colonized, for one reason or another, and 390 others were colonized but failed to become permanently established, presumably for one or more of the following reasons: they were not colonized in sufficient numbers; they were not released at the right time; there were no alternate hosts to carry them over the winter; or they were unable to survive unsuitable climatic conditions. The remaining 95 species, comprising 81 parasites and

[6] C. P. Clausen, *Biological Control of Insect Pests in the Continental United States* (Washington: USDA Technical Bulletin No. 1139, June 1956).

In 22 rooms of the insectary at Santa Paula (Ventura County), California, about 30 million *Cryptolaemus* lady beetles are produced each year for control of mealybugs; 18,000 acres in all are served by this insectary. Here, production room showing purpose attached to walls and ceiling and to sides of trays. (Host mealybugs feed on potato sprouts growing in these trays.) Burlap on walls and exposed side of trays afford pupation sites for the beetles. (*K. L. Middleham.* courtesy *T. W. Fisher*)

14 predators, became established. Of the parasites, 32 are chalcid wasps used mainly for control of scale insects and mealybugs in California, and 15 are tachinid flies. It should be borne in mind, on the one hand, that some of the established species may not persist, and on the other, that some not known to be established may turn up later.

In Canada a total of 85 species (4 of them predators, the rest parasites) have been liberated in attempts to control 27 species of agricultural pests. Against 36 forest pest species (16 of foreign

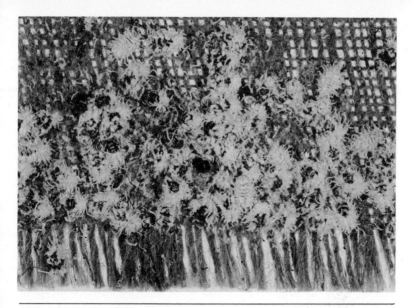

Close-up of pupae and newly emerged *Cryptolaemus* adults on burlap.
(*K. L. Middleham,* courtesy *T. W. Fisher*)

origin), 104 beneficial species have been released, only 15 of
which were predators—again a large disparity as compared with
parasites, especially since 13 of the 15 were released against the
balsam woolly aphid (*Chermes piceae*), for which no parasite is
known. On the basis of later recoveries, 25 of the species released
against forest pests appear to have become established, and 11
others are left in some doubt.[7]

Some of the more recent liberations against forest pests in the
United States[8] have been against the spruce budworm (*Choristoneura fumiferana*) in Maine; the larch casebearer (*Coleophora
laricella*) in Idaho; the elm leaf beetle (*Galerucella xanthomelaena*) in Arkansas and California; and the balsam woolly aphid
(*Chermes piceae*) in Maine, Washington, Oregon, New York,

[7] J. H. McLeod, B. M. McGugan, and H. C. Coppel, *A Review of the
Biological Control Attempts Against Insects and Weeds in Canada* (Farnham
Royal, Bucks, England: Commonwealth Agricultural Bureaux, 1962).

[8] Philip B. Dowden, *Parasites and Predators of Forest Pests Liberated in
the United States Through 1960* (Washington: USDA Agricultural Handbook No. 226, July 1962).

Collecting adult beetles in calibrated plastic tube from screen cloth covering window. They are scooped up by pushing funnel up against screen. (*T. W. Fisher*)

and North Carolina. The most active of these programs has been against the balsam woolly aphid. Canada has achieved far more than the United States in introducing and releasing parasites and predators of forest insect pests and in the use of other biological control agents.

INSECT CONTROL—FOREST AND FARM

In the relatively stable and complex environment of a forest, with its many species of plants, insects, and other animals, the chances for permanently establishing an introduced predator or parasite are much better than in the rapidly changing environment in which agricultural crops are grown, with monoculture the rule. By the same token, in the forest the effects of chemical insecticides can be more far-reaching. It is an axiom of biological control that the more complex and stable the biotic environment, the greater the chance the introduced species have of surviving and playing a part in natural control of pest species. "For this reason," says R. E. Balch, "the forest entomologist is particularly interested in biological control and is less inclined to be discouraged by its limitations. He needs economical, self-perpetuating methods rather than control at extremely low densities. His approach is essentially ecological."[9] The product of the forest—the wood in the trunks of trees—is less easily damaged than are agricultural crops. Severe defoliation and infestations can be tolerated for a time, and control of the pest at fairly high densities can be satisfactory. To avoid severe loss of agricultural crops, low pest density is usually necessary.

ASSESSMENTS OF BIOLOGICAL CONTROL

The assessment by Turnbull and Chant of the biological control projects in Canada, where a very considerable effort has been made in this direction, gives us some idea of its possibilities. As has already been indicated, in that country nearly a billion parasites have been released against sixty insect pests. Twenty-nine of these were minor or local pests against which surplus parasites were used, in operations of which no records were kept, so that the results cannot be assessed. In evaluating the thirty-one that remain to be considered, "any measurable reduction of damage" will be regarded as "a degree of control"; complete control will be deemed to have been effected where the damage is reduced to a level that is tolerable from an economic standpoint. On this basis, twelve of the thirty-one projects can be classed as successful, and two as partially successful (giving an appreciable reduction of the pest but not controlling it); three have been without success to date but are continuing and have a good chance of being successful. Five of the successful projects were against forest pests, seven against agricultural pests (see Appendix C).

This is a remarkable achievement, and the list might well have been expanded significantly if sufficient information had been available to assess the effect of the release of parasites and predators against the twenty-nine other pests. The investigators, although not complacent, with the failures outnumbering the successes, "were gratified by the percentage of documented cases

[9] R. E. Balch, "The Approach to Biological Control in Forest Entomology," *The Canadian Entomologist,* April 1960.

Oviposition cages (*interior view*) for production of *Leptomastix* wasps at Santa Paula. Housed 200 feet from the *Cryptolaemus* insectary, the two are operated independently to avoid cross-contamination. About 22,000 wasps per tray are produced by the method employed here. (*T. W. Fisher*)

that were successful." In their estimate of the biological control projects relating to forests alone, McGugan and Coppel believe that "a satisfactory degree of success was obtained" and that the number of species established and the impact of the more successful ones is "sufficient to justify the entire programme of releases." Of the 25 species released against forest pests and known to be established, 12 are widely distributed in the hosts' range and exerting a measurable degree of control.

Of the biological control projects initiated throughout the world, Sweetman lists 80 cases as being successful to date, "only those instances which are highly successful or decidedly beneficial to the extent of eliminating or greatly reducing other methods of control [being] included." This shows considerable progress, in comparison with the same author's findings twenty years earlier, when, with adjustments made for incomplete information, 37 successful cases of biological control could be claimed. According to his present list, control was achieved in 48 instances with parasites, in 24 instances with predators, and in 8 with a combination of parasites and predators. About 25 per cent of the successful projects were in the continental United States (see Appendix D), and about the same number in the Hawaiian Islands, where biological control has had a high degree of success. The projects listed are not confined strictly to insects, but include control of the black widow spider in Hawaii, two mites in California, and a snail (by introduction of another snail predatory upon it) in several islands of the Pacific. The beneficial predators of insects also include several animals other than insects: a fish used to control mosquitoes, a lizard and a toad to control certain beetles, a bird to control a locust, and the domestic hog to control a moth.[10]

In many instances control was accomplished with two or more parasites or predators, or combinations of the two. In some notable instances full control was the work of a single insect, a natural enemy of the pest species. The ten instances that follow are taken from a compilation by Charles A. Fleschner.[11]

A survey by Paul DeBach shows that a total of 97 species of insect pests have been controlled partially or completely by the introduction of their natural enemies. Thirty-eight or 40 per cent of these pest species are scale insects and mealybugs (coccids) distributed over fifty different countries.[12] The success with coccids is due partly to the relatively greater attention given to these pests, for the reasons cited elsewhere. It does not come as a surprise that there is some disagreement in evaluating these projects; in fact, Turnbull and Chant believe that any assessment "must be intuitive and cannot be supported by scientifically acceptable evidence."

[10] Harvey L. Sweetman, *The Principles of Biological Control* (Dubuque, Iowa: Wm. C. Brown Co., 1958).

[11] Charles A. Fleschner, "Parasites and Predators for Pest Control," *Biological and Chemical Control of Plant and Animal Pests:* A Symposium, ed. by L. P. Reitz (Washington: American Assoc. for Adv. of Science, 1961).

[12] Paul DeBach, "Biological Control of Scales and Mealybugs (Coccidae)," in *Handbook on Biological Control of Plant Pests* (Brooklyn Botanic Garden, 1960).

PEST	IN	CONTROLLED BY	FROM
EUCALYPTUS SNOUT BEETLE (*Gonipterus scutellatus*)	Union of S. Africa	CHALCID WASP (*Anaphoidea nitens*)	Australia
SATIN MOTH (*Stilpnotia salicis*)	U.S.A. and Canada	BRACONID WASP (*Apanteles solitarius*)	Europe
WOOLY APPLE APHID (*Eriosoma lanigerum*)	Many countries	CHALCID WASP (*Aphelinus mali*)	United States
COCONUT SCALE (*Aspidiotus destructor*)	Fiji	LADY BEETLE (*Cryptognatha nodiceps*)	Trinidad
SUGAR CANE LEAFHOPPER (*Perkinsiella saccharicida*)	Hawaii	PREDACEOUS BUG (*Miridae*) (*Cyrtorhinus mundulus*)	Fiji
CITRUS BLACK FLY (*Aleurocanthus woglumi*)	Cuba	CHALCID WASP (*Eretmocerus serius*)	Malaya
SPINY BLACK FLY (*Aleurocanthus spiniferus*)	Japan	CHALCID WASP (*Prospaltella smithi*)	China
COCONUT MOTH (*Levuana iridescens*)	Fiji	TACHINID FLY (*Ptychomyia remota*)	Malaya
COTTONY CUSHION SCALE (*Icerya purchasi*)	U.S.A. (Calif.)	LADY BEETLE (*Rodolia cardinalis*)	Australia
CITROPHILUS MEALYBUG (*Pseudococcus gahani*)	U.S.A. (Calif.)	CHALCID WASP (*Tetracnemus pretiosus*)	Australia

BIOLOGICAL CONTROL IN AUSTRALIA

In Australia—the happy hunting ground of the early search by Koebele and others for the natural enemies of citrus pests—the importation and release of biological control agents has lagged. According to Frank Wilson, the introduction of natural enemies of insect pests in this region has been slow in view of "the number of pests requiring control and the large number of natural enemies that could be introduced."[13] In Australia and in Australian New Guinea, "useful results" have been achieved against insect pests in twenty out of forty-three attempts at control by release of their enemies. Eight of these are classified as a "higher" and twelve as a "lower" degree of biological control. Most of the success has been with "exotic" pests—those of foreign origin—and with "cosmopolitan" pests, whose origins are doubtful and that are thus likely to belong to the "exotic" category.

Among the reasons given for this lag in the importation of biological control agents is the limited financial support given to this kind of control at a time when the use of chemicals has predominated. Wilson writes, "It is becoming increasingly evident . . . that chemical means tend to magnify the problems they cope with, and to create fresh problems in the process." The complexity and expense of spray schedules, and the resurgence of once innocuous pests, he adds, "point to the desirability of basing the control of pests so far as possible upon natural controls, and of employing chemical controls in such a manner that they supplement rather than replace natural controls."

THE BALANCE OF NATURE

Nature, the sum total of all the physical and living factors in an environment, is governed by a system of checks and balances. In agricultural and landscaped areas, as in the natural and more stable communities, there are "ecosystems," each operating within

[13] Frank Wilson, *A Review of the Biological Control of Insects and Weeds in Australia and Australian New Guinea* (Farnham Royal, Bucks, England: Commonwealth Agricultural Bureaux, 1960).

a given area and comprising the plants and animals that interact with one another, together with the physical properties of that environment. Normally all the species within this system, although they undergo constant fluctuations, are held in a balanced relation to one another. The harmful insects and other arthropods are normally held within bounds by insect predators and parasites, by diseases, and by birds and other small animals. "Explosions" occur when some new factor or disturbance enters the picture, and insects which have previously gone unnoticed suddenly gain pest status because the balance has been tipped in their favor.

The situation in the avocado orchards of southern California illustrates this point. Here excellent biological control of avocado pests is maintained, mostly with native species of predators and parasites; insecticidal treatments are normally required in only a fraction of 1 per cent of the total acreage. Although potential pests are present, they are generally held in almost perfect biological balance. Such potential pests as the long-tailed mealybug (*Pseudococcus adonidum*), the black scale (*Saissetia oleae*), and the soft (brown) scale (*Coccus hesperidum*), are controlled by introduced parasites. The avocado brown mite (*Oligonychus punicae*) and the six-spotted mite (*Eotetranychus sexmaculatus*) are controlled largely by native predators, such as *Stethorus picipes,* a small black lady beetle; *Oligota oviformis,* a small staphylinid beetle; and predatory mites of the genus *Typhlodromus.* The omnivorous looper (*Sabulodes caberata*) is controlled by two small native wasps, *Apanteles caberatae* and *Meteorus tersus.*

An experiment conducted by Fleschner shows what happens when this balance between insect pests and their enemies are upset by man. When all parasites and predators were removed from a portion of an avocado tree for a period of eighty-four days, the omnivorous looper, six-spotted mite, long-tailed mealybug, avocado brown mite, and latania scale (*Aspidiotus lataniae*) increased to very damaging levels. It was necessary to remove the larvae of the omnivorous looper by hand to save the leaves; but at the same time it was found that over 90 per cent of the very young larvae were parasitized by their two wasp enemies. During the test period no other significant damage was noticed on the rest of the test tree, or on any other trees in the orchard. The Argentine ant, which protects the scales and mealybugs from their enemies; accumulations of dust on the avocado leaves; and ill-advised spraying with insecticides all have the same effect as the physical removal of the beneficial insects in the experiment. It is interesting to note that avocados are one of the few fruits that remain free of insecticidal residues, as determined from allergic reactions in persons sensitive to such chemical contaminants, according to Dr. Theron G. Randolph, a Chicago allergist who has made a study of this problem.[14]

The most important disturbance to the ecosystems has been the accidental transport of insects and other animal species across the boundaries of one area to the other, without the enemies and diseases that held them in check in their native environment. The introduction of plant species favorable to the increase of insects already in an area has also been a disturbing factor. In the past this challenge of the insects was usually met by the use of biological control techniques, with varying degrees of success. With the advent of the spectacular new insecticides that came into use after World War II the interest in biological control declined; DDT and the related chlorinated hydrocarbons, and later the phosphate compounds, looked like the answer to all our insect problems. Their most spectacular success (mainly using DDT) has been in the eradication of the mosquito, tsetse fly, and other insect vectors of disease in many tropical countries. The residual nature of DDT has proved to be its greatest virtue—and perhaps also its greatest drawback. In any event, the problems arising from its use and from the other organic insecticidal compounds as well, are the cause of increasing concern.

[14] Theron G. Randolph, M.D., *Human Ecology and Susceptibility to the Chemical Environment* (Springfield, Illinois: Charles C. Thomas, 1962).

PROBLEMS WITH PESTICIDES

The problems arising from the use of the new insecticides may be briefly summarized as follows: (1) poison residues on food and forage crops; (2) hazards to wildlife and to workers handling the poisons; (3) pollution of streams, lakes, and ground water; (4) development of immunity in insects to these poisons (77 species are reported to be resistant in Canada,[15] and the list is growing in all areas where these chemicals are used); (5) resurgence of secondary pests previously held in check by their natural enemies; (6) buildup of the primary pests coming in from untreated fields and unchecked by their natural enemies; (7) repeated applications of pesticides necessitated by the previous two conditions, with consequent increase in risks and in costs.[16]

The problems of residues on food, hazards to wildlife and workers, and environmental pollution are now being widely discussed and debated. They are also under investigation by a special committee appointed by the President and in special hearings conducted by the Senate.[17] Since they are outside the scope of this book, they will not be dealt with here.

The problem of insect resistance to pesticides may well bring about a change in our approach to the control of insect pests. This problem, along with the others that have just been enumerated, was recognized by the FAO Conference on Pesticides in Agriculture held in Rome November 12-17, 1962, whose report contains this statement:

---

[15] A. W. A. Brown, "Tactics of Insect Control, Particularly in Medical Entomology" (Symposium: Strategy and Tactics of Insect Control, Centennial of Entomology in Canada, Ottawa, Sept. 3–6, 1963).

[16] Vernon M. Stern, Ray F. Smith, Robert van den Bosch, and Kenneth S. Hagen, "The Integration of Chemical and Biological Control of the Spotted Alfalfa Aphid: The Integrated Control Concept," *Hilgardia*, Oct. 1959.

[17] See Rachel Carson, *Silent Spring* (Boston: Houghton Mifflin, 1962); also *Use of Pesticides: A Report of the President's Science Advisory Committee, Washington, D.C.*, May 15, 1963. The Senate Subcommittee conducting these hearings is headed by Hubert H. Humphrey of Minnesota.

Resistance has now been reported in at least 65 species of arthropod pests in agriculture and there are already indications that resistance may also include fungicides and herbicides. Although it has so far proved possible to meet resistance with alternative pesticides, sometimes by a very narrow margin, the Conference stressed the urgent need to anticipate the grave situation in which no safe alternative was available. Authorities consider that resistance has the potential of becoming an economic problem of primary importance to agriculture, possibly of equal significance to that of residues.[18]

The difficulties arising from the killing of beneficial species as well as pests with insect sprays, is the root of all the other problems enumerated. The FAO conference also "considered the adverse effects of pesticides to beneficial organisms . . . and recognized the importance of the pesticide hazards, both real and potential, to such organisms, including wildlife, beneficial insects, fish, and to the soil flora and fauna." Some entomologists have long been apprehensive of the great reliance placed on insecticides. One of these, A. D. Pickett of the Kentville Research Station in Nova Scotia, has said that "dependence on chemical control alone is a snare and a delusion from which we must extricate ourselves sooner or later,"[19] and has demonstrated in the apple orchards of the Annapolis Valley how this can be done through a "modified" (or integrated) control program.

A similar point of view was expressed some years ago in an editorial by Leonard Haseman:

We must work more with and less against nature. . . . Through widespread use of the newer high-powered insecticides we have done more to increase the lopsided balance of nature in connection with insects and agriculture in the last ten years than in the previous one hundred years. We economic entomologists, in our present unbridled chemical warfare against insects, need to stop and take stock of just where we are headed. If we cannot succeed in controlling

[18] *Report of the FAO Conference on Pesticides in Agriculture, Held in Rome, Italy 12–17 November 1962* (Food and Agriculture Organization of the United Nations).

[19] A. D. Pickett, in a letter to the *Commercial Grower*, January 15, 1960.

insects by working with nature through the soil, we can at least slow down our further drive at destroying her natural balance.[20]

Unfortunately not all entomologists have this "ecological" approach; there is the view that man has altered his environment to the point where the so-called "balance of nature" is a figment of the imagination, and that biotic factors are of little importance and can be ignored. Those who hold this view believe that insects can be controlled by means of chemicals alone. In any event, the problems arising from the reliance on chemicals alone are still with us, and the view is widely held today that biological control techniques coupled with cultural practices, and integrated with chemicals as required, are the only solution. Entomologists who share this opinion believe that insecticides have not solved our insect problems, that they never can, and that they should be used as a supplement to, not in place of, biological control measures. Chemicals are only a short-term factor in the biotic environment and cannot permanently change the pest population density, as can introduced or native parasites, predators, and disease pathogens. Applications of pesticides must be repeated at intervals; beneficial insects and disease organisms can adjust themselves automatically, responding to changes in the size of the pest population.

It is interesting to note that the FAO conference had something to say on this question also; it "recognized the importance of the integration of biological, cultural, and chemical control methods of controlling agricultural pests, especially since biological control is equally effective against susceptible as well as resistant strains of a pest. It was pointed out that adequate attention should be given by member governments to this approach."

INTEGRATED CONTROL

Successful integrated control programs have been worked out in California, notably with the spotted alfalfa aphid and the alfalfa

[20] Leonard Haseman, "Controlling Insect Pests Through Their Nutritional Requirements," *Journal of Economic Entomology,* June 1950.

caterpillar. In some areas native predators are capable of controlling the aphids throughout the year; in others they hold them to noneconomic level throughout most of the growing season, some insecticidal treatments being required. The most important enemies of the spotted alfalfa aphids are lady beetles (principally the genus *Hippodamia*), lacewings (*Chrysopa*), bugs (*Nabis* and *Geocoris*), and the larvae of syrphid flies. Insecticidal treatments are designed to restore the balance and to allow biological control factors to reassert themselves. Low dosages of Systox have been found to be "selective"—preserving the aphids' natural enemies in sufficient numbers to take care of those aphids that come in from other fields after the treatments. Malathion and parathion were found to be "non selective"; the natural enemies of the pests were destroyed along with the pests and repeated treatments were required.

An example of the integrated control of soil organisms is the treatment for root maggots on rutabagas, cabbages, and related plants worked out in the maritime provinces of Canada. Instead of being broadcast, the insecticide (heptachlor or aldrin), or a fertilizer-insecticide mixture, is applied in bands 1½ inches below the seed in the seeding ridge. In this way the chemical does not come into contact with the beneficial soil-inhabiting insects. At least five beneficial species of predators and parasites attack the root maggots in one form or another; and although these do not give sufficient control by themselves, if they are destroyed by misuse of chemicals the injury to the crop by the root maggots is likely to be more severe than if no chemicals were used.[21] Two flies (*Coenosia tigrina* and *Scatophaga stercoraria*) attack the maggot adults in flight or on the plant; a rove beetle (*Aleochara bilineata*) in the adult stage destroys the maggot eggs at or near the soil surface, and its larvae attack the maggot pupae inside the puparia; a wasp (*Trybliographa rapae*) parasitizes the root maggot larvae;

[21] D. C. Reed, *Control of Root Maggots* (Hylemya brassicae) *in Rutabagas, Cabbages, and Related Plants in the Maritime Provinces* (Ottawa: Research Branch, Canada Department of Agriculture, May 1960).

and an assortment of ground (carabid) beetles, in the adult form, destroy root maggot eggs at or near the soil surface.

One of the outstanding examples of integrated control is in Annapolis Valley, the apple-growing area of Nova Scotia. An investigation of the long-term effect of pesticides on apple insects was begun in 1943 under the direction of A. D. Pickett.[22] The four major pests at the start were the oystershell scale (*Lepidosaphes ulmi*), The European red mite (*Panonychus ulmi*), the eye-spotted bud moth (*Spilonota ocellana*), and the codling moth (*Carpocapsa pomonella*). The pesticides generally in use at the time were dormant oils, dinitro compounds, bordeaux, sulphur, lead arsenate, and nicotine sulphate. The substitution of ferbam for sulphur as a fungicide, and the elimination of the oil, permitted the parasite *Aphytis mytilaspidis* and the predaceous mite *Hemisarcoptes malus* to develop in sufficient numbers to bring the scale under complete control in two years. It was found that most of these pests could be manipulated at will with certain sprays because of their effect on beneficial insects; sulphur was particularly damaging to the latter. This phenomenon was noted even in the case of the codling moth, which is the worst single pest of apples and for which no satisfactory biological control measures have been found. By substituting copper for sulphur as a fungicide, the damage from codling moths was greatly reduced. This is believed to be partly due to the detrimental effects of sulphur on the fungus *Beauveria bassiana;* also, the substitution permitted a substantial increase in the predaceous thrips *Leutothrips mali.*[23]

The eye-spotted bud moth, for many years the most serious pest of apples in Nova Scotia, was shortly reduced to the role of a minor pest; this is believed to have been due to the restoration of certain natural control factors following the use of selective sprays. One of these, the braconid wasp *Agathis laticinctus,* was seen to have increased sharply and to have accounted for a 90 per

    [22] A. D. Pickett, "Utilization of Native Parasites and Predators," *Journal of Economic Entomology,* Dec. 1959.
    [23] A. D. Pickett, "Utilization of Native Parasites and Predators," *Journal of Economic Entomology,* Dec. 1959.

cent mortality in the overwintering larvae; several predators—anthocorids, mirids, and pentatomids among the bugs; lady beetles, thrips, and the predaceous mite *Anystis agilis*—were also effective against the moth at low densities.

Ryania, a plant-derived poison that is nontoxic to warm-blooded animals, was found to be very selective and to give good control of the codling moth. The records show a gradual decline in fruit injuries following the substitution in the spray schedule of ryania for DDT and parathion. An interesting comparison was made of the amount of damage sustained by the apples from codling moths in the year following applications of DDT to a five-acre orchard, and in the year following application of ryania in the same orchard, after these respective insecticides were discontinued. The stings and deep entries of the moth larvae in the apples increased many fold the year following DDT treatments, but little difference was noted the year following ryania treatments. Counts of beneficial insects indicated that the difference was due to the difference in the survival rate of the predators and parasites; very few were noted in the orchard the year following DDT treatments, but they were abundant the year following ryania treatments.

CONCLUSIONS FROM MODIFIED PROGRAMS

After fifteen years of investigations and observations, Pickett concludes that pesticides, by destroying predators and parasites, frequently create more problems than they solve; that several apple pests of economic importance would present no problem if natural control factors were allowed to operate; that biological control, to be effective, must be practiced over a wide area; that once the parasites and predators have been eliminated over a wide area, it will take several years for them to become re-established; that more emphasis should be placed on developing selective pesticides, on their timing to avoid the most susceptible stages of the beneficial species, and on minimum dosages; and that the proper approach to orchard insect control is through a complete ecological study of the problems involved.

Although no claim could be made that the program worked out in Nova Scotia would fit another apple-growing area, "there are indications that a New York modified control program, for example, would work as well in New York as the Nova Scotia program does in Nova Scotia."[24] LeRoux's studies in Quebec indicate that the faunal relationships in Nova Scotia are not unique, and that nonselective pesticides created the same problems there as in Nova Scotia. A five-year study of two 1200-tree plots in Quebec—one operated with the regular commercial spray program and one with a modified spray program—showed the latter to give equally good control of pests at half the cost, not to mention the other advantages.[25]

Stern *et al.* point out that to carry out integrated control projects of this nature, our population sampling methods are not speedy enough. Nor are growers often able to evaluate the status of pest populations and determine what should be done; this requires a trained entomologist. The answer to this problem might be to have "supervised control," such as has been tried in California, Arizona, Arkansas, and elsewhere. A farmer or orchardist, or a group of these, contracts with a professional etomologist, who makes the necessary population counts; on the basis of his knowledge of the pests and their natural enemies, and of other factors, he is able to predict population trends, and to determine when to apply controls and what kind to use. Equally important is his knowledge of when it is *not* necessary to do anything, and his dispensing with so-called "insurance" treatments.

THE FUTURE?

To Theodore Fisher, as to other workers in the field, the future of biological control "couldn't be brighter"; he points to the fact that there are many major insect pests (and weeds) that have

[24] A. David Crowe, "Nova Scotia's Modified Control Program," *American Fruit Grower,* March 1960.

[25] A. D. Pickett, Wm. L. Putman, and E. J. LeRoux, "Progress in Harmonizing Biological and Chemical Control of Orchard Pests in Eastern Canada," *Proceedings,* Tenth International Congress of Entomology (1958).

Parasites being released. The cover of the box is raised and wasps allowed to escape as insectary worker walks through the citrus grove. The combined net cost of the *Leptomastix* and *Cryptolaemus* program to the cooperative grower-member is about $10 per acre for three releases per year of each. (*T. W. Fisher*)

never been studied to determine the possibilities of biological control. He sees the lack of an adequate budget as the only hindrance to progress.[26] Funds spent by the United States Department of Agriculture on insect control research in recent years have been heavily in favor of chemical controls. During a television interview in April 1963, Secretary of Agriculture Freeman reported—with apparent satisfaction—that his department spends about one and a half million dollars each year for research in biological controls. It has been pointed out that the chemical industry will spend twice this amount or more to develop, test, and market one new pesticide.

It would appear, however, that a more serious drawback is that there are so few entomologists trained in this specialty. The lack of funds can be remedied quickly enough if our lawmakers can be convinced of the need, but trained personnel in an exacting discipline are hard to come by. According to Fisher, in the United States not more than forty academically trained entomologists

[26] Theodore W. Fisher, "What is Biological Control?" in *Handbook on Biological Control of Plant Pests* (Brooklyn Botanic Garden, 1960).

(or 2 per cent of the total) are devoting full time to research in biological methods of insect control; and he might have added that most of them are in California. Much of the remaining talent, even in the universities, is devoted to the development and testing of insecticides for the chemical companies, which furnish them an endless stream of funds—for some reason called "donations" —for this purpose. Funds for basic research in biological control come almost entirely from public sources. Fortunately—for us too, since knowledge can be and is shared—biological control has not suffered the same neglect in Canada as in the United States.

It is the belief of Turnbull and Chant that biological control should be regarded as a science in its own right, "one that may draw heavily on other disciplines but no more." As they see it, workers in this field have a dual function: to make basic or long-term ecological studies to determine the underlying principles of biological control; and to carry out short-term projects of applied biological control, involving the importation and distribution of natural control agents, so as to cope, as they arise, with problems that cannot wait long for answers.

B. N. Smallman envisages the day when the pendulum will have swung back too far in the direction of biological control, to the neglect of chemicals. Biological control is mainly for the strategic long pull, while chemicals must remain the tactical protective measures. It is pointed out that insect-resistant varieties of plants, cultural methods, and biological controls, as we have practiced them, have all been found wanting; we cannot take the chance of relying on these to the neglect of insecticides. Anything that has threatened the survival of insects has met with resistance, and the use of biological control could encounter the same difficulties as insecticides if they are pushed too far. "We will need to match the variables of nature with a variety of controls."[27]

[27] B. N. Smallman, "Perspectives of Insect Control," Symposium: Strategy and Tactics of Insect Control (Centennial of Entomology in Canada, Ottawa, September 3–6, 1963).

Man can control his destiny particularly if the knowledge gained by biologists can be furthered and applied as rapidly as that of the physicists and chemists.

—LORD BOYD ORR

APPENDIX A

Classification of the Arthropods

Some comment on the naming and classification of insects seems appropriate here. The use of scientific names is necessary both for the sake of accuracy and because in many instances there are no others. The need for a system of naming insects and other organisms has been explained by the English biologist, E. B. Ford, in this way:

It would be almost impossible to study animals if they were treated merely as a chaotic mixture of forms. For convenience they must inevitably be classified into groups on some logical system, and that adopted is based upon relationship. Thus all members of a group are more closely related to each other by descent than they are to any other living creatures. A *species* is a group of animals so much akin that they can interbreed and produce fully fertile offspring.[1]

THE JOINTED-LEGGED ANIMALS

The animal kingdom is divided into phyla, which in turn are divided into classes. We are concerned here with the *phylum*

[1] E. B. Ford, *British Butterflies* (Harmondsworth, Middlesex, England: Penguin Books, Ltd., 1951).

Arthropoda (Greek for jointed legs) and especially the *class Insecta* or *Hexapoda* (which means six-legged). The Arthropoda include some other classes which are commonly grouped with insects: *Chilopoda,* the centipedes; *Diplopoda,* the millipedes; and *Arachnida,* the scorpions, harvestmen or daddy longlegs, spiders, mites, and ticks. The other main class in this phylum is that of the *Crustacea,* which include the crayfish, lobsters, crabs, sowbugs, pillbugs, barnacles, water fleas, and cyclops.

The next divisions below the classes are the *orders.* These in turn are divided into *families* and further into *genera* and finally *species* the natural reproductive unit. Animals and plants are identified by the genus and species, which are always printed in italics, with the genus capitalized and the species begun with a small letter. This is called the binomial system of nomenclature and was first suggested by Linnaeus, the great Swedish botanist, in the eighteenth century. Latin was used because at the time it was closest to being a universal language. It now has the further advantage of being a "dead" language, thus undergoing no change. It is important in the exchange of information for names to be precise and to mean the same to all scientists working in the field. This system is used by scientists for both the plant and animal kingdom, including the microorganisms.

SCIENTIFIC NAMES

The genus name is followed by the abbreviation *sp.* when the species has not been certainly identified. Man belongs to the genus *Homo,* of which he is the only living species, *sapiens.* After the species name, entomologists and other scientists often add the name of the person who first identified it as a distinct species, for convenience in referring to the literature describing it. Since this practice is hardly necessary for our purpose, we have omitted it. The single names given in parentheses, beginning with a capital letter and ending in *ae,* refer to zoological families. It is often easier to think in terms of the broader classifications of order and family, where more precise identification is not required.

All the members of an order have the same general structure of wings, mouth, parts, and other appendages, and also undergo the same kind of metamorphosis. They may have marked differences in size, color, and even shape, but the similarities that place them in the same order will be apparent. Finer distinctions are made in dividing orders into families, and likewise with the genera and species.

The orders are listed in the accompanying table showing the number of described species, as is customary, in the order of their complexity. Perhaps this order is customary because, as Ralph Swain has suggested, "Complexity, at least to mortals, seems to signify progress."[2] The "higher" forms have a complete metamorphosis—that is, they develop in successive stages, from egg to larva to pupa, before reaching the adult stage. The "lower" forms have a simple or gradual metamorphosis, with only one distinct stage between egg and adult—that is, the nymph. With the lowest there is no metamorphosis; in other words, the young resemble the adults.

WHAT IS AN INSECT?

An insect has *three* pairs of legs and the body is made up of *three* distinct parts: head, thorax, and abdomen. It usually has one or two pairs of wings attached to the thorax. The legs are segmented, with five joints, and are also attached to the thorax. It breathes by means of tubes called tracheae, which open along the sides of the body. Aquatic insects that do not depend on occasional trips to the surface for air have these tracheae modified to form tracheal gills, which extract oxygen from the water and permit carbon dioxide to escape. These gills differ from the blood gills of fish and other animals in that the oxygen is transported in the form of gas instead of being received and carried by the

[2] Ralph B. Swain, *The Insect Guide* (Garden City, N. Y.: Doubleday & Company, Inc., 1952).

blood cells: indeed, insect blood does not contain red cells and has no part in respiration. Though the vision of insects is poor, the adult and nymph forms typically have two kinds of eyes—compound eyes and simple eyes, or *ocelli*. The latter are very small and are not possessed by all insects. The larvae have simple eyes, if any—never compound ones—and butterflies, on the other hand, never have ocelli. The huge compound eyes of the dragonfly, of which most of its head consists, are made up of 30,000 separate units, are a special adaptation to its livelihood of catching insects on the wing.

There is considerable evidence that insects have a delicate sense of smell—what Charles T. Brues calls "an acute and discriminate chemical sense"[3]—which guides them to the plant or other host of their choice. The voracious caterpillars of the cabbage butterfly refuse to eat if placed on plants they are not accustomed to and will starve in the midst of plenty unless the plants are smeared with sap from their food plants or with mustard oils. This sense is even more acute in the adults, especially if the food of the two stages differ, as it does in butterflies and moths. The latter feed on the nectar of flowers, but must select the proper plant for deposition of their eggs, since the caterpillars obviously lack the searching ability of the winged forms and can be very discriminating, as we have seen.

SPIDERS

A spider is not an insect. It has only *two* distinct body parts—head and thorax combine as the cephalothorax—and *four* pairs of legs. It does not have antennae, true jaws, or compound eyes. Its poor vision comes from eight simple eyes, usually arranged in two rows. The harvestman or daddy longlegs is not a spider. It belongs to another group or order known as Phalangida, while the spider belongs to the order Araneida. The harvestman has the same

[3] Charles T. Brues, *Insect Dietary* (Cambridge: Harvard University Press, 1946).

number of legs as the spider, but the cephalothorax and abdomen are united into one, and it has no silk glands.

MITES AND TICKS

Other noteworthy members of the Arachnida are the mites and ticks. They resemble the spiders in having four pairs of legs and in some cases being able to spin silk, but the body and head are fused into one part. The newly hatched young have only three pairs of legs; breathing is by means of tracheae or directly through the skin. The difference between a mite and a tick is one of size —in other words, ticks are simply large mites. Some, such as the red spider mite, are plant pests, and some are parasites on cattle and on man. The cattle tick that causes Texas fever, and the tick causing Rocky Mountain spotted fever, are among our most obnoxious pests. Some ticks show a remarkable capacity for survival. Those that cause relapsing fever in man have been kept alive in a laboratory for five years without food, and during that time the disease organisms they harbor have remained virulent. Some mites, however, are predators of other mites and are therefore beneficial.

CENTIPEDES AND MILLIPEDES

Another arthropod commonly thought of as an insect is the centipede, which is the closest relative of the insects in the entire group. Its name means "hundred-legged," but the number of legs vary from the fifteen pairs of the house centipede to as many as 173 pairs in some other species. Like the insects, centipedes have a pair of antennae and breathe by means of tracheae. They differ from the insects in not having a thorax or wings and in generally having two clumps of simple eyes, as well as in the number of legs—a pair for each segment of the body. The house centipede is distinguished from the others by its long, delicate legs, and by its possession of compound eyes. House centipedes like damp places and are often found in basements. Should you be tempted to stamp on one, you might consider the fact that they do no harm and that they prey on cockroaches and other insects. Unlike worms, centipedes have a head; a pair of curved, hollow claws, on the first segment back of the head are used to paralyze their prey. They attack insects, slugs, grubs, worms, and even lizards and mice. Some tropical centipedes are over a foot long and may inflict painful bites on man, but as a group the Chilopoda are beneficial.

The millipedes differ from the centipedes in having rounded bodies, with two pairs of legs to each body segment. The head resembles that of a centipede, having two antennae and chewing jaws, but millipedes do not have poison claws. The name means "thousand-legged"—but about the best the common species can claim is 115 pairs! In spite of this elaborate locomotive machinery, millipedes are much slower-moving than the centipedes. In appearance they suggest the wireworms, and are sometimes mistaken for them. Commonly found under stones and in shady places in the garden, they are timid souls and curl up spirally when frightened. Millipedes generally feed on decaying plant material, and in this activity are beneficial. At times they become pests by eating the roots of living plants.

ORDERS OF THE CLASS HEXAPODA

ORDERS	EXAMPLES	EST. NO. OF SPECIES DESCRIBED
INSECTS WITHOUT METAMORPHOSIS		
Thysanura:	Bristletails, silverfish	325
Collembola:	Springtails, snowfleas	1,250
INSECTS WITH A GRADUAL OR SIMPLE METAMORPHOSIS		
Orthoptera:*	Roaches, crickets, grasshoppers, kataydid, walking sticks	20,000
Dermaptera:*	Earwigs	900
Ephemeroptera:*	Mayflies, shadflies	800
Odonata:*	Dragonflies, damselflies	4,900
Plecoptera:*	Stoneflies, salmonflies	2,000
Isoptera:	Termites, "white ants"	2,000
Corrodentia:	Book lice, bark lice	850
Mallophaga:	Chewing lice, bird lice	2,300
Thysanoptera:*	Thrips	1,500
Homoptera:	Aphids, scale insects, cicadas, leafhoppers	26,500
Hemiptera:*	Chinch bug, squash bug, bedbug, stink bugs, leaf bugs, aquatic bugs	31,000
Anoplura:	Bloodsucking lice, "cootie," hog louse, cattle lice	400
INSECTS WITH A COMPLETE OR COMPLEX METAMORPHOSIS		
Coleoptera:*	Beetles, weevils	250,000
Strepsiptera:*	Twisted-wing parasites	175
Neuroptera:*	Aphid lions, ant lions, dobsonflies	4,000
Mecoptera:*	Scorpionflies	300
Trichoptera:*	Caddisflies	2,850
Lepidoptera:*	Butterflies, moths, skippers	120,000
Hymenoptera:*	Bees, wasps, ants, sawflies	89,000
Diptera:*	Flies, mosquitoes, gnats, sheep "tick"	78,000
Siphonaptera:	Fleas	850
Minor Orders:	Zoraptera, Embioptera, and other lowly forms	100
	TOTAL INSECTS	640,000

Condensed from *Destructive and Useful Insects* by C. L. Metcalf and W. P. Flint, rev. by R. L. Metcalf (New York: McGraw Hill Book Co., 1951).* Orders containing the more important beneficial species, which are discussed in this book.

APPENDIX B

Some Insects Having Virus Diseases[1]

NAME	TYPE OF VIRUS DISEASE
LEPIDOPTERA	
SALT-MARSH CATERPILLAR *Estigmene acrea*	Polyhedrosis, granulosis
FALL WEBWORM *Hyphantria cunea*	Polyhedrosis
SILKWORM *Bombyx mori*	Nuclear polyhedrosis
CALIFORNIA OAKWORM *Phryganidia californica*	Nuclear polyhedrosis
GREATER WAX MOTH *Galleria mellonella*	Polyhedrosis
LODGEPOLE NEEDLE MINER *Recurvaria milleri*	Granulosis
WINTER MOTH *Operophtera brumata*	Cytoplasmic polyhedrosis, result of cross-infection with polyhedra from painted lady butterfly (*Vanessa cardui*)

[1] Compiled from Kenneth M. Hughes, "An Annotated List and Bibliography of Insects Reported to Have Virus Diseases," *Hilgardia*, May 1957.

NAME	TYPE OF VIRUS DISEASE
OMNIVOROUS LOOPER *Sabulodes caberata*	Polyhedrosis, granulosis
EASTERN TENT CATERPILLAR *Malacosoma americanum*	Polyhedrosis
GREAT BASIN TENT CATERPIL-LAR *Malacosoma fragile*	Nuclear polyhedrosis
WESTERN TENT CATERPILLAR *Malacosoma pluviale*	Nuclear polyhedrosis
DOUGLAS FUR TUSSOCK MOTH *Hemerocampa pseudotsugata*	Polyhedrosis
BROWN TAIL MOTH *Nygmia phaeorrhoea*	Polyhedrosis
GYPSY MOTH *Porthetria dispar*	Nuclear polyhedrosis Cytoplasmic polyhedrosis, result of cross-infection with polyhedra from another insect
PAINTED LADY BUTTERFLY *Vanessa cardui*	Nuclear polyhedrosis
CODLING MOTH *Carpocapsa pomonella*	Polyhedrosis
EYE-SPOTTED BUD MOTH *Spilonota ocellana*	Nuclear polyhedrosis
ALFALFA LOOPER *Autographa californica*	Nuclear polyhedrosis, granulosis
ARMY CUTWORM *Chorizagrotis auxiliaris*	Polyhedrosis, granulosis
TOBACCO BUDWORM *Heliothis virescens*	Polyhedrosis
CORN EARWORM, BOLLWORM, TOMATO FRUITWORM *Heliothis zea*	Nuclear polyhedrosis Cytoplasmic polyhedrosis
FALL ARMYWORM *Laphygma frugiperda*	Polyhedrosis, granulosis
VARIEGATED CUTWORM *Peridroma saucia*	Polyhedrosis, granulosis

NAME   TYPE OF VIRUS DISEASE

WESTERN YELLOW-STRIPED ARMYWORM *Prodenia praefica*	Nuclear polyhedrosis
ARMYWORM *Pseudaletia unipuncta*	Nuclear polyhedrosis, granulosis Noninclusion virus
CABBAGE LOOPER *Trichoplusia ni*	Nuclear polyhedrosis
ALFALFA CATERPILLAR *Colias philodice eurytheme*	Nuclear polyhedrosis
EUROPEAN CABBAGE BUTTER-FLY *Pieris brassicae*	Granulosis
IMPORTED CABBAGEWORM *Pieris rapae*	Granulosis Nuclear polyhedrosis, result of cross-infection with polyhedra from *Colias philodice eurytheme*
WATTLE BAGWORM *Cryptothelea junodi*	Nuclear polyhedrosis
PANDORA MOTH *Coloradia pandora*	Polyhedrosis
RANGE CATERPILLAR *Hemileuca oliviae*	Polyhedrosis
SPURGE HAWK MOTH *Celerio euphorbiae*	Polyhedrosis
PRIVET HAWK MOTH *Sphinx ligustri*	Nuclear polyhedrosis
WEBBING CLOTHES MOTH *Tineola bisselliella*	Nuclear polyhedrosis
BLACK-HEADED BUDWORM *Acleris variana*	Nuclear polyhedrosis
RED-BANDED LEAF ROLLER *Argyrotaenia velutinana*	Granulosis
SPRUCE BUDWORM *Choristoneura fumiferana*	Nuclear and cytoplasmic polyhedrosis, granulosis
WESTERN GRAPE LEAF SKELETONIZER *Harrisina brillians*	Granulosis

NAME   TYPE OF VIRUS DISEASE

HYMENOPTERA

EUROPEAN SPRUCE SAWFLY
Diprion hercyniae

Nuclear polyhedrosis; also reported to be susceptible to polyhedrosis of *Neodiprion pratti banksianae*

BALSAM FIR SAWFLY
Neodiprion abietis

Polyhedrosis

RED-HEADED PINE SAWFLY
Neodiprion lecontei

Polyhedrosis

JACK PINE SAWFLY
Neodiprion pratti banksianae

Nuclear polyhedrosis

EUROPEAN PINE SAWFLY
Neodiprion sertifer

Nuclear polyhedrosis; also susceptible to polyhedrosis of *Neodiprion pratti banksianae*

LARCH SAWFLY
Pristiphora erichsonii

Polyhedrosis

BLACK CURRANT SAWFLY
Nematus olfaciens

Nuclear polyhedrosis

DIPTERA

BLUEBOTTLE FLY
Calliphora vomitoria

Polyhedrosis

WHEAT MIDGE
Sitodiplosis mosellana

Polyhedrosis

LEATHERJACKET
Tipula paludosa

Polyhedrosis
Noninclusion virus

APPENDIX C: Insect Pests Controlled by Introduction of their Enemies in Canada[1]

PEST	CONTROL AGENT	REMARKS
(1) EUROPEAN WHEAT STEM SAWFLY *Cephus pygmaeus*	ICHNEUMONID WASP *Collyria calcitrator*	Pest native to Europe. Parasite introduced from Europe between 1937 and 1940.
(2) APPLE MEALYBUG *Phenacoccus aceris*	WASP (Platygasteridae) *Allotropa utilis*	Pest native to Europe and Asia. Parasite introduced from Nova Scotia to British Columbia in 1938. This project rated an outstanding success.
(3) WOOLLY APPLE APHID *Erisoma lanigerum*	CHALCID WASP *Aphelinus mali*	Pest native to eastern North America. Parasite introduced from Ontario to British Columbia in 1921 and 1929.
(4) EUROPEAN EARWIG *Forficula auricularia*	TACHINID FLY *Bigonicheta spinipennis*	Garden pest of foreign origin. Parasite introduced from England to west coast between 1928 and 1931.
(5) HOLLY LEAF MINER *Phytomyza ilicis*	CHALCID WASP *Epilampsis gemma* BRACONID WASP *Opius ilicis*	Pest of foreign origin. Five parasites imported from England into British Columbia between 1936 and 1938; four established with these the most important. *O. ilicis* became established from a release of only 10 individuals!

[1] Based on evaluations by A. L. Turnbull and D. A. Chant in "The Practice and Theory of Biological Control of Insects in Canada," *Canadian Journal of Zoology*, Oct. 1961.

(6) LARCH CASEBEARER
    Coleophora laricella

BRACONID WASP
Agathis pumilis
CHALCID WASP
Epilampsis laricinellae

Pest native to Europe. Five parasites imported into Canada from Europe between 1931 and 1939. This braconid and chalcid complement one another effectively.

(7) SPRUCE SAWFLY
    Diprion hercyniae

TACHINID FLY
Drino bohemica

ICHNEUMONID WASP
Exenterus vellicatus

Pest native to Europe. Six of 27 parasites introduced from Europe became established. Virus (polyhedrosis) disease also important factor in control. This project an outstanding success.

(8) SATIN MOTH
    Stilpnotia salicis

BRACONID WASPS
Apanteles solitarius
Meteorus versicolor
TACHINID FLY
Compsilura concinnata

Four parasites introduced into British Columbia from New Brunswick and Massachusetts between 1929 and 1934; three became established.

(9) OYSTERSHELL SCALE
    Lepidosaphes ulmi

PREDACEOUS MITE
Hemisarcoptes malus

Pest long established in Canada. The predaceous mite introduced into British Columbia from eastern Canada in 1917.

(10) GREENHOUSE WHITEFLY
     Trialeurodes vaporariorum

CHALCID WASP
Encarsia formosa

A cosmopolitan pest of greenhouse plants. Parasite introduced into Canada from England in 1931. Was supplied to greenhouses regularly by the Belleville laboratory until 1953.

(11) CITRUS MEALYBUG
     Pseudococcus citri

CHALCID WASPS
Leptomastix dactylopii
Leptomastidea abnormis

Pest generally found in greenhouses. Parasites from California and Ontario reared and shipped to growers across Canada from 1938 to 1939. As with the greenhouse whitefly parasite, periodic introductions are necessary but effective.

PEST	CONTROL AGENT	REMARKS
(12) EUROPEAN FRUIT LECAN- IUM *Eulecanium coryli*	CHALCID WASP *Blastothrix sericea*	Shade tree pest native to Europe. Parasite introduced into British Columbia from England in 1927 and 1929.
(13) LARCH SAWFLY *Pristiphora erichsonii*	ICHNEUMONID WASP *Mesoleius tenthredinis*	Introduced from England into eastern and central Canada between 1910 and 1935, and British Columbia in 1934. Native tachinid *Bessa harveyi* and chalcid *Tritneptis klugii* also control factors.
(14) PEA MOTH *Laspeyresia nigricana*	BRACONID WASP *Ascogaster quadridentata* ICHNEUMONID WASP *Glypta haesitator*	Pest native to Europe. Parasites introduced into Canada from England in 1936. Rated partial success. Early success in British Columbia later obscured by other factors.
(15) ORIENTAL FRUIT MOTH *Grapholitha molesta*	BRACONID WASP *Macrocentrus ancylivorus*	Pest native to Japan. Parasite introduced into Ontario from New Jersey in 1929. Complemented by native ichneumonid *Glypta rufiscutellaris*. Project rated partial success though chemicals are now used.
(16) EUROPEAN PINE SAWFLY *Neodiprion sertifer*	VIRUS (Polyhedrosis)	The virus was imported into Canada from Sweden in 1949. Tests in pine plantations of Ontario gave good control.[2] Rated by Turnbull and Chant as "without success to date," but with "prospects of eventual success." (See Appendix D, item 4.)

[2] F. T. Bird, "On the Artificial Dissemination of the Virus Disease of the European Pine Sawfly, *Neodiprion sertifer* (Geoffr.)," *Bi-monthly Progress Report*, Canada Dept. of *Agriculture*, May–June 1952.

(17) JACK PINE SAWFLY
Neodiprion swainei

VIRUS (Polyhedrosis)

The virus was found in Quebec and northeastern Ontario. Disseminated by airplane in infested area of Quebec in 1960 and 1961. Disease spread rapidly and gave satisfactory control.[3]

(18) EUROPEAN PINE SHOOT
MOTH
Rhyacionia buoliana

ICHNEUMONID WASPS
Temelucha interruptor
Orgilus obscurator
Exeristes roborator
Pimpla turionellae

CHALCID WASP
Tetrastichus turionum

Between 1928 and 1959, twelve species and 86,000 individuals released in southern Ontario. Only four or possibly five established; most valuable is *O. obscurator*. Fifteen species and 300,000 individuals released in eastern United States from 1931 to 1938. Turnbull and Chant "were tempted to rank this project as a partial success" since some valuable species have been established and probably aid in control. This project still in progress and believed to hold promise.

(19) BALSAM WOOLLY APHID
Chermes piceae
(*Adelges*)

BEETLE (Derodontidae)
Laricobius erichsonii
LADY BEETLE
Pullus impexus
FLIES (Chamaemyiidae)
Cremifania migrocellulata
Leucopis obscura
(All predators—no known parasites of *C. piceae*)

Importations from Europe initiated in 1933. Of 13 species colonized, 4 became established in the maritime provinces. *Laricobius* most effective but none gives satisfactory control. Turnbull and Chant rate this project a failure but their "judgment is conditional and may have to be revised at some future date." (See Appendix D, item 36.)

[3] W. A. Smirnoff, J. J. Fettes, W. Haliburton, "A Virus Disease of Swaine's Jack Pine Sawfly, *Neodiprion swainei* Midd. Sprayed from an Aircraft," *The Canadian Entomologist*, May 1962.

APPENDIX D: Insect Pests Controlled by Introduction of Their Enemies in the Continental United States[1]

PEST	CONTROL AGENT	REMARKS
(1) JAPANESE BEETLE *Popillia japonica*	BACTERIA ("milky disease") *Baccillus popilliae*	Origin of pest: Japan. Bacteria first found in New Jersey in 1933. Mass production begun in 1939. Program of distribution between 1939 and 1948. Two parasites imported from the Far East, *Tiphia popilliavora* and *T. vernalis*, are important control agents.
(2) ALFALFA CATERPILLAR *Colias eurytheme*	VIRUS (polyhedrosis) *Borrelina campeoles*	Seasonal applications give commercial control in California. *Bacillus thuringiensis* also effective control agent. The parasite *Apanteles medicaginis* important in natural control at times.
(3) SPRUCE SAWFLY *Diprion hercyniae*	VIRUS (polyhedrosis) TACHINID FLY *Drino bohemica* ICHNEUMONID WASP *Exenterus vellicatus*	Pest and parasite origin: Europe. Virus first appeared as epizootic in eastern Canada and Maine in 1940.

[1] H. L. Sweetman, *The Principles of Biological Control* (Dubuque, Iowa: Wm. C. Brown Co., 1958); C. P. Clausen, *Biological Control of Insect Pests in the Continental United States* (Washington: USDA Technical Bulletin No. 1139, June 19 56).

(4) EUROPEAN PINE SAWFLY *Neodiprion sertifer*	VIRUS (polyhedrosis)	Virus obtained from Canada in 1951. Used on Scots and red pine plantations in New Jersey and Illinois. Ground applications very successful. Virus bank established by Forest Service in New Haven, Connecticut.[2]
(5) GRAPE MEALYBUG *Pseudococcus maritimus*	CHALCID WASP *Acerophagus notativentris* GREEN LACEWING *Chrysopa californica*	Pest is native of North America. Parasite introduced into California in 1943. Colonization of green lacewing effective with three releases of 250 eggs per tree.
(6) COMSTOCK'S MEALYBUG *Pseudococcus comstocki*	CHALCID WASP *Pseudaphycus malinus*	Parasite introduced from Virginia to Ohio in 1940; has controlled this pest on apples. Importations from Japan began in 1939 and included the wasp *Allotropa burrelli* (Platygasteridae) which is also effective.
(7) YELLOW SCALE *Aonidiella citrina*	CHALCID WASP *Comperiella bifasciata*	Pest is native of Australia. Parasite imported into California from Far East beginning in 1906. Controls pest if not hindered too much by ants.
(8) FLORIDA RED SCALE *Chyrsomphalus aonidum*	CHALCID WASPS *Pseudhomalopoda prima* *Prospaltella auranti* *Aspidiotiphagus lounsburyi* *Aspidiotiphagus citrinus*	This complex of parasites has given good control. Recent (1959) importation from Israel, *Aphytis holoxanthus*, is established.
(9) SOFT (BROWN) SCALE *Coccus hesperidum*	CHALCID WASP *Aphycus luteolus*	This parasite controls the soft scale wherever it occurs in California.

[2] *Use of Diseases to Kill Plant Insect Pests* (USDA Agricultural Research Service, ARS 22-74, October 1961).

PEST	CONTROL AGENT	REMARKS
(10) OLIVE SCALE *Parlatoria oleae*	CHALCID WASP *Aphytis maculicornis*	Pest is worldwide; occurs in California on olive and deciduous fruit. Parasite imported from Persia in 1951. Gives commercial control but not consistently.[3]
(11) GREENHOUSE WHITEFLY *Trialeurodes vaporariorum*	CHALCID WASP *Encarsia formosa*	Used more successfully in Canada and Australia (see Appendix C).
(12) NIGRA SCALE *Saissetia nigra*	CHALCID WASP *Aphycus helvolus*	Pest of ornamental plants mostly, in California. Parasite imported from South Africa in 1938 gives good control.
(13) BLACK SCALE *Saissetia oleae*	CHALCID WASPS *Aphycus lounsburyi* *Aphycus helvolus* EGG PREDATORS *Scutellista cyanea* *Lecaniobius utilis* LADY BEETLE *Rhizobius ventralis*	Lady beetle imported from Australia into California in 1891 and 1892; still present in coastal region. *A. lounsburyi,* imported from Australia in 1919 effective until hyperparasitized. *A. helvolus,* imported from South Africa in 1937, now controls scale. The egg predators have been effective on olives in Peru.
(14) WOOLLY APPLE APHID *Eriosoma lanigerum*	CHALCID WASP *Aphelinus mali*	Pest is worldwide. Parasite has been introduced into 50 countries, gives adequate control in some areas, in others reduces infestations markedly.

[3] C. B. Huffaker, C. E. Kennett, and G. L. Finney, "Biological Control of Olive Scale, *Parlatoria oleae* (Colvée), in California by imported *Aphytis maculicornis* (Masi) (Hymenoptera: Aphelinidae)," *Hilgardia*, July 1962.

(15) CITROPHILUS MEALYBUG
Pseudococcus gahani

LADY BEETLE
Cryptolaemus montrouzieri
CHALCIDG WASPS
Coccophagus gurneyi
Tetracnemus pretiosus

Lady beetle first imported into California from Australia in 1891 and 1892 to control citrus mealybug. Mass production and yearly releases began in 1917 and provided control of *P. gahani* until the two parasites were imported from Australia in 1928. These quickly gave permanent control.

(16) CITRUS MEALYBUG
Pseudococcus citri

LADY BEETLE
Cryptolaemus montrouzieri
CHALCID WASPS
Leptomastidea abnormis
Leptomastix dactylopii

Parasite imported into California from Sicily in 1914, effective in some areas. In others, the lady beetle and a chalcid wasp, *Leptomastix dactylopii*, are mass produced and released periodically. *C. montrouzieri* effective on gardenias and chrystanthemums in greenhouses when mealybug infestations are heavy.

(17) LONG-TAILED MEALYBUG
Pseudococcus adonidum

CHALCID WASPS
Anarhopus sydneyensis
Tetracnemus peregrinus
LADY BEETLE
Cryptolaemus montrouzieri

Pest of citrus and avocados. A. *sydneyensis* imported into California from Australia in 1933, *T. peregrinus* from Brazil in 1934. They have been very effective. Lady beetle was used before 1934.

(18) CALIFORNIA RED SCALE
Aonidiella aurantii

CHALCID WASPS
Aphytis chrysomphali
Aphytis lingnanensis
Aphytis melinus
Aphytis coheni
LADY BEETLE
Chilocorus confusor

A. *chrysomphali* introduced into California with the scale. A. *lingnanensis*, imported from China in 1947, more effective of the two. A. *melinus* came from India and Pakistan in 1956 and 1957, A. *coheni* from Israel in 1960. Earlier imports control scale in coastal and intermediate areas but not in interior valleys. Lady beetle has controlled the scale in Texas, but the two older parasites are also present there.

PEST	CONTROL AGENT	REMARKS
(19) COTTONY CUSHION SCALE *Icerya purchasi*	LADY BEETLE *Rodolia cardinalis* PARASITIC FLY (Agromyzidae) *Cryptochaetum iceryae*	Both enemies of the scale came to California from Australia in 1888. Lady beetle generally given most of the credit for control. The lady beetle and a fungus, *Spicaria javanica*, control the pest in Puerto Rico and Cuba.
(20) WESTERN GRAPE LEAF SKELETONIZER *Harrisina brillians*	BRACONID WASP *Apanteles harrisinae* TACHINID FLY *Sturmia harrisinae* VIRUS (granulosis)	The two parasites brought to California from Arizona in 1950 and 1951. Virus believed to have been brought in accidently at this time with host and parasite material. Control established in two to three years. Program terminated in 1956, rated "an outstanding success."[4]
(21) CALICO SCALE *Lecanium cerasorum*	CHALCID WASP *Blastothrix longipennis* WARBLER (vertebrate–predator) *Dendroica auduboni auduboni*	This pest of walnuts in California is controlled by a parasite and a bird.
(22) SOUTHERN CORN STALK BORER *Diatraea crambidoides*	ANT *Solenopsis xyloni*	Ant holds this pest of the southern states in check during the winter months, preventing it from doing serious damage.

[4] Curtis P. Clausen, "Biological Control of Western Grape Leaf Leaf skeletonizer (*Harrisinia brillians* B. and McD.) in California," *Hilgardia*, Dec. 1961.

(23) CITRUS RED MITE
Panonychus citri

LADY BEETLES
Lindorus lophantae
Chilocorus sp.
CHALCID WASP
Aphytis sp.
MITES (predaceous)
Typhlodromus sp.

This pest is controlled by lady beetles in unsprayed orchards in California. Most effective predators are several species of Typhlodromus mites.

(24) CYCLAMEN MITES
Steneotarsonemus pallidus

MITES (predaceous)
Typhlodromus reticulatus
Typhlodromus bellinus

These two mites control cyclamen mites on second to fourth year plantings of strawberries in California. They can be introduced onto plants for earlier control.

The following biological control projects should be rated at least partially successful—the parasites established are a valuable permanent addition to the biotic environment and in some cases they provide satisfactory control:

(25) GYPSY MOTH
Porthetria dispar

BRACONID WASP
Apanteles melanoscelus
TACHINID FLIES
Blepharipoda scutellata
Compsilura concinnata
EGG PARASITES
Anastatus disparis
Ooencyrtus kuwanai
PREDATOR (ground beetle)
Calosoma sycophanta

More than 40 species imported; 9 parasites and 2 predators established. Over 92 million parasites released between 1905 and 1927. Combined effects of this excellent complex of enemies gave substantial control in New England in the past. Present situation obscured by the use of chemicals. A virus ("wilt disease") is an important natural control factor. Bacillus thringiensis, used as a "microbial insecticide," is an effective control agent.

(26) SATIN MOTH
Stilpnotia salicis

BRACONID WASPS
Apanteles solitarius
Meteorus versicolor
TACHINID FLY
Compsilura concinnata

Parasites imported from Europe. Effective control maintained by these and the gypsy moth–browntail moth complex of parasites.

PEST	CONTROL AGENT	REMARKS
(27) BROWNTAIL MOTH *Nygmia phaeorrhoea*	BRACONID WASPS *Apanteles lacteicolor* *Meteorus versicolor* TACHINID FLIES *Townsendiellomyia nidicola* *Compsilura concinnata*	Since establishment of these parasites, this pest has presented no problem in New England.
(28) IMPORTED CABBAGEWORM *Pieris rapae*	BRACONID WASP *Apanteles glomeratus*	First insect intentionally imported (1875) into this country for biological control. Spread was phenomenal; now found wherever cabbages are grown.
(29) ORIENTAL FRUIT MOTH *Grapholitha molesta*	BRACONID WASPS *Macrocentrus ancylivorus* *Agathis diversa*	A. *diversa* was imported from Japan. Most of the importations (20 in all) did not become established. Native parasite of strawberry leaf roller, *M. ancylivorus*, took to the moth and became the most important control agent. Large scale colonizations in the peach-growing areas, in combination with native parasites, gave fairly good control until DDT came into use.
(30) EUROPEAN CORN BORER *Ostrinia nubilalis* (*Pyrausta*)	ICHNEUMONID WASPS *Horogenes punctorius* *Phaeogenes nigridens* CHALCID WASP *Sympiesis viridula* BRACONID WASP *Macrocentrus gifuensis* TACHINID FLY *Lydella stabulans grisescens*	Large scale colonization program extended from 1919 to 1940 with 22 species of parasites imported and colonized. Five species known to be established. Federal-state co-operative plan after 1943 gave much better control than was thought possible. Very good results from program in north central states.

(31) ALFALFA WEEVIL
Hypera postica

ICHNEUMONID WASP
Bathyplectes curculionis

BRACONID WASP
Microtonus aethiops

CHALCID WASP
Tetrastichus incertus

Program of importations started in 1911. *B. curculionis* most valuable of early imports. Parasitizes 90 to 100 per cent of weevils on first crop in Utah; early cutting destroys many of the parasites and reduces their effectiveness. Parasite gave economic control in lowland middle California. *M. aethiops* and *T. incertus* are recent importations (1957 to 1961).

(32) SPOTTED ALFALFA APHID
Therioaphis maculata

BRACONID WASPS
Praon palitans
Trioxys utilis

FUNGUS DISEASE
Entomophthora exitialis

Parasites imported into California from the Near East between 1955 and 1957, hold high promise as enemies of the aphid. Dissemination of fungus has been very effective. Native predators very important factors in control if not destroyed by insecticides; these are: predatory bugs (*Nabis* sp., *Orius* sp., *Sinea* sp., *Geocoris* sp.), larvae of the green lacewing (*Chrysopa* sp.) and syrphid fly, and most important of all, lady beetles (*Hippodamia* sp.). This parasite-predator-disease complex is capable of holding the aphid below economic levels throughout the year in many areas of Southern California and in others for much of the growing season.[5]

(33) EUROPEAN EARWIG
Forficula auricularia

TACHINID FLY
Bigonicheta spinipennis

Parasite became established on eastern seaboard and in Idaho, Washington, and Utah. Control is generally satisfactory.

[5] Vernon F. Stern, Ray F. Smith, Robert van den Bosch, and Kenneth S. Hagen, "The Integration of Chemical and Biological Control of the Spotted Alfalfa Aphid," *Hilgadia*, October 1959.

PEST	CONTROL AGENT	REMARKS
(34) EUROPEAN PINE SHOOT MOTH *Rhyacionia buoliana*	(See Appendix C, item 18)	
(35) ELM LEAF BEETLE *Galerucella xantho-melaena*	TACHINID FLY *Erynnia nitida* CHALCID WASP *Tetrastichus brevistigma*	Tachinid imported from France in 1934 and 1935. Not successful in eastern states but became quickly and widely established in California. The chalcid is a native of eastern U.S. and became quickly established in California also. Injury to elms greatly reduced as result of these introductions.
(36) BALSAM WOOLLY APHID *Chermes piceae* (*Adelges*)	DERODONTID BEETLE *Laricobius erichsonii* LADY BEETLE *Scymnus* (*Pullusq Impexus* FLIES *Leucopis obscura* (Chamaemyiidae) *Aphidoletes thompsoni* (Cecidomyiidae) (All predators—no known parasites of *C. piceae*)	Close to a million predators and 17 species colonized in New England, North Carolina, and Pacific northwest from 1955 to 1960—4 species established. *Scymnus* and *Leucopis* established in New England; latter spread naturally from New Brunswick. *Leucopis*, *Laricobius* and *A. thompsoni* established in Pacific northwest. (Last named not established in Canada—see Appendix C, item 19.)

APPENDIX E

Biological Control of Insects in the Pacific Area

Following an analysis and listing of 125 successful control projects in the Pacific area,[1] DeBach summarizes the results in the table below. Only projects involving control by imported species are included; the cases of control occurring naturally through the action of native species, which are of course far more numerous, are another matter. A few cases of control by agents other than insects are included, but not cases of biological control by disease. The 125 cases involve 87 species of pests in 23 regions; they represent more than half the 221 worldwide cases of successful biological control in some 65 countries. "Partial successes," DeBach points out, "tend to be overlooked or discounted but nonetheless they often represent a considerable saving as measured by reduction in damage or lessened need for treatment."

[1] Paul DeBach, "An Analysis of Successes in Biological Control of Insects in the Pacific Area," *Proceedings of the Hawaiian Entomological Society,* 1962.

CASES OF BIOLOGICAL CONTROL OF PEST INSECTS IN THE PACIFIC AREA BY "COUNTRIES"

	CONTROL RESULTS[1]		
	C	S	P	Total
Australia		5	5	10
Bali			1	1
Bismarck Archipelago		1	1	2
Canada, British Columbia	2	4	3	9
Caroline Islands (including Ponape)		1	1	2
Celebes		2	1	3
Chile	2	1	3	6
Colombia	1			1
Costa Rica	2			2
Ecuador		1		1
Fiji	3		3	6
Japan	4			4
Mariana Islands (including Guam)	1	3	1	5
Mexico	1	1		2
New Zealand	3	5	3	11
Panama	1			1
Peru	1	3	1	5
Tasmania		2	5	7
U.S.A. (California)	2	9	8	19
U.S.A. (Hawaii)	2	10	12	24
U.S.A. (Pacific Northwest)	1	1	2	4
	26	49	50	125

[1] C=complete; S=substantial; P=partial

This study of biological control in the Pacific area does not bear out some common beliefs concerning the reasons for success of these projects. More successful projects have actually occurred *outside* the tropics—56 per cent of successful ones are north of 30 degrees latitude. Nor are islands necessarily best suited to biological control: over the world, more successes have occurred on continents than on islands (52 per cent of the Pacific cases were on islands). This study would also seem to indicate that success is in proportion to the effort made. Hawaii leads with a total of 24 recorded successes, and California is second with 19; Hawaii has been very active in this work since the 1890's and leads all others in importations, with California again the runner-up.

The British Commonwealth countries, long active in biological control, also have a large share of the successes, due here as elsewhere in no small measure to the efforts of a few "enthusiastic workers who have kept the work going and who have obtained support for their projects."

GLOSSARY

ABDOMEN—The posterior region of the body, behind the thorax of insects and divided into similar segments or rings.

ALDRIN—A chlorinated hydrocarbon insecticide, which is converted to dieldrin in man and in the environment; in either form it is many times more toxic to vertebrates than DDT.

AMPHIBIAN—A vertebrate that reproduces in aquatic environment. Frogs, toads, and salamanders belong to this class (Amphibia); they differ from snakes in that their eggs are not fertilized by coition and are not protected by either a shell or an embryonic membrane.

ANTENNA (pl. ANTENNAE)—A segmented sense organ found in pairs on the head of an insect.

APHID—A small homopterous insect that sucks plant juices; sometimes called plant louse.

ARACHNID—Any arthropod belonging to the class Arachnida, including spiders, mites, ticks, harvestmen, scorpions. Arachnids have four pairs of legs and two body segments; they do not have antennae or wings.

ARANEIDA—Arachnid order composed of spiders.

ARTHROPODS—Any member of the phylum Arthropoda, which consists of animals with jointed legs and jointed skeletons including insects, spiders, mites, harvestmen, scorpions, millipedes, centipedes, and crustaceans.

BACTERIA (sing. BACTERIUM)—One-celled, microscopic, plantlike animals which multiply by fission. Some are destructive as disease organisms of man and other animals; some are beneficial to man as disease organisms of insects and in breaking down organic matter.

BEETLE—An insect with a pair of hard, protective wings covering a second pair of membranous wings (the latter are more important in flying). Beetles comprise the order Coleoptera, which means "sheath-winged."

CERCI—Paired appendages protruding from the hind end of many insects; they take a variety of forms and sometimes have a sensory function.

CHALCID—Parasitic wasp belonging to the superfamily Chalcidoidea, order Hymenoptera.

CHLORDANE—*See* HEPTACHLOR.

COCCID—An insect of the family Coccidae, which includes the diaspine or armored scales, soft scales, fluted scales, and mealybugs (order Homoptera).

COCCINELLID—Any beetle of the family Coccinellidae. Almost all the species in this family are beneficial, two exceptions being the squash beetle and the Mexican bean beetle.

COCOON—Silklike protective covering spun by the larvae of many insects prior to the pupal stage.

COLEOPTERIA—*See* BEETLE.

CONIDIOPHORE—A filamentous growth resulting from the germination of specialized hypha of certain fungi which produces conidia or spores. In insects, the hyphae usually grow outward and burst through the host's integument in spongy masses, which vary considerably in appearance and are usually white but also range from bluish to greenish hues. In some species the hyphae develop within the body of the host. Each conidiophore gives rise to a single conidium which is violently discharged into the air (or within the insect) when its development is completed.

CONTROL, BIOLOGICAL—In a strict sense, the use of predators, parasites, and disease organisms to control insect pests. The term is often loosely applied to other forms of control without the direct use of chemicals—such as the release of sterile male insects, insect attractants, and traps—and to other "unconventional approaches," as well as to cultural practices affecting insect populations.

CONTROL, MICROBIAL—Biological control by means of microorganisms pathogenic to insect pests.

CONTROL, NATURAL—Maintenance of insect populations within more or less definite limits through the interaction of plant-feeding insects, their enemies (including disease organisms), and other factors in the environment. The control of pests by this means may or may not be at an economically acceptable level.

CONTROL, INTEGRATED—Combination of natural and biological control with chemical control, limiting the use of chemicals to the extent necessary to restore the balance between pest and beneficial species at an acceptable level.

CRUCIFERS—Plants of the mustard family (Cruciferae), including cabbage, broccoli, kale, kohlrabi, brussels sprouts, cauliflower, turnip, radish, and some common weeds.

CRUSTACEAN—A class (Crustacea) of arthropods, mostly aquatic and usually with a hard shell, including crabs, crayfish, lobsters, sowbugs, pillbugs, barnacles, shrimps, waterfleas, and cyclops.

CYTOPLASM—All the protoplasm of a cell excepting the nucleus.

DDT—A chlorinated hydrocarbon insecticide noted for its residual and persistant nature. Related compounds are aldrin, dieldrin, endrin, toxaphene, lindane, methoxychlor, chlordane, and heptachlor.

DERRIS—Any of a group of woody pants (legumes), found in the East Indies; rotenone is extracted from the roots.

DIAPAUSE—Arrested or suspended development in insects. It may be induced by external factors such as temperature, moisture, food, or by internal factors such as enzymes and hormones. It varies in degree and may occur in any stage of metamorphosis but is most pronounced in the egg and pupal stages. In other immature stages it occurs for short periods during molting and longer periods during estivation (*which see*) and hibernation (*which see*).

DIELDRIN—*See* ALDRIN.

DIPTERA—An order of insects notable for having only one pair of wings; a pair of knoblike halteres in place of second pair is believed to have a balancing function. The Diptera include flies, mosquitoes, gnats, and midges.

ECOLOGY—The study of the relation of animals and plants to their environment.

ECTOPARASITE—A parasite that feeds from the outside of the host. An *external parasite.*

ELYTRA (sing. ELYTRON, ELYTRUM)—Hardened front wings of beetles.

ENDOPARASITE—A parasite that feeds inside the host. An *internal parasite.*

ENTOMOGENOUS—Growing in or on the body of an insect; used of fungi causing disease in insects.

ENTOMOLGY—The study of insects.

ENTOMOPHAGOUS—Insectivorous. Entomophagous insects are the predators and parasites.

ENTOMOPHTHORACEOUS—"Insect-devourers." Fungi belonging to the family Entomophthoraceae; best known are in the genus *Entomophthora.*

EPIZOOTIC—Disease of epidemic proportions causing severe and rapid reduction of insect populations.

ESTIVATION—A dormant state similar to hibernation (*which see*) but induced by opposite conditions—occurs in the Tropics due to high temperatures.

FUNGUS (pl. FUNGI)—Any plant growing in irregular masses, not differentiated by roots, stems, and leaves, and lacking the chlorophyll of green plants. Fungi include molds, yeasts, mushrooms, toadstools, mildews, and rusts. Some species infect insects and are conspicuous by the presence of mycelia and fruiting bodies on the insect remains. Fungus infections are called *mycoses*. Some fungi are also important agents, together with bacteria and other organisms, in decomposing plant and animal residues; other species are predaceous and destroy harmful soil organisms.

GENUS (pl. GENERA)—Grouping used in classifying plants and animals. Usually a number of similar species comprise a genus, and similar genera make up a family. In the binomial system of nomenclature, animals and plants are designated by genus and species.

GRANULOSIS (pl. GRANULOSES)—a virus infection of insects producing granular bodies in the invaded cells.

HALTERES—*See* DIPTERA.

HEMIPTERA—The order of true bugs, having jointed beaks at *front* of head for sucking plant or animal juices (*see* HOMOPTERA). The forewings are thickened at least halfway out from the base, and are membranous the rest of the way.

HEPTACHLOR—A chlorinated hydrocarbon insecticide, closely related to DDT but more toxic—as is chlordane.

HIBERNATION—A dormant state similar to estivation (*which see*) occurs in temperate or frigid areas due to low temperatures. Insects may hibernate in all stages of development. *See also* DIAPAUSE.

HOMOPTERA—An order of insects having jointed beaks, which are quite long, at *base* of head, for sucking plant juices (*see* HEMIPTERA). With some minor exceptions, all are plant feeders. They include cicadas, scales, mealybugs, aphids, treehoppers, leafhoppers, planthoppers, spittlebugs, psyllids, and whiteflies.

HYMENOPTERA—An insect order comprising ants, wasps, bees, sawflies, and horntails. All have membranous wings; mouthparts are usually of the biting type, sometimes with a proboscis ("tongue") for lapping up nectar and other exudates. Except for sawflies, horntails, and some ants, they are almost all beneficial.

HYPERPARASITISM—Parasitization of one parasite by another, the *hyperparasite*. *See also* SECONDARY PARASITE.

ICHNEUMON or ICHNEUMONID—A parasitic wasp of the family Ichneumonidae, sometimes also called an ichneumon fly.

INSECT—An animal belonging to the class Insecta or Hexapoda (meaning "six-legged") of the phylum Arthropoda. Insects have a pair of antennae, usually one or two pairs of wings, and three distinct body parts (head, thorax, abdomen); they breathe by means of tracheae.

INTEGUMENT—Outer covering or skin of insect or plant.

LADY BEETLE (also LADYBUG or LADYBIRD BEETLE)—The common name for coccinellids.

LARVA (pl. LARVAE)—*See* METAMORPHOSIS.

LEPIDOPTERA—An order comprising moths, butterflies, millers, and skippers—insects having membranous wings with fine scales, whose mouth parts (consisting of a long, coiled proboscis or tongue) are used for lapping up nectar. Butterfly antennae end in knobs; moth antennae are featherlike. Larval forms, hairy or otherwise, are called caterpillars and are mostly plant feeders.

LUCIFERASE—An enzyme in the cells of fireflies, which reacts with luciferin to produce luminosity.

MALATHION—*See* PARATHION.

MARSUPIAL—An animal that carries its young in a marsupium or pouch.

METAMORPHOSIS—A marked change in form between birth or hatching and maturity. The young of many species closely resemble the adults, except for the absence of wings and genitalia; they undergo gradual or simple metamorphosis and the young are called *nymphs*. Among the higher insects, the young or immature stage usually assumes two forms, *larva* and *pupa*, which do not resemble the adult; these insects have a complete or complex metamorphosis. Caterpillars, grubs, and maggots are the larval forms of moths and butterflies, beetles, and flies respectively. In the pupal stage, locomotion and feeding cease and the larva gradually changes to the adult form; after shedding of the pupal skin, the transformation is rapidly completed.

MICROORGANISM—A single-celled organism of microscopic size. Bacteria, viruses, rickettsiae, protozoa, and fungi belong to this category.

MICROSPORIDIAN—A microorganism of the phylum Protozoa and the class Sporozoa. These organisms are parasitic on a wide range of animals, including insects.

MITE—An arachnid belonging to the order Acarina, along with ticks, which are larger. Body segments are not as well defined as those of spiders.

MULTIPLEPARASITISM—Attack simultaneously by two or more primary parasites of different species on the same host.

MYCELIA (sing. MYCELIUM)—Filamentous, branching vegetative structure of fungi.

NEMATODE—A threadlike parasitic worm, also called a roundworm.

Some nematodes parasitize mammals, including man, others attack insects. Certain species transmit bacteria that are fatal (rather than their feeding) to the host insect; others destroy their insect hosts by feeding and injury in emerging. Nematodes (also called eelworms) attack plants, usually the roots, and some are predaceous on other nematodes. They range in size from the microscopic forms found in the soil to those of several feet in length found in mammals.

NEUROPTERA—An order including lacewings, dobsonflies, alderflies, and ant lions—the "nerve-winged" insects.

NYMPH—*See* METAMORPHOSIS.

OCELLI (sing. OCELLUS)—Minute, simple eyes possessed by many (but not all) insects.

ODONATA—An insect order comprising dragonflies and damselflies.

ORDER—A plant or animal group composed of families with similar characteristics.

ORTHOPTERA—An insect order including grasshoppers or locusts, katydids, and crickets. Walkingsticks, roaches, and mantids are also generally included, though some classifications place them in separate order.

OVIPAROUS—Bringing forth eggs, as distinguished from giving birth to living young.

OVIPOSITION—Act of depositing or laying egg by female insect.

OVIPOSITOR—Instrument possessed by female insects for depositing eggs.

PAEDOGENESIS—A rare form of insect reproduction, in which young are produced by the larvae or pupae.

PARASITE—*See* PREDATOR.

PARATHION—An organic phosphorus insecticide, related to malathion, TEPP, and phosdin. Chemicals of this group are generally more toxic but less persistent than chlorinated hydrocarbons—though parathion has been found to persist in the soil for a considerable time.

PARATHENOGENESIS—Reproduction by development of egg without fertilization.

PHAGOCYTE—A blood cell capable of engulfing foreign matter that enters the body. The process of envelopment is called *phagocytosis*. Most multicelled animals, including insects, possess this defense mechanism.

PHORESY—The habit, found in some insects, of attaching themselves to another in order to be transported; some parasites find their hosts in this way. It may be the larvae that are transported (usually to reach the colony of their hosts), or an adult female parasite (to attack the host's eggs as soon as they are laid).

PHYLUM (pl. PHYLA)—Division of plant or animal kingdom made up of related classes.

PHYTOPHAGOUS—Herbivorous.

POLYEMBRONY—The process of repeated division in a fertilized egg, giving rise to numerous embryos which develop independently.

POLYHEDROSIS (pl. POLYHEDROSES)—A virus infection of insects producing polyhedral (many-sided) crystals in invaded cells.

PREDATOR—An animal living at the expense of another. A predatory (or predaceous) insect usually requires more than one host insect to complete its development—in contrast to a *parasite*, which can complete its development by feeding on a single host.

PRIMARY PARASITE—A parasite that attacks a pest or other insect that is not itself a parasite. Primary parasites that attack pest species are beneficial to man.

PUPA (pl. PUPAE)—*See* METAMORPHOSIS.

PYRETHRUM—A repellent and insecticide derived from the pyrethrum flower, *Chrysanthemum cinerariaefolium,* which is cultivated in Kenya for this purpose. It is nontoxic to warmblooded animals.

ROTENONE—An insecticide derived mainly from derris root (found in the East Indies) and from cube or timbo (found in South America), and described as "highly toxic to many insects but relatively innocuous to mammals." It is reported to be present in 68 species of plants.

RYANIA—A plant-derived insecticide, innocuous to warmblooded animals.

SAPROPHAGOUS—Living on decaying organic matter; organisms that do so are *saprophytes.*

SECONDARY PARASITE—A parasite that attacks a primary parasite. Since secondary parasites attack a beneficial insect, they reduce the value of that insect to man. Secondary parasites may be attacked by a *tertiary parasite* which is thus beneficial to man. All parasites that attack other parasites are called *hyperparasites.*

SEPTICEMIA—An infection carried throughout the body by the blood.

SPECIES—The smallest unit of biological classification; its members closely resemble one another and can breed with one another but not with those of another group.

SPERM—Male reproductive cell.

SPERMATHECA—Organ in female insect for receiving and storing sperm.

SPIRACLES—Breathing pores (*see* TRACHEA).

STREPSIPTERA—An insect order composed of *Stylops,* or twisted-wing parasites.

SUPERPARASITISM—Attack on a single host by two or more individual parasites of the same species but not the same parent.

SYMBIOTE—An organism that lives in association with another. Most symbiotes are harmless to their hosts or are distinctly beneficial to them; in some cases the host cannot live without its symbiote.

SYSTEMIC—Generally distributed throughout an organism. Systemic poisons applied to plants as insecticides are taken up by the sap stream and distributed throughout the plant. All parts of the plant are thus poisonous to the insect when eaten and for a time, until the poison undergoes chemical change within the plant.

SYSTOX—A systemic insecticide.

TARSUS (pl. TARSI)—An insect's "foot," excluding the claws and pads (pretarsi) at the end of the leg; it is commonly divided into from two to five segments. An insect's legs are composed of six independently moving parts; the tarsus is the fifth leg segment from the thorax.

TEPP (*tetraethyl pyrophosphate*)—*See* PARATHION.

THORAX—A group of three segments between the head and abdomen of an insect; the legs and wings are attached to the thorax.

THYSANURA—A small order of primitive, wingless insects called bristle-tails. It contains a few species known as silverfish, fishmoths, slickers or firebrats that are household pests. Most of the species are scavengers. With the Collembola, they differ from all other insects (including the wingless kind) in never having had wings in their evolution and in having no metamorphosis; they change in size as nymphs but not in form.

TICK—see *mite*.

TOADFLAX—A noxious weed, *Linaria vulgaris*.

TRACHEA (pl. TRACHEAE)—In insects, a respiratory tube that distributes air from the spiracles to various parts of the body.

TRICHOPTERA—An insect order including the caddisflies.

VIRUS—Any of a group of infectious agents, not visible under the ordinary microscope, which can pass through a thick porcelain filter and cannot be grown outside their hosts.

VIVIPAROUS—Bringing forth active young; characteristic of mammals, in which there is a vascular connection between mother and embryo, the placenta.

WEEVIL—A kind of beetle. Typical weevils belonging to the family Curculionidae have snouts with chewing mandibles—not to be confused with the beaks of homopterans and hemipterans, which are used for sucking.

INDEX